The Last Paradises

THE LAST PARADISES

ON THE TRACK OF RARE ANIMALS

Eugen Schuhmacher

Zoological Appendix by

Gerd Diesselhorst

Irenäus Eibl-Eibesfeldt

Theodor Haltenorth

Walter Hellmich

Translated by

Gwynne Vevers and Winwood Reade

DOUBLEDAY & COMPANY, INC.

NATURAL HISTORY PRESS

GARDEN CITY, NEW YORK

1967

Die Letzen Paradiese was first published in Germany
by Bertelsmann Verlag, Gütersloh, 1966

Library of Congress Catalog Card Number 67-17545

Plates printed in Germany by Mohn and Co.
GMBH Gütersloh
Text printed in Great Britain by Collins Clear-Type Press,
London and Glasgow

Contents

Foreword

As President of the World Wildlife Fund the publication of this beautiful book, *The Last Paradises* gives me great pleasure. Eugen Schuhmacher's illustrations provide an impressive photographic record of species that are in danger of extinction. International conservation bodies carry the heavy and difficult responsibility of ensuring that the fauna of the world is preserved for the enjoyment of future generations. It is my hope that this book will be seen by many people and that the information it contains will be assimilated by a wide public, so that the fight for the preservation of these last traces of 'Paradise' will receive full support.

PRINCE BERNHARD OF THE NETHERLANDS
Soestdiik, July 1966

Seven years' filming on all continents

The cliffs and reefs off the Newfoundland coast are pounded by the relentless power of the sea. Generations of seafarers have experienced the rise and fall of the foaming swell under lowering skies. A strong wind whips up the salt-laden spray and tosses it like whirling snowflakes against the rocks. The sea is seldom calm in this storm-centre of the North Atlantic Ocean.

In the year 1578 a small fishing vessel bobbed like a cockle-shell on the turbulent water and came to rest in a small bay sheltered by low-lying cliffs. Several bearded men jumped ashore, watched by hundreds of densely packed birds which stood quietly on the rocks, each one as tall as a goose. They showed no sign of alarm as the men made the boat fast and balanced heavy planks to make a swaying gangway to the shore.

The huge black-and-white birds did not take to the wing. They were incapable of flight, using their wings only for swimming and diving. Although they resembled penguins, they were in fact the largest member of the auk family—no penguin has ever occurred in the north. These flightless giant auks were not alarmed by the sight of humans. Equally the fishermen and sailors of that period were not afraid of the large birds, regarding them only as fat prey which could be killed easily because they were incapable of flying away.

Armed with cudgels the men started to round up the birds which still showed no sign of alarm. As the men advanced on them, shouting and driving them closer together, the birds made a move but did not attempt to attack the intruders or to defend themselves in any way. They were driven towards the boat and up the swaying gangway until the boat could hold no more. Many of the birds were killed in the process, being trodden underfoot, stunned and pushed over the side where they were swept underwater and dashed against the rocks. The men appeared to be unmoved by the fate of these birds; after all, those in the boat would meet the same fate in the end. The heavily laden boat then sailed away with hundreds of giant auks on board. Shortly afterwards the birds would be skinned and salted, to make valuable food which would keep in a satisfactory condition for a long time.

From time immemorial this gruesome slaughter had taken place. Throughout the centuries, the birds were taken year after year, not only on the Newfoundland coast but on the cliffs of Iceland and anywhere that garefowl—another name for the giant auk—were known to be present. Later, when ships were driven by steam, the birds were even used as fuel for the ships' boilers. Wood and coal were more costly than the corpses of giant auk which had a high content of fat.

In 1831 twenty-four giant auks were caught on the cliffs of Eldey off Iceland. In 1844 there were only two and these were probably the very last living specimens of this bird. Today there are only about eight skins, two skeletons and approximately seventy blown eggs of this species. These valuable remains of an extinct animal species are carefully guarded in museums.

In the 17th century another group of birds was exterminated by man: the dodos and the solitaires. They were large and plump. According to the anatomical structure of their bodies, they were related to the pigeons but like the giant auk they were also flightless. At that time the dodos and solitaires lived on the islands of Mauritius, Réunion and Rodriguez in the Indian Ocean. We have far less information about them than for other extinct animals. We know, however, that they were easily captured by crews of passing ships and that, similar to the giant auk, their fleshy carcasses provided a welcome change to the monotony of ship's rations in those days. A few skeletal parts, one bill and three feet are all that remain as evidence of this sad story.

When the Boers colonised Africa they moved up from the south, taking the land by force. They penetrated far into the interior and found themselves amongst herds of mountain zebra, white-tailed gnu, bontebok, blesbok, bluebok and quagga. In the extensive areas through which the Boers trekked, these herds numbered millions of animals. Time and again their wagon columns were held up by huge concentrations of wild animals and the treks were often forced to wait a long time while animals crossed their route.

With the advance of the white man and his settlement of the country, the decimation of the population of wild animals began. Animals were slaughtered senselessly. Skins were used to make sacks for corn and potatoes but only a small proportion of dead meat was eaten by the native workers. For the most part, carcasses were just left to rot in the sun. Compassion did not enter into the picture and animals were killed without any kind of forethought or plan.

The resulting toll: the last bluebok was killed in 1799. By 1858 only two quaggas remained alive in the wild and the last two specimens in captivity died in the Berlin Zoo in 1875. Today there are scarcely more than 800 bontebok still surviving, about 85 mountain zebra and little more than 1,000 head of white-tailed gnu. These last survivors would have suffered the same fate if it had not been for the last minute efforts of animal-loving farmers and nature conservationists.

In the same way the passenger pigeon was exterminated by the white man after his discovery and settlement of the New World. Up to the turn of the 19th century there were still millions of passenger pigeons to be seen. They darkened the skies, landing in trees and breaking the branches with their weight as they settled down to rest or to breed. When the passenger pigeons arrived in a neighbourhood, everyone who could carry a gun ran out and shot at random into the flock, using lead shot or small stones which also served as projectiles. At that time they were sold for a penny a bird. The end of the passenger pigeon in the wild came in 1907. The last captive specimen died in the Cincinnati Zoo in 1914.

These few examples are sufficient to bear witness to the trail of disaster to wildlife left by man as he moved into new areas all over the world. Up to 1800, some 33 large animal species had been exterminated by man; from 1800 to 1900 the number was much the same. During the last 50 years man has been responsible for the disappearance of yet another 50 species.

This senseless destruction of wildlife still goes on. Leaving aside the position of invertebrates and plants, there are 1,000 species of vertebrates which are threatened with the fate of the giant auk, the dodo and others. Over and above this, habitats everywhere are in danger of being destroyed—habitats not only of wild animals and plants but also those of man. Signs that the whole of nature is in jeopardy lie all around us: the air is polluted, the freshwaters of the land are contaminated, the soil is eroded or poisoned, even the sea is polluted; everywhere the pressures of human population are resulting in land being built-up or taken over in the name of progress. As civilisation advances, it brings its own destructive forces to the countryside.

These are some of the factors to be borne in mind if we are to plan for the future. The destruction must not only be brought to a halt but damage as a result of earlier mistakes must be rectified and nature restored wherever this is still possible.

Two large organisations have already been established for protection and conservation: the International Union for the Conservation of Nature and Natural Resources (IUCN) and the World Wildlife Fund (WWF). As an animal lover and conservationist I soon gravitated towards these two international bodies. I managed to stimulate their interest in the idea of making a documentary film about nature protection—a dream which had been taking shape in my mind for several years—and I offered my services. With the aid of photographs and films the concept of nature protection and the need for conservation could be carried to all parts of the world.

The film would have to be a colour documentary, backed by natural sounds, covering all the rare and threatened species wherever they still survived. Such a film could provide absorbing entertainment to hundreds of people. Inevitably the locations would be in the beautiful landscapes of the more important national parks and nature reserves, as it is only in such places that rare animals and plants still survive in unspoilt, natural surroundings.

These protected areas, which have been saved at the last minute from the foolish exploitation of man, are now publicly owned. They are important centres of research. They are also living examples of bygone ages, the last paradises in the best sense of the word. If it were not for these protected areas, the world would be even poorer than it already is in beautiful, natural scenery.

I started work on the film in the spring of 1959. It was the largest assignment—and without any doubt the most important—in my 35 years of film-making. The film was called *Die Letzten Paradiese* and parts of it were shown on BBC TV under the title of *The Rare Ones*. The idea for this book was conceived at the same time. It was intended that both the film and the book should be widely distributed in order to arouse the interest of people of every nationality in the need for conservation measures. Conservation is the concern of every one of us, wherever we live. By continually breaking the laws of nature man has already imperilled his existence all over the world and it is already apparent that he who destroys nature destroys himself.

Modern man has acquired a great deal of knowledge about technology and he is proud of his progress in this field. He knows far too little about the value and beauty of nature and he remains surprisingly indifferent. He does not realise that it is only in nature that he will find the wealth and power which he needs in order to develop into a complete human being instead of turning into a mechanical robot.

Producing the film and preparing the book has been a difficult but wonderfully rewarding task. The work has taken seven years to complete, seven years which have been arduous and fully occupied in every respect. I have travelled on all continents, undertaking one journey after another, searching continually for rare animals, hunting for them in their last strongholds and then stalking them with my cameras. Sometimes it was necessary to make two or even three journeys through the same area in order to achieve my aim. I had many adventures in my attempts to get close enough to the animals and it was a constant battle to outwit the weather and the changing seasons. It has been a race from one half of the globe to the other, passing through friendly countries and others less friendly, experiencing all climatic zones and varying habitats from one pole to the other.

Although the species in which I was interested were living in protected areas, many of the places where I was looking for them held only small numbers. In some cases the total world population of a threatened species was down to fifty, sometimes only two dozen or as few as eight or ten specimens were still surviving. It is only as a result of their protection in these nature reserves that they have been saved from extermination.

The International Union for the Conservation of Nature and the World Wildlife Fund opened the way for me, gaining access to many places which would otherwise have been difficult or even impossible for me to enter. Both organisations have given me constant assistance in the protracted business of film-making. For their constant encouragement and support throughout my undertaking of the film and this book, I offer these two organisations my sincere thanks.

I also wish to acknowledge with gratitude the assistance given to me in the completion of both projects by the Agfa organisation of Leverkusen and the Perutz Film factory of Munich, the Ministry of Culture of North Rhine-Westphalia and the head of the Nature Conservation organisation in Bavaria.

I must also thank the governments, state and private nature conservation establishments, the national park authorities, conservation agents and officials, the many wildlife wardens, rangers, assistants and private persons in the Antarctic, Argentina, Australia, Austria, Belgium, Borneo, Brazil, Canada, Chile, Ecuador, France, Germany, Great Britain, Greece, Holland, India, Indonesia, Italy, Japan, Kenya, Malaya, New Guinea, New Zealand, Norway, Peru, Poland, Sarawak, Spain, Spitsbergen, Switzerland, Tanzania, Turkey, Uganda, the Union of South Africa and the United States of America.

My thanks are also due to my colleagues Helmut Barth, Erwin von Dessauer and Peter Höser. Whereas Peter Höser could only take part in a few expeditions, Erwin von Dessauer and his wife undertook most of the photography in South America. Helmut Barth, however, accompanied me for five whole years, working indefatigably under all kinds of conditions. At many critical moments he remained at my side as I filmed. He also carried out many difficult assignments, working on his own in remote places. Many of the photographs in this book were taken by him.

I would also like to thank the authors of various zoological publications: Dr G. Diesselhorst, Dr I. Eibl-Eibesfeldt, Dr T. Haltenorth and Professor W. Hellmich.

THE AUTHOR

Grünwald near Munich—Summer 1966

Europe

NORWAY AND SPITSBERGEN

Six months after returning from New Guinea I decided to make for Norway and Spitsbergen. It was early in the summer of 1960 and I had just finished working on the colour film of the *Land of the Spirits*, shot in the South Seas. My young friend, Peter Höser and I were just completing our preparations for the journey when Helmut Barth, a young commercial artist, turned up at the last minute and asked if he could join the expedition as second camera assistant. Although a good photographer, he had not done any filming for a long time; he was so keen to join us that in the end I agreed to take him, even though we had scarcely enough room for a third man in our party. I had already decided to use my car for the entire expedition or at least for as long as it would stand up to the conditions. In spite of being somewhat reluctant to take Helmut Barth in the first place, it turned out that he eventually became my constant companion.

We had to put in a long stay on the island of Röst in the Lofotens. The high cliffs provided sites for breeding colonies of kittiwakes, guillemots, razorbills and puffins. We had no difficulty in photographing these sea birds and we found the work completely absorbing. Although my principal objective was to find the last refuges of rare species, the variety of species and the presence of such large numbers of individuals in the colonies were so impressive that I could not resist them. Adults with young were present in hundreds of thousands on these cliffs. It is usually necessary to approach wildlife with considerable care when filming but it was comparatively easy to get near to these sea birds as they were preoccupied with rearing their young and took no notice of us. They behaved so naturally that when we came to leave Röst, we looked rather like house-painters, our clothes and equipment being splashed with white droppings.

In Norway and farther north into Lapland we were looking primarily for the snowy owl and its nest-sites. Unfortunately our search proved in vain. It was a year when the lemmings were scarce and the owls therefore lacked the necessary inducement to breed freely. Lemmings are the favourite prey of the snowy owl and when numbers of these small mammals are low the bird is also rarely to be found. At this time of year mosquitoes are so numerous that one is almost eaten alive by them. We could scarcely take a breath without swallowing them and they descended on us like a cloud whenever we had a meal. Our soup seemed to be perpetually full of mosquitoes bent on committing suicide and in these conditions it was almost impossible to continue the search for the snowy owl. My determination to persevere finally waned when I was arrested as a spy and taken to the police station by a particularly suspicious policeman. In any case, we could not afford to lose any more time as the main objective of my journey north was to get to the island group of Spitsbergen in time for the few remaining weeks of summer.

In Harstad we found a ship of the Great Norwegian Spitsbergen Coal Company which was prepared to take us to Spitsbergen. The voyage took only a few days and we had a pleasant trip as neither storms nor poor visibility hindered the ship's progress. At midnight the sun was suspended over the horizon of the sea like a ball of fire. It rose again, without disappearing, to greet the new day.

We arrived at Spitsbergen at the Norwegian coaling port of Longyearby and our search for the musk-ox, the cattle of the Arctic, began. We had already seen these long-haired animals in central Norway. In Dovrefell, south of Trondheim, we had spent a few days chasing them over mountains and across high plateaus; we had not managed to film or photograph them, but had had to content ourselves with observing them from a distance. There is only one small herd of musk-ox in Dovrefell. The animals had only been introduced a few years before our visit there and had not really settled down in their new home. They wandered about the whole time and were masters at hiding themselves in this extensive area of mountains.

A much larger number of musk-ox live in Spitsbergen. The animals are distributed in various herds throughout the island group. The Sheriff at Longyearby told me that one of these herds was always to be found in a valley known as Advent Dale. Pilots of the Caltex Oil Company, who regularly flew there in helicopters looking for oil and other natural resources, confirmed this and so we set off for the valley full of optimism. There is no traffic on Spitsbergen, roads and streets are non-existent. There was no kind of transport available and the oilmen were not able to take us as passengers in their helicopters. Pack-horses and porters were equally unobtainable by money or any other form of persuasion. Shanks's pony was inevitable and we had to set out on foot, carrying all the bulky gear ourselves. The only help for the solitary traveller in Spitsbergen is the existence of small refuge huts. Each one lies about a day's march from the next and the Coal Company in Longyearby gave us permission to use them. This meant that at least we always had a roof over our heads and there was no need to carry tents and cooking equipment with us.

The summer was still pleasantly discernible in this country lying far north of the Arctic Circle. Snow lay only on the higher mountains. Walking was not difficult and even the many streams could be crossed relatively easily.

On the third day we came upon a herd of musk-ox. We were making our way slowly round a rise in the terrain when we caught sight of them, standing just behind the rising ground. I feared they would take to their heels when they saw us but on the contrary, they moved closer together and stared inquisitively at us. They then formed a circle, with heads facing outwards, as musk-ox do when danger approaches. I was able to take my first film shots of these animals from only a short distance away. I had never been so close to musk-ox before. At the time I did not realise that the outcome of this meeting at such short range could well have been different. These animals, as I was to learn later, can be very dangerous when they suddenly switch to the attack. When this happens the phalanx formation is not maintained.

When the herd finally started to move off, they withdrew into the length of Advent Dale and we left them in peace. There was still sufficient time for us to come across them again. We halted at the refuge hut which was not far away and, tired out by our long walk, we ate and then fell asleep. When we woke up again it was not possible to tell whether it was midday or one o'clock in the early hours of the morning. In summer, the sun stands so high in the sky that it never sets, and it is light even when the skies are cloudy or totally overcast. We were able to expose film just as successfully at midnight as during the day. We finally decided to eat only when we were hungry and so we did not really know whether we were eating breakfast, lunch or dinner. We slept when we were tired and did not bother ourselves about the time of day when we woke up and got under way again.

The photography of the musk-ox almost ended in disaster for my two assistants. Working according to a carefully prearranged plan they started driving the herd towards me, trying to get them nearer to the camera, when suddenly the animals turned on them and went into the attack. Only a hasty flight and a steep river bank saved them from the leader of the herd which was already snorting at their heels. I shall never forget the sight of the two men running for their lives, chased by a black-haired colossus. Although the scene was not lacking in comedy for me, my two companions found it far from humorous. Some time later I was myself attacked by an angry musk-ox, in quite a different place, in Copenhagen Zoo. I believe I blanched somewhat, even though I was separated from the aggressor by a fence of thick planks.

Unfortunately the first film shots of the musk-ox had to be rejected on technical grounds after they were developed and only part of the sequence was usable. Helmut Barth returned to the same area in the summer of 1963 and after a strenuous trip on his own he succeeded in re-taking the shots.

SWITZERLAND, ITALY, AUSTRIA AND THE GERMAN ALPS

Soon after our journey into the land of the midnight sun the three of us went to the Swiss Nature Reserves and to the Italian Gran Paradiso National Park in the Valley of Aosta. We were looking for the alpine ibex and we found most of them with the assistance of the Italian National Park authorities, who directed us to the best area and assigned men with local knowledge to help us. We were fortunate in that the weather worked in our favour: a week of constant rain was followed by a snowfall. Ibex try to avoid new snow and consequently they were driven down to the lower altitudes and we were able to photograph them without having to go very far or climb too high.

I was able to film several sequences of this mountain species, which at one time came perilously near to extinction. Deeply rooted beliefs in the medicinal powers of certain parts of the animal's body—the horns and bezoar stones—were at one time prevalent amongst people living in the mountains. Many an alpine ibex must have lost its life on account of this superstition. Poachers who were caught in the act were either shot by keepers working for the owners of the hunting estate or ended their lives on the gallows.

Towards the end of the summer in 1964, Helmut Barth and Peter Höser got some more remarkable pictures of the alpine ibex in the Gran Paradiso. With the additional material they obtained, an important film sequence on the life of this rare alpine animal was completed.

After we had spent the winter months of 1960–1 in South and East Africa, we continued our search for the vanishing species of wildlife in Europe. Our immediate aim was to film the great bustard.

As we were not allowed to use cameras in East Germany and there were also filming difficulties in Hungary, I could only go to the Burgenland of Austria. The best time to film this huge bird is in the spring when courtship display takes place. Courting males show off their attractive plumage to advantage and the display is particularly interesting to watch. Unfortunately the results of our first trip into bustard country were not completely satisfactory and three years later additional film material had to be obtained. My friend Erwin von Dessauer and his wife helped me to complete this part of the film successfully.

We erected a hide made out of reeds and rushes in the shade of watch towers and barbed wire, close to the Austro-Hungarian frontier. We sat for days in this hide from dawn to noon and succeeded in filming the wonderful courtship display of this big shy bird. The male bustards looked like white balls rolling about on the extensive grassy plains as they displayed for hours on end. They never seemed to tire of showing off their dazzling white plumage to the females, although the latter showed no apparent interest and merely went on feeding.

The great bustard used to be present in considerable numbers in the Burgenland but the population is now at a dangerously low level. Hunting them for sport still persists and the population has been decimated by over-shooting. Although the species is on the danger list, the will to conserve them is weaker than the hunter's ambition to possess a stuffed bustard, however questionable the glory of possessing such a trophy. The perpetual destruction of their habitat by agricultural improvements adds to the pressure on this species. Drainage and ploughing operations are changing the landscape from extensive hayfields, on which no man set foot, into smaller areas of arable land. Here the birds are subject to disturbance and they are not able to find the peace and privacy which they need. The sight of a great bustard—perhaps the heaviest bird in the world capable of flight—spreading its wings over the newly cultivated arable fields of Andau may soon be lost for ever. Unless shooting is stopped immediately and the law strictly enforced, this species will soon be driven from one of its few remaining breeding areas in Europe.

During the summer and autumn of 1962 we were busy photographing in the German Alps. In the Berchtesgaden area we filmed the golden eagle at its eyrie, also alpine marmots, chamois and other alpine animals. The scenery in the nature reserve area around the Königsee is particularly beautiful, more so than in any other part of the Bavarian Alps, and it provided a remarkably attractive setting for our film. Only four or five pairs of golden eagle are still resident within the borders of Germany. These birds of prey are protected the whole year round in West Germany, but unfortunately this does not apply to Austria. A mockery is made of the German protection laws when the neighbouring country of Austria still allows the golden eagle to be shot because now and again it kills a young chamois or takes a lamb. It is not in accordance with international thinking on nature conservation for such a rare bird to be protected in one country but permitted to be shot in another as soon as it flies over the border.

The fact that the golden eagle is primarily a scavenger is not taken into account. If owners or tenants of mountain estates are not able to endure the thought of an eagle occasionally taking one or two wild animals, then their attitude to nature conservation needs putting right and unfortunately it shows these people to be hunters at heart and not conservationists. Happily there are still some sporting owners and professional hunters who are proud to have a pair of golden eagles breeding in their area of the mountains. If it were not for their helpful attitude, these regal birds might soon disappear from Germany even though they are protected.

Two years were then spent in long journeys overseas and it was the summer of 1964 before I was able to resume my various filming projects in Europe. I had long wished to visit the Austrian bird refuge on the Neusiedler See. I planned to make a film there and I realised that this undertaking could only be successful with the co-operation of Professor Otto Koenig, Director of the Wilhelminenburg Biological Station in Vienna. I therefore got in touch with this well-known behaviour expert and conservationist. He readily offered me every possible assistance without delay. It was June when Professor Koenig personally escorted me to the Neusiedler See. Half-grown young of the great white egret, which were what particularly interested me in this nature reserve, were already present in the nests. This was the best time at which to film them without causing too much disturbance to the adults. Two tall, spacious observation towers were quickly erected, one near the nesting sights of the great white egret and the other in a neighbouring colony of spoonbills. G. Grafe and H. Digruber worked fast and with great thoroughness.

Every morning for ten successive days Digruber punted me across the lake to the hide. These daily boat trips across the shallow lake, slipping through narrow channels where the reeds formed dense thickets up to 15 feet high, were a remarkably stimulating experience. Only a man with local knowledge could have found the way through this labyrinth, which one would normally have expected to find in the Amazon jungle rather than in a lake on the doorstep of a city with a population of a million people. Great reed warblers and reed warblers sang against each other and bearded tits slipped secretively through the reeds. Sometimes the croak of a little bittern sounded across the water, and the great bittern could be heard booming now and again. Great crested grebes disappeared like lightning beneath the surface of the water when our boat glided out from the reed thicket into one of the numerous pools. And all the time the snow-white great white egrets and spoonbills circled above us, with now and again a purple heron or a grey heron. All these species nest in the almost inaccessible wilderness of reeds which lines the shores of the lake, making it a unique bird paradise lying at the gates of eastern Europe.

Every evening more film was taken of the great white egret which is one of the rarest birds in Austria. There are about 260 pairs on the Neusiedler See which is the only breeding site in western Europe. The nesting sites of these large birds, immaculate in their dazzling white plumage, should be guaranteed for all time and every attempt to make them more accessible to the ever-increasing stream of tourists should be prevented. Professor Otto Koenig and his colleagues are the best guarantors of this.

GERMANY, HOLLAND AND BRITAIN

We started our next journey in May 1962, beginning on the north coast of Germany, moving on to Holland and then over to Britain.

It was essential that the final film *The Rare Ones*, should include shots of Germany's largest sandwich tern colony—with some thousands of breeding pairs—on the isle of Norderoog. The initial credit for having safeguarded this unique site in Germany for breeding sea birds, saving it from all kinds of hazards, must be given to the organisation in Hamburg known as 'Verein Jordsand e.v.'

A chorus of bird calls greets the visitor as he wanders along the shore of the island on which the sandwich terns nest. The extensive breeding colony runs like a white band through the long grass. The birds stoop at every intruder who dares to invade their territory, darting down to attack with their bills and only leaving the intruder alone when he moves sufficiently far away from the colony. Members of the public are not allowed to land on the islet of Norderoog as and when they please. During the nesting season a warden watches over the colony to ensure that the birds are not disturbed. This is the only way of retaining the sandwich terns and the many other sea birds on the little island, which year by year is being eroded by the tides and constantly reduced in size. If it is to remain a refuge for sea birds, basic fortifications are urgently needed in many places. It is to be regretted that so little of the present wealth of Germany is devoted to nature conservation.

In neighbouring Holland we were anxious to film spoonbills. There is a breeding colony in a reserve at Zwanenwater but the owner of the land demanded such a high fee in return for allowing us to film that I had to abandon my plans to film there. Through the co-operation of the Dutch Nature Conservancy organisation, I then obtained permission to film the spoonbills nesting on the island of Texel. We arrived at exactly the right time. There were already young in the nests and there was a lively concourse of spoonbills in the breeding colony, the adults arriving with food for their young and then flying off again. There are only a few places remaining in Europe where these birds with spoon-shaped bills still breed in the wild.

I was also allowed to film the cormorant colony in the Nardermeer which is the oldest nature reserve in Holland. It is an extensive inland water and it offers a home and refuge to many other water birds.

In June we crossed the English Channel and visited various British nature reserves. Great Britain is well-known for her vigorous attitude towards conservation, which is supported not only by the government but also by many private protection societies. It has long been realized that nature protection and conservation must have the backing of the whole population if it is to be successful. In Great Britain many influential persons, headed by His Royal Highness the Duke of Edinburgh, work hard for the protection of nature. Such behaviour is indeed worthy of imitation.

I readily obtained access to the Farne Islands off the coast of Northumberland, with permission to film there, through Mrs Grace Hickling of the Hancock Museum in Newcastle-upon-Tyne. This group of islands is a sea bird refuge with a special appeal. Eider ducks, puffins, guillemots, shags, kittiwakes, storm petrels, terns—including the rare roseate tern—and gulls nest here every year in fantastic numbers. The grey seals are also regular visitors to this group of islands. In the autumn they haul out on the shore and the white-coated pups are born. A great many tourists and naturalists come to the islands to admire and study the bird life. In places the birds are so accustomed to humans that it is even possible to stroke them while they are sitting on their eggs. This is a happy example of the fact that man and animal can indeed exist side by side. It is only constant persecution that makes animals wary of humans.

From near Edinburgh we went on a fishing boat to the Bass Rock, a steep cliff stack rising out of the sea. About 8,000 pairs of gannets nest there every year, and also herring gulls. The nesting birds sit far enough apart so that they cannot touch each other. In places they are so numerous that the cliff appears to be covered with a white carpet. With the continual coming and going of birds to and from their nests, there is an atmosphere of perpetual restlessness. Thousands of gannets sit on their eggs, thousands are in the air, thousands swim on the water which washes against the steep cliffs. From the summit of the rock one appears to look down through a snowstorm at the sea. There are white shapes gliding, flapping and swimming; there are gannets to be seen wherever one looks.

At Woburn Park, the Duke of Bedford's estate, we filmed a great zoological rarity: Père David's deer, or Milou, from China. These deer became extinct in their country of origin a long time ago but here at Woburn they have found a last refuge. Père David's deer would have vanished from the face of the earth, like many other species, if this English nobleman and his ancestors had not thought it important to care for them and save them from extinction.

The French missionary Père Armand David discovered them in 1866 living in the grounds of the Imperial Palace in Peking. The species had long since disappeared in the wild but survived there in captivity. The first Père David's deer arrived in Europe in 1870. The stock in Woburn Park, and in many of the world's zoological gardens, originates from the animals which were brought to Europe. The herd in Woburn Park numbers about 300 head at the present time.

TURKEY

During the last week of May 1964 I received a cable from Dr H. Kumerloeve in Turkey. This well-known ornithologist had been doing scientific work in the Near East for some time and his research programme included routine visits to the breeding colony of the bald ibis on the Upper Euphrates. Before his departure on one of these visits, we had arranged that he would inform me as soon as the young birds were almost fledged. It did not take us long to fly to Adana via Athens and Ankara. From there we travelled by bus by way of Gaziantep to Birecik on the Upper Euphrates, where Dr Kumerloeve and his charming wife awaited us. They met us in the afternoon and took us straight to the bald ibises. One could scarcely miss these large, dark brown birds with their long, curved bills because they nest in the high, steep cliffs immediately above the edge of the town.

The Kelaynaks or bald-pates, as the Turks call them, have nested alongside the human population of Birecik since time immemorial. Their dark silhouette in flight is as much a part of the town as the slender minaret, the ruined citadel and the broad sweep of the river which flows past Birecik. Often the nests of the birds lie scarcely a stone's throw above the house tops, beneath which the inhabitants come and go, on which they occasionally work and where they even sleep on hot nights. This disturbs the birds just as little as it does the humans. Moreover, the bald ibises enjoy complete protection in Birecik; nobody would dare to touch a single feather of them. They are sacred birds.

I have included the bald ibis in this chapter even though it no longer occurs in Europe. Some hundreds of years ago they were known in Austria, Germany and Switzerland by the popular name of 'Waldrapp'. In 1955 the Swiss naturalist Conrad Gesner, described these birds in his country as 'Waldraben'. For a long time doubt was thrown on this early record of them in the region of the Alps and it was finally completely denied. They were known to breed in former times in the Salzburg area, in the region of Graz, Kehlheim, Passau and in other places. But for reasons that are uncertain the bird soon disappeared for ever from Europe. Today the bald ibis is only known to breed at a few places in Morocco and here in Birecik. So it has in fact become a very rare bird. Even in the Turkish colony it has recently appeared in ever decreasing numbers. In 1953 Dr Kumerloeve estimated the population of old and young bald ibises at about 1300, in 1954 C. Kossig reported about 600 to 800 pairs. When we were filming here, there were at the most 65–70 pairs—an alarming decline.

It was frightfully hot as we filmed the bald ibises at their various nest-sites, at quite short range from the roofs of the houses. The mayor of Birecik had given us a policeman as guide. His main job was to keep away the many inquisitive onlookers but he may also have been detailed secretly to watch that we did not get too close to the birds. It was purgatory working on the roof-tops. The nests were built on crags and narrow ledges in the high cliff which towered above the houses. There was no shade of any kind and the glare of the sun, reflecting from the steep cliff, was very trying. Only the endless supply of tea, served by friendly householders, helped to refresh us somewhat. In spite of the heat we spent the whole day near the nests. We did not want to miss anything that might be important from the filming or ornithological point of view. After all, no one knows how much longer opportunities will still exist for observing the bald ibis at the nest.

There were young in many of the nests, some half-grown, others already fledged. They were all being fed constantly by their parents. Begging for food continued throughout the day and there was a steady procession of adults on the wing, flying to and from the nests. They searched for food either in the surrounding countryside or down in the river. Others stood at their nests, keeping watch. Even the birds were troubled by the heat. Some of them panted with their bills open, like dogs, and others stood with their wings spread out, shading their young. Towards evening the bustling activity died down. Birds flew in from all directions, returning to the colony in large and small groups to spend the night there.

We found no other location, either before or afterwards, where rare species could be photographed so easily at such close range without any restrictions. The filming was completed in four days. In spite of the burning heat, our short stay at the breeding place of one of the rarest birds, in the company of like-minded friends, was a memorable experience.

POLAND

My journey to Poland in September 1964 was the only one behind the Iron Curtain. I had not even been allowed to enter the eastern half of Germany, in spite of many efforts to do so. The Soviet Union and China also steadfastly refused permission to film, although IUCN and WWF had repeatedly made requests on my behalf. These countries also have various nature reserves where rare and vanishing species are protected. An international conservation film, such as the one I envisaged, should have included film of the animals in these reserves but it was through no fault of mine that these large countries failed to be represented.

I was received in a very friendly manner by the leading nature conservation authorities in Warsaw. I am most grateful to Professor V. Goetel of Craców, the Polish delegate to IUCN, for the facilities he arranged. In no time we were taken to the world-renowned Bialowieza National Park near Bialowieza. Although the eastern part of this extensive National Park is today under Soviet administration, the area remaining in Poland is still so large that it provides a habitat for many large European animals. Deer, wild pigs, elk, bears, lynx, wolf, beaver, eagle owls, black storks and wisent are still resident today in Bialowieza Forest. Even the tarpan, a type of horse from bygone ages, is once again breeding successfully there.

The Director of the National Park, Mr Andreas Kawecki, spared no efforts to see that my work on the film of this important reservation should be really successful. Accommodation and transport were provided, and Mr Potoka—a wildlife ranger with local knowledge—was constantly at my disposal. My major film objective in the Bialowieza National Park was the wisent or European bison.

The trees in the forest were just beginning to take on their autumn tints. Morning mist drifted through the virgin forest. Later, when the sun broke through, its rays filtered through the trees and the sunlight revealed the primitive cattle standing in the centre of a scene which was reminiscent of the Middle Ages. It was as though one had been transported into a bygone age: at any minute one expected a medieval hunt to go by, with horses ridden by knights armed with spears and crossbows, and the music of hounds and hunting horn ringing through the forest as they sallied forth.

Slowly and calmly, without any sign of alarm or haste, the wisent walked through the fairy-tale forest with their heads held low. Vapour exuded from their nostrils as they snorted; leaves and earth were scattered by their hooves as they pawed at the forest floor with their forelegs. They stood before us like statues incarnate, the embodiment of primitive strength, belonging to an epoch from the distant past. We walked for hours on end through the forest with them, filming as we went. There were bulls, cows and calves; sometimes we saw solitary aged bulls and there were herds of up to fifteen head.

On occasions we were forced to get out of their way quickly. A fallen tree with its huge roots torn out of the ground and pointing up into the sky, provided an effective screen; sometimes a hedge gave us sufficient cover or we jumped on to the small truck which accompanied us on our expedition through the silent forest. We had to be particularly careful of cows with calves. Should they attack suddenly, they are much faster than the heavier bulls. The latter are also not always to be trusted; they are unpredictable when there is a cow on heat in the vicinity. However, our guide, Mr Potoka, knew the wisent like a shepherd knows his sheep. The animals also knew him and his voice; when he spoke to them they soon settled down again.

It is delightful to see these primitive cattle in their natural surroundings, living and behaving as completely wild animals. What a difference between these animals, living here in the primeval forest of Bialowieza, and others behind bars in a zoo. It is true that there are also bars and railings in this National Park, behind which the wisent live, but the enclosures are so spacious and there is so much natural vegetation that one scarcely notices the limitations to their habitat. We had to observe as much care when filming the animals inside the enclosures as outside. The wisent in the Bialowieza region have increased to such an extent that they are now allowed to live outside the enclosures and today some herds are living in complete freedom. It is wonderful to think that there are now wisent living wild in the deep forest as they did hundreds of years ago.

The enormous forest complex of Bialowieza has always been a well stocked hunting chase. Up to the First World War it belonged to Russia. Every year the Tsar spent some weeks in Bialowieza and hunted deer, boar, bears and the wisent. The old hunting lodge is now in ruins, but the park, laid out on a grand scale, and the entrance-gates together with various other buildings, still bear witness to this period. The 1914–18 war and the confusion of the post-war period had a disastrous effect on the population of wild animals and after 1918 there was not a single wisent left alive in the Bialowieza Forest.

Fortunately there were still some surviving in various zoos in Europe. From this stock a few individuals were brought back to Bialowieza and there they formed the basis for a new breeding herd. The wisent got through the Second World War much better, indeed they even increased in numbers at this time. Today, including those in the enclosures and those living completely wild, there are 118 wisent living free in the Bialowieza Forest area alone. There are other herds in other Polish reserves. At present Poland has over 223 pure-blooded wisent, a total population which is sufficient to make the future of this primitive type of European cattle secure.

FRANCE AND SPAIN

Much as I wanted to include the flamingoes of the French Camargue Reserve in my film and book, it was not possible. Every spring I was all set to go to the reserve at the mouth of the Rhône and I merely waited for news that these elegant birds were breeding there. But throughout my seven years of filming they failed to breed in the Camargue. Nobody knows why, after so many years, the flamingoes have stopped breeding in this area. Could it be due to climatic changes, unfavourable weather, changes in the habitat due to man, or to difficulties regarding food? We do not know the answer. Only a small number of flamingoes now spend the spring and summer months in the Camargue. They stand around in the shallow salt-water lakes or fly about over the area. It would be a tragedy if this unique attraction of the Rhône delta were to disappear altogether.

In June 1965, I stayed in the Coto Doñana Nature Reserve in the region of the Guadalquivir estuary in South Spain. There I filmed the imperial eagle at the nest and various breeding colonies of cattle egrets, spoonbills, heron, white storks and other birds. The whole of South Spain was suffering from an unusually severe drought, such as had not occurred for decades, and the number of breeding water birds was therefore much less than in normal years when wide stretches of this region are under water. Our vehicle was constantly sinking into soft sand or being bogged down in sticky mud. Sometimes it needed a powerful Land-Rover to haul us out again. One becomes hopelessly lost as a stranger in this region. Endless grass steppes and bushy sand flats stretch for miles into the distance. The number of sand dunes increases towards the sea coasts and there are sparse plantations of pine in the dunes. Mature cork-oaks grow in the bushy parts. These are favoured as nesting trees by egrets and also by the Spanish form of the imperial eagle, which still breeds here in small numbers.

The administration of this unique bird reserve is under the care of Dr José Valverde in Seville. It is usually impossible to gain access to this reserve but Dr Valverde was in complete sympathy with my aims and gave me permission to film there. With his support and the help of French film colleagues from the Natural History Museum in Paris, I was able to obtain beautiful shots of the rare imperial eagle in a comparatively short time. The best information on the Coto Doñana Nature Reserve and its fauna is given in the report issued by the press section of the German branch of WWF. The author, Herr Werner Koep, has given me permission to reproduce it here: 'Unnoticed by the world at large, something has recently happened in Spain which is of the greatest importance to nature conservation throughout the world. After several years of endeavour and lengthy negotiations, the World Wild-life Fund, with headquarters in Morges, Switzerland, has now been able to hand over to the Spanish Government the recently established Coto Doñana Nature Reserve in the estuary area of Guadalquivir.

'With its 25 sq. miles the Spanish nature reserve is not only among the most important reserves in Europe from the viewpoint of surface area, but also with regard to its wildlife and particularly the birds; it is an area of the most interesting natural landscape of western Europe still remaining in its original condition. The Reserve accommodates no fewer than half of all the bird species occurring in Europe, including large egret colonies with populations of up to 15,000 birds. The Coto Doñana is also however one of the last refuges of two of the most threatened animal species in Europe: the Spanish imperial eagle, of which there may still be only about 200 specimens, and the Spanish lynx, with a population of approximately a couple of hundred pairs. Together with the famous buildings and works of art, this Reserve now belongs to the Spanish people for all time and, in addition, it is there in perpetuity for the whole world.

'For hundreds of years the Marismas, a triangle of land at the mouth of the River Guadalquivir between Seville, Huelva and Jerez, was the property and hunting ground of the Dukes of Medina

Sidonia. Virtually cut off from the outside world for a very long time, this area is one of the most interesting original areas of natural countryside on our continent.

'Within a few years of the World Wildlife Fund being founded, it has launched one of the most significant projects for nature conservation that is taking place in Europe today. The initial finance, however, could only be raised largely on the basis of loans and further donations are needed to support the project.'

From the Coto Doñana we took a trip down to the Rock of Gibraltar where there is a small colony of Barbary apes. They were probably introduced there at some time, and thus they are the only monkeys living wild in Europe. So far, the British have tolerated them on the Rock, and it is said that the British will continue to hold this naval fortress as long as the Barbary apes continue to live on Gibraltar.

Politics are no concern of mine but as a naturalist and conservationist, I can but hope that these attractive monkeys will remain undisturbed on the Rock for a long time, regardless of whatever flag happens to be flying over Gibraltar. On the continent of Europe free-living monkeys are a rarity and all rare animals, wherever and under whatever conditions they exist, deserve special efforts for their preservation.

To the tourist at Gibraltar, the Barbary apes are just as great a sightseeing attraction as the deep caves. They are as much a part of the local scene as the ships lying in the harbour. There is no difficulty in finding them and every taxi driver knows where to direct people. Half-way up the Rock, with a magnificent view overlooking the town and harbour, it is easy to get photographs of these tame animals. The apes are completely at home with members of the public and some of them are almost importunate. They are quick to see titbits held by tourists and if they are not offered them fast enough, they know how to grab them without ceremony.

GERMANY

In July soon after my return from Spain, I went to the nesting sites of the black stork in Lower Saxony. Herr H. Makowski of Hamburg and Herr L. Müller-Schessel of Rotenburg helped me to get the necessary permit, as these birds are legally protected at the nest in Lower Saxony. This protection order also includes the prohibition of filming and photography. During the past years amateurs have all too often disturbed these rare storks at their nests.

Herr Müller-Schessel looks after the few black stork nests in Lower Saxony. He knows more about their habits than anyone else. He also knows the number of breeding pairs and where they nest. He showed me several nests with young storks of different ages, and I was able to decide on the most suitable way to get film of them. Dr Gisela Mauermayer of the State Zoological Museum in Munich assisted me with the filming.

The site of the spacious nest was in an old pine tree growing in a large stand of mature conifers and deciduous trees. It was solidly constructed in the fork of two branches about 45 feet above the ground.

There were four young in it, already fairly large and almost fledged. There were still a few down feathers on the head and neck but these became fewer as each day passed. The young storks spent most of the day standing in the nest. They lay down and went to sleep only after they had eaten a lot of food. They were never all lying down at the same time as only those which had succeeded in getting the largest share of the food brought to the nest were ready for a rest.

We erected the hide on the ground among tall ferns under a spreading fir tree, at a distance of about 90 feet from the nest. From the hide I was able to film everything that was of interest and particularly the typical behaviour of the young storks. The young were fed several times a day by the adults which took turns in bringing food. We were not able, however, to distinguish between the male and female. Although the adults did not keep to a regular time interval between feeds, nevertheless we could count on a feeding session every 2 to 3 hours. This was always an exciting time for the young birds and also of course for my filming. Feeding, however, was not the only point of interest and the young storks kept us busy. Some of the typical behavioural shots included their preening routine, the exercising of their wings as they tested their strength and their method of excreting, in which they squirted in a low trajectory over the side of the nest.

Although the weather was mostly bad and there were constant squalls of rain, I was able to get some good film sequences and a number of photographs. The result naturally gave me considerable personal satisfaction as this species is one of Germany's rarest birds and I was particularly pleased that my conservation film would include shots of the black stork and its young.

I went to Bavaria hoping to film the great eagle owl but here I was unfortunate enough to run up against the profit motive. People who were knowledgeable about birds knew where there were occupied nests which were suitable for filming, but they were only prepared to show me the sites for an excessively high sum of money. Such behaviour amongst country people is beyond my comprehension, especially as great eagle owls and their nests are not privately owned, but the property of everyone. I have not come across this attitude in any other country. Americans, British, Japanese, even the most primitive bush people have shown themselves to be friendly and helpful.

In spite of this I was able to film the great eagle owl with the help of Herr H. Weinzierl, the Vice-president of the German Nature Conservation Circle, and of Herr H. Zahn and of Herr A. Steinhauser. I am most grateful to them for their assistance.

Nature is being threatened on all sides by the encroachment of civilisation. How much longer shall we be given to enjoy the unspoilt beauty of natural scenery like this breathtaking view of the Matterhorn? So far, mountain ranges have largely escaped being opened up and utilized in the name of progress. In the Alps, for instance, plants and animals which are no longer to be found anywhere else have managed to survive.

In 1921 King Victor Emmanuel III presented large areas of the Aosta Valley to the Italian nation. At that time the Valley was already renowned and it now forms the Gran Paradiso National Park. About the middle of the last century the alpine ibex was saved from extinction in this area by the efforts of King Emmanuel II.

For centuries, the alpine ibex was hunted ruthlessly. Popular belief attributed magical properties to its heart septa and stomach stones or bezoars; consequently the animal was so much in demand that poachers frequently risked their lives to obtain it. By the nineteenth century, when it was placed under strict protection in the Aosta Valley, the entire stock had already been reduced to fifty head.

If Germany should ever establish a National Park, the most suitable place for it would be the wonderful nature reserve around the Königsee in Upper Bavaria. At present this area is used to an increasing extent for hunting, alpine pasture and forestry.

Right. Only a few young golden eagles are fledged each year in the German Alps. There are only four to five pairs from Allgau to the Alps around Berchtesgaden. This regal bird enjoys complete protection in Germany but when it flies over the border it is, unfortunately, not completely secure from persecution.

Nowadays it is an unusual experience to hear the call of a great eagle owl and one needs a great deal of luck to see one in the wild. The eagle owl has become so rare in Germany that since 1965 the organisation 'Nature in Danger' has been considering its extensive reintroduction.

Most children have heard of white storks but the fact that there are also black storks is not so well known. A few of the latter still nest in Germany in secluded stands of mature trees. Their number is so small that information about their breeding sites is kept secret by foresters and a few experts.

There is a unique bird refuge on the small island of Norderoog. Each year storms batter this unprotected island, reducing its size. Up to now a German conservation group has done everything possible with the resources at its disposal to preserve this island. But unless substantial fortifications can be built soon this unique refuge for sea birds will be seriously threatened.

A clamour of harsh cries greets anyone who approaches the colony of Sandwich terns on Norderoog. Birds fly up in a cloud, stooping at intruders and attempting to drive them away. The colony of terns extends like a white ribbon through the grass. Arctic terns, oystercatchers and other sea birds nest in the same area.

During their nesting season in Holland, spoonbills are guarded day and night by the Dutch conservation authorities. We obtained permission to visit the colony on the island of Texel and to take pictures of these rare and beautiful birds with their remarkable bills.

From time immemorial eider-down has been in demand. The soft down feathers, plucked by the eider duck from her own breast to line her nest, were regularly collected by people living along the coasts of North Europe. Unfortunately they mostly took the eggs as well. Today the eider is protected in most countries.

The great bustard likes to roam undisturbed over many miles of open grassy plains each day. Until now this bird has found suitable country in the Burgenland district along the Austria-Hungarian border. But now, even here, schemes for drainage and arable cultivation are threatening to destroy the great bustard's habitat.

The display of the great bustard is one of the most remarkable sights of the European bird world. In this picture the male is just starting his display. He fluffs up his white feathers, turning himself into a billowing white ball; in this posture he moves backwards, forwards and sideways within sight of the female.

At one time the plumes of the great white egret were much in demand by the nobility and for ladies' fashions. The bird was hunted so persistently that today there is only one place in Western Europe, the Neusiedler Lake, where about 260 pairs nest.

Right. The Barbary apes on the Rock of Gibraltar are the only monkeys occurring naturally in Europe. They are lively animals but comparatively tame.

Visitors to the Coto Doñana Reserve in the estuary region of the Guadalquivir in Spain cannot fail to be impressed by its unique landscape. Old cork-oaks, with huge colonies of egrets, tower above extensive grass steppes. The World Wildlife Fund recently managed, at the eleventh hour, to save this practically untouched area where an extensive programme of urbanisation had been planned.

The Coto Doñana Reserve offers refuge to nearly half the total number of bird species occurring in Europe. Amongst these is the Spanish form of imperial eagle of which only about 250 specimens still survive. The Spanish imperial eagle is distinguished from the golden eagle by its slightly smaller size and pure white shoulders. It nests in open, park-like country.

Above and *right*. We were struck by the peaceful way in which the rare bald ibis lives side by side with the inhabitants of Birecik on the Upper Euphrates. The Turks call this beautiful ibis 'kelaynak' or bald-pate. The bald ibis nests just above the roofs and the people go in and out of their dwellings below the birds without disturbing them. They also work on their roofs from time to time and even sleep on them when the weather is very hot.

The extensive forests around Bialowieza in Poland were formerly a hunting ground of the Tsars, who came here each year. A large castle and park, together with various other buildings, still bear witness to its former use. The area has now become the Bialowieza National Park, where we had the memorable experience of observing European bison or wisent in the wild.

The European bison often stood in front of us like some living representative of a bygone age. Then we saw them moving slowly through the fairy-tale forest, their heads held low as they withdrew calmly, showing neither alarm nor haste. As they pawed the ground with their forefeet, they snorted and blew small eddies of vapour from their nostrils.

The wild horse or tarpan of the deciduous woodlands of Europe was already extinct when attempts were made to re-establish it in the Bialowieza National Park where it had previously survived until 1812. To obtain its original form, horses were back-crossed and now a magnificent herd of this grey wild horse lives under exceptionally favourable conditions in the Park.

In 1898 the Duke of Bedford obtained a few specimens of Père David's deer; they had originally been found only in the Imperial Park in Peking and had never been seen in the wild. He formed a herd on his estate at Woburn Park near London where they have steadily increased, and there are now several in various zoos throughout the world.

Above and *left*. Puffins have a clown-like appearance. They look distinctly odd as they return from a successful feeding trip carrying sand-eels in their bills. When excavating their nesting burrows, these birds undermine the ground to such an extent that one cannot walk over the area without falling through.

Overcrowding is the order of the day on a guillemot cliff. Guillemots breed in their thousands, closely packed, on rock stacks in the Farne Islands, known as the Pinnacles. They lay their single egg on the bare rock. The egg is tapered and this helps to prevent it from rolling over the edge into the sea.

Shags also nest on rocky cliffs but they lay their eggs in a real nest, not on bare rock like guillemots; the nest is built of seaweed and other local plants. Shags belong among the cormorants, which are persecuted on many fishing grounds because they are excellent catchers of fish.

As we approached the Bass Rock in a fishing boat in the Firth of Forth, the massive stack reared up out of the sea and appeared to be covered with a white carpet. Approximately 8000 pairs of gannets find nest-sites on this rock.

Young gannets are nidicolous. They are helpless and require a long period of parental care before they finally fledge. An adult gannet is roughly the size of a goose but is a much superior flyer.

When we tracked down a herd of musk-ox on Spitsbergen, the animals did not run off as I had feared they would. Instead they took up a defensive position and formed a circle with their heads facing outwards. On one occasion my two assistants went too close to a herd and were summarily charged by these shaggy beasts. Only a hasty retreat and a steep river-bank saved them from the fury of the leader of the herd.

Polar bears are continually on the move. Indefatigable, they strike out across the endless icy wastes of the Arctic and even swim across long stretches of open water. Polar bears tend to be very inquisitive but are normally harmless to man; strictly speaking it is only the female who is dangerous when she fears for the safety of her cubs.

The snowy owl replaces the great eagle owl in the Arctic. Lemmings are its chief prey and a considerable number of them are eaten during the nesting season. In years when lemmings are particularly scarce, the snowy owl appears not to breed and is then practically impossible to find.

America and the Antarctic

ALASKA

The summer and autumn of 1961 were spent in North America. Leaving the Old World at eight o'clock one morning, we flew from Copenhagen non-stop over the Pole and landed at Anchorage, Alaska at about noon. The jet plane defied distance and time and even gained us a few hours into the bargain. The highlights of our Alaska tour were to be Mount McKinley National Park, Kenai Wildlife Reserve, McNeil River Reserve and Walrus Island.

When summer comes to this region, thousands of caribou wander from the low-lying tundra up to the cooler pastures high up on the massif of Mount McKinley. At this height they are no longer bothered by swarms of mosquitoes and they also find lusher pasturage. Mount McKinley, the highest mountain in North America, is enveloped in cloud for 350 days in the year. It is permanently covered in snow and ice. We were only able to go there once in search of the wandering caribou. There is no darkness in the summer months and it was shortly after midnight when we saw the peak of this giant mountain sparkling under the cloudless northern skies.

Grizzly bears follow the tracks of the caribou herds. The caribou go long distances and weaker members of the herd which fail to keep up are occasionally eaten by the bears. Every day we came across *Ursus horribilis*, this awesome omnivore of the northern forests. The Alaskans say that its nose is so keen that it can scent prey on the other side of a mountain. We saw the grizzlies at close quarters devouring chance prey. We also noticed how they sought the coolness of the snowfields and ate lush grass with the same gusto as a cow.

The short summer brings a radiance to this wilderness of the far north and the Dall's sheep withdraw higher up into the mountains. We were forced to climb high to reach them and we found the going very laborious with the additional burden of our heavy filming equipment. But these wild white sheep, with their rounded horns, are so characteristic of the mountains of Alaska that we could not afford to miss them.

We saw dozens of Alaskan brown bears catching salmon. These are the largest carnivores in the world. They are a little larger and more powerful than their relatives in Kamchatka on the other side of the Bering Strait. Old, experienced males, over 8 feet tall, mothers with awkward cubs and unskilled beginners—all congregate at the rapids where the salmon leap on their way to their spawning grounds which are up near the sources of the rivers. The salmon were making the return journey to the same place where they had hatched years before, after spending the main part of their lives at sea. The adult bears were remarkably skilful at getting the salmon out of the rapids. Every minute a 10 to 12 pound salmon ended up in their jaws. Some of these extremely skilled fishers are real gourmets. They open up the fish, eat only the roe and then let the rest fall into the river again. The fish then float downstream to where the young bears are waiting for their share below the rapids. At this age, they are still too clumsy to catch the live fish themselves.

As we approached the bears for filming, they stood their ground until we were only 15 to 18 feet away from them and then only withdrew hesitantly. Neither bears nor humans disturbed each other and there was sufficient space for us to avoid one another. The abundant supply of fish makes the bears lose their aggressiveness. The spawning period of the salmon lasts for six weeks and the bears then disappear again to other hunting grounds. By hook or by crook they must strive to put on plenty of fat before arriving at their winter-quarters as they lie up and sleep during the winter.

At about this time of year 1700 to 1800 adult walrus bulls lie peaceably together in a very restricted area on a small island, Walrus Island, in the Bering Strait. Each of them weighs two to three thousand pounds; they have two powerful tusks of pure ivory, as in elephant tusks. The boulder beach is too small to hold all of them and their corpulent bodies lie in a heap, packed close together and even piled on top of one another. Walruses do not lie about on rocks like sea-lions and other seals. We saw many of them swimming about in the water, waiting for a free place on shore where they could rest and sun themselves. Only the bulls assemble on this beach. Why the females do not come here is still a mystery. The intense sunshine causes blisters the size of a man's hand and there are pink patches on their brown skin. Walruses with sunburn blisters on a beach in Alaska are one of the more curious sights of the animal world!

The voyage to the walrus beach nearly developed into a journey into eternity for our party which consisted of the boatmen, Putwin, my Swedish friend Sven Gillsäter and myself. The sea was relatively calm when we set out but we were soon riding the waves in a stormy sea. On the return journey we smashed the rudder on a rock off Walrus Island. Helpless and with only a thin saw-blade as an improvised rudder, we set sail on seas which became increasingly rough. Only an offshore wind and the determination of our imperturbable boatman, together with a stout hull, brought us back alive. Our unique film, however, suffered irreparable damage on the return journey.

Surrounded by the turbulent Bering Sea, the walruses are eminently well protected on their beach. Eskimos may take a few now and again but it will be a long time before tourists drive the walruses away.

CANADA

We went on southwards to Canada. My wife joined us in Edmonton. We drove through the National Parks of Banff, Jasper, Kootenay, Yoho and Waterton in the Rocky Mountains. I had no difficulty in finding the best places to film the more important animals as I was familiar with the region. I had been there on two previous occasions in 1956 and 1957, hunting for animals with my camera while making the colour film *The Land of the Black Bear*. My Swiss friends Rentsch and Hürlimann had been with me on the first trip; Paul and Veronika Eipper were my companions on my second visit. The parks contain moose (elks), wapiti, bighorn sheep and Rocky Mountain goats. These are among the species in danger and only complete protection, such as they enjoy in these Canadian wildlife refuges, have saved them from extermination. Outside the reserves they had almost disappeared from places where they were once common. Trophies of Canadian big game still attract numerous hunters from all over the world.

UNITED STATES

We crossed the US–Canadian border near Hot Springs. For some weeks we drove through the United States and visited the principal national parks and wildlife reserves where the scenery is of outstanding beauty. The largest canyon in the world, the Grand Canyon, Arizona, was the southernmost point of our journey through the United States.

On its northern edge the Kaibab Plateau lies like a dark green island in the middle of a yellow desert. Tall Ponderosa pines cover the high uplands from which one enjoys an awe-inspiring view into the depths of the Grand Canyon. The pine forests are the home of the Kaibab squirrel which is found nowhere else in the world. It has been restricted to this habitat from time immemorial. It cannot extend its range either into the surrounding desert or into the deep canyon as it would starve; it feeds only on the seeds of the Ponderosa pines. This little dark grey rodent with the bushy white tail kept us very busy for several days.

The Canyon, one of the wonders of the world with its remarkable rock formations and its enormous scale, offers a unique view of a cross section through the evolutionary history of the earth's crust. The continuous play of sunlight and the changing colours of this panorama are of exceptional beauty.

Bryce Canyon in the State of Utah, on the other hand, looks like a dried up sea-basin. Mysterious formations resembling aurochs, toadstools, obelisks, pyramids, bridges, chapels and miniature castles in salmon-pink, yellow, pink and white limestone and sandstone, allow the fantasy free rein.

We spent a few days looking around Yellowstone Park, the oldest National Park in the world. Here there is plenty of wild life to be seen in beautiful surroundings. In addition, there are several hot springs and geysers numbering about 300 in all. They are unique in size and variety; their power has remained undiminished for thousands of years. In intensity they are far superior to their opposite numbers in Iceland and New Zealand.

The idea of National Parks was conceived in Yellowstone Park almost a hundred years ago. Since then the concept has spread throughout the world, a remarkable rate of progress in only a hundred years. In Red Rock Wildlife Reserve and in Jackson's Hole Reserve we saw the rare trumpeter swans. In 1930 there were only 37 specimens but, as a result of strict protective measures, there are now more than 2000.

In the Montana National Bison Range we came across the largest wild animal of the New World, the Indians' buffalo or American bison. The achievement of American conservationists who succeeded in saving this species when it was on the brink of extinction will not be forgotten. Around 1800 some sixty million head of bison grazed the prairies of North America. By 1900 there were no more than 1000 head, which the white man had left alive in the wild. This must surely be the most sordid page in the history of wanton destruction of wildlife. For the continued survival of this wild species we have to thank the energy of far-seeing men and a few animal-loving farmers who kept a handful of bison on their properties. Today there are 30,000 head of bison on the American Continent, skilfully distributed among various wildlife reserves so that any potential disease or hazard could not easily endanger the survival of the species.

In the Montana National Bison Range we were able to film these animals on historic ground. A hundred and fifty years ago the Flathead Indians hunted bison on the same grassy slopes where the herds range today. In those days the Indians, mounted on agile horses and armed only with bows and arrows, succeeded in bringing the steers down. This bloodshed however was of no real significance. The former masters of this country were too wise to squander their resources; the bison represented all that the Indians needed for survival. They fed their families on its meat, they built their wigwams from its hides, and its horns adorned the medicine men in the practice of their magical arts.

We returned home late in the autumn of 1961, enriched by our contact with American wildlife and with plenty of valuable pictures.

SOUTH AMERICA (BRAZIL, ARGENTINA)

In January 1962 we travelled to Brazil and Argentina. In Brazil we planned to photograph animals characteristic of the tropical rain-forests, such as ant-eaters and sloths, hummingbirds, the maned wolf, South American tapirs and others. Erwin von Dessauer did splendid work in several countries in South America. He and his wife, who accompanied him on his long travels, spared no effort on behalf of the film and this book. In the Peruvian Andes he filmed vicunas, chinchillas and the rare spectacled bear; in Southern Chile, he also filmed the small pudu deer and the condor.

With Erwin I flew on southwards to the Argentinian Nahuel Huapi National Park, with its fjord-like lake and neighbouring cordilleras making attractive landscapes. I had already been to this park to make a film some 25 years earlier. As companion to the zoologist Professor Hans Krieg I had become familiar with the many animals of Patagonia and also with those of northern Argentina, Paraguay and southern Brazil. At a later date I also travelled through Tierra del Fuego, Chile, Peru and Bolivia. In the course of four expeditions I have spent a total of 47 months in this sub-continent and the animal life of South America is well-known to me.

In spite of such a long absence I found that very little had changed in the Nahuel Huapi National Park; even the friendly hospitality of the people was the same. Our main objectives were the flightless steamer ducks, the huemuls or Andean deer and the guanaco which has already become very rare; we were also particularly keen to find the nest of a condor with young. Scarcely any film was known to exist of a nest with young of this largest of all flying birds. Condor nests are usually well-hidden and often in inaccessible places, such as crags or cliffs.

The condor is subjected to considerable pressure by the cattle and sheep farmers of the cordilleras. High rewards are still paid for the shooting of these harmless birds, although they are officially protected everywhere. Unfortunately one cannot rid the farmers of South America of the erroneous idea that it kills calves and sheep. The condor is not by nature a killer; it feeds chiefly on carrion and offal. It is a vulture and is incapable of overpowering healthy living animals; it does not have the sharp bill and the powerful talons with which birds of prey are equipped. The condor has to find corpses if it is to eat. Its habits therefore make it a useful scavenger and sheep farmers ought to value its presence.

After a long search Erwin and I eventually found a pair of condors, with one almost fully grown young in the nest, in the area of the estancia San Ramon. Herr Lahusen of Buenos Aires gave us a great deal of support in this part of our work and his bailiff Don Udo Frank acted as an extremely valuable assistant to us. He succeeded in finding a well-camouflaged position for our camera, screened by a stunted tree in the vicinity of the condor's nest which was in a rock face.

The giant birds looked like sail-planes as they floated past us, only a few yards away, gliding on the thermal up-currents, and the wind made a sussurating sound as it passed through their powerful wings. There was no sign of movement from them except for their heads turning this way and that, their sharp eyes trying to detect what was happening on the cliff face near their nest. They came so close that often the camera could not get the whole bird in the picture. They have a total wingspan of over 9¾ feet.

We identified the young bird as a male from its comb which was already clearly visible although quite small. We were able to film it, together with the parents, as it left the nest. It was already a match for its parents in soaring and gliding and at a distance, it could only be distinguished from them by the different colour of its juvenile plumage. However, when the parent birds found a dead sheep, the young condor was not able to make much progress on its own, and did not seem to know how to make a start on the carcass. It beat its wings up and down in an agitated manner and gave begging calls until the parents ripped open the sheep carcass. Before very long it would be flying away, out over the wide plains of Patagonia, guided by the adult condors.

Shortly afterwards we found one of the last guanaco herds in the region of the estancia Ramon. These wild camels of South America formerly inhabited the plains of Patagonia in hundreds of thousands. But because a guanaco eats seven times as much grass as a sheep, it has been mercilessly hunted by the sheep farmers since they settled in this gigantic area of pasture land. Nowadays, it is a rare stroke of luck to come across these animals living in the wild. There are plenty of them in zoos as they breed well in captivity. The numbers of wild guanaco are dwindling in South America and the only large species of animal, which appears to be on the increase is the llama. Zoologists believe that the latter, a multi-coloured mountain form, was descended—ages ago—from the guanaco.

From San Carlos de Bariloche, an attractive small town on Lake Nahuel Huapi, we flew out across Patagonia to Puerto Madryn on the Atlantic coast. The immense sheep country of Chubut stretched beneath us right up to the coast. The Valdes Peninsula projects far out into the sea with a steep shoreline of rugged cliffs and boulder-strewn beaches. The poor soil bears only a meagre covering of grass, so that in places a single sheep requires 17 acres, in order to have sufficient grazing for a year's supply of food. It is a bleak and desolate looking countryside. The coastline of the peninsula is deeply indented by quiet inlets where the sea-lions can bring their young into the world undisturbed and without fear of being hunted. We arrived at precisely the right time. At this time of year there are some hundreds of these large eared seals with their young on a plateau jutting out into the sea.

The young pups romp about and the scene is reminiscent of an overcrowded children's playground. We watched a group of young sea-lions being led to the paddling pool. Some of the mothers kept order there and after a while the young obediently came out of the water when they were called. There appeared to be a kind of division of labour among the female sea-lions; as well as being mothers, each one played a secondary role as governess.

Mothers repeatedly showed the young pups the best way of jumping off the edge of the rocks into the water. In spite of this, the pups tumbled in head over heels. But, as born swimmers, they were naturally in their element in the water even though they were still unskilled at diving into it. After bathing the young were suckled. The female sea-lions have so much milk that the young are not able to take it all and we saw the excess milk flowing into the sea like white rivulets.

Here nothing disturbs the rearing of the sea-lion pups. No seal-hunter is allowed to put in an appearance as the owner of this large peninsula, Don Emilio Ferro, does not allow the eared seals to be slaughtered. Everywhere else along the coast of Patagonia the gruesome slaughter takes place but on the Valdes Peninsula the seals are left in peace.

On the open shores of the South Atlantic, an hour's car journey away, the orders of Don Emilio also prevail. A few dozen elephant seals assemble here each year at the breeding season. This is the only place on the South American subcontinent where the elephant seal, the largest species in an extensive group, still occurs. It is the most northerly breeding place in their range. The true homes of the elephant seals living in this region are the sub-antarctic islands lying between the southern tip of South America, Africa and Australia on the one side, as well as the pack-ice girdle of the Antarctic Continent on the other side. When they are not wandering about somewhere in the southern seas, they withdraw to the Tierra del Fuego Archipelago, South Georgia, the Falkland Islands, Diego Ramirez, Kerguelen and the Macquarie, Campbell, Antipodes and Auckland Islands.

It was a great advantage to us to have the elephant seal so close to us. It saved us a lot of time and money as we would otherwise have had to charter a ship to reach the islands where they are to be found. It took us only a few days to take the necessary pictures of this bulky inhabitant of the sea. The seals lie motionless on the shore and spend most of the time asleep. The only sign of movement amongst them is when a bull has to drive his harem closer together. With inflated upper lip he rears up above the sand, gives his chosen ones a hard dig in the ribs and looks aggressive. But elephant seals are harmless by nature, and this frequently costs them their lives. Seal-hunters are not misled by their aggressive appearance and show them no mercy.

USA

From Buenos Aires, where Erwin stayed behind, I flew on to Texas, via Lima and Miami, in order to look for America's rarest bird in the Aransas Wildlife Refuge. This small protected area on the west side of the Gulf of Mexico is one of the most important in the world. Here the few surviving whooping cranes spend the winter. In 1962 only 32 specimens were counted. A tiny population, but nevertheless one which justifies optimism when one realises that the population had recently been only fourteen. Even today there are not much more than 50 whooping cranes in the world, including those living in a few zoos in the United States. No other species of crane is so threatened.

Faithfulness to a particular locality is one of the remarkable characteristics of these large birds. The last breeding places of the few remaining whooping cranes lie in northern Canada, in Wood Buffalo National Park. It is the largest wildlife reserve in the world and its 17,000 square miles are the only place in this vast continent where the whooping cranes still go to breed. There, in the area of forest, moor and tundra lying between Lake Athabaska and the Great Slave Lake, which is larger than Switzerland and Luxembourg put together, they breed and rear their young until they are fully grown and able to fly.

For as long as man can remember they have come every year to Texas, arriving with their offspring in the autumn. These large white birds fly some 2500 miles over North America, notwithstanding the many hazards they meet on the long journey. In spring, they fly back along the same route. Ornithologists, conservationists and rangers watch them passing on migration. Continuous reports are made of the direction, locality, speed of flight and the numbers of birds sighted. The whooping crane is surely the most strictly protected and the most closely observed of all birds.

Nevertheless their population continues to fluctuate in an alarming manner. Natural mortality among the young, bad weather conditions, accidents in landing and taking off owing to fences and other wires, together with irresponsible shooting by man, are always bringing these birds close to extinction. A single disease or one natural catastrophe would be sufficient for the tiny world population to be lost for ever. In such circumstances attempts to breed these cranes in zoos are essential, but in the long run they must be able to exist in freedom.

No visitor is allowed to enter the winter quarters of the cranes in Aransas, exception is granted only on the highest authority. Although I had the full backing of IUCN and leading American conservationists, I too was not allowed into the reserve area. As in the case of other visitors, I had to make do with filming the birds either from a high observation tower on the edge of the refuge or from the bank of the canal. This was adequate for distant shots but not for close-ups. At the end of my first visit I had to leave with my material only half completed. In April 1964, on the return journey from New Zealand and Hawaii, I paid another visit to the Aransas Reserve. Once again I was not allowed in but I obtained some good pictures of America's rarest birds from the canal bank.

It is not so long ago that the Everglades National Park was established on the opposite side of the Gulf of Mexico at the southernmost tip of Florida. The Superintendent, Mr W. Hamilton, was most helpful and understanding, and I was allowed a completely free hand. The swamps cover an immense area. The land is only a few feet above sea level and the waters of Lake Okeechobee and of many rivers and lakes flow south in a wide stream, flooding the land of the Everglades before they reach the sea. These waters flow almost imperceptibly. They are full of fish and other aquatic animals. This wealth of food makes the Everglades National Park into a first class refuge for swamp and water birds.

White, blue, grey, green and reddish egrets, white and brown pelicans, storks, ibises, the roseate spoonbill, flamingoes, gulls, terns, stilts, snipe, cormorants, sun-bittern, rails, ducks, birds of prey and many song birds live here. There are also numerous alligators, otters, racoons and the American crocodile in the swamps, in which the original Seminole Indians still live in places. This is the habitat of a subspecies of the white-tailed deer and sometimes one sees the rare Everglades Kite, of which there are now only very few breeding pairs left. Manatees also live in the water-courses and ponds of the Everglades. Unfortunately I did not find the kite but on my first day there I saw a manatee as it came up momentarily to breathe at the surface.

Every day I was able to observe and film this wealth of bird life from very close range. Otters, racoons, alligators, and manatees added variety to the scenes we filmed. For the animal photographer the Everglades National Park is an Eldorado. The park authorities have arranged attractive jungle paths and boat trips, making it easy for visitors to get to the animals. There is a wonderful variety of wildlife readily accessible to every visitor with the minimum of effort.

HAWAII AND GALAPAGOS

In Hawaii, the fiftieth state in the USA, there is the same concern for protection and conservation of threatened species as on the mainland.

Mr D. Woodside of the Fish and Game Department in Honolulu, on the island of Oahu, gave us considerable help by laying on facilities without delay. He sent us to Hilo, the capital of the island of Hawaii where we were met by Ranger E. Kosaka, a Japanese, who like so many of his compatriots was born in the State of Hawaii.

In Pohakuloa Camp we saw the first animals which we hoped to film in Hawaii. These were Hawaiian geese, known here as ne-ne. They are kept in pairs in fine spacious enclosures where they are bred. The project of building up the seriously reduced population of ne-ne, by breeding them in captivity, has been in operation since 1949. As part of this scheme the ornithologist Peter Scott, Director of the Wildfowl Trust at Slimbridge in England and son of Captain Scott, the polar explorer, has also been very successful at breeding them. So much so that he was able to send an aeroplane full of these geese, which had been reared in captivity in England, for release into the wild on the island of Maui in Hawaii, where the ne-ne used to be found.

A hundred and fifty years ago there were over 25,000 ne-ne living on the two main islands of Hawaii and Maui. By about 1940 there were less than a dozen left and so it was decided that these few survivors should be captured and taken to selected places where they could be bred in captivity, and later released to restock the former habitat. Today there are about 340 Hawaiian geese on Hawaii and Maui; in addition, as a safety measure, a further 150 are being kept in various zoos throughout the world.

Operation Hawaiian Goose is a model example of nature conservation in action. It has since been followed by similar operations in various parts of the world, including Germany. IUCN, WWF and certain national conservation bodies are all actively engaged in undertakings designed to save species in danger.

Tourist brochures depict Hawaii as a resort of slender palms, tropical vegetation and white beaches. In fact there are only a few places like this and if you go inland, much of the landscape is totally different. Volcanoes still rumble on these Pacific islands and throughout the ages there have been constant eruptions. Today the land is scarred and desolate with a crust as hard as stone. It certainly does not look like a tropical wonderland, but this uninviting landscape is the habitat of the Hawaiian goose.

The ne-ne is not only the rarest but also the most strange of the wild geese. It lives in a hot, tropical region whereas all the other geese live in cold or temperate regions of the north or south. Continental geese migrate in autumn and spring; the ne-ne does not. Other geese like and seek water; the ne-ne lives on dry lava fields. The Hawaiian goose is well adapted for a life on these porous, mostly waterless lava wastes. The webs on their feet are much reduced. They seek their food on areas of pasture which are surrounded by the rough lava. When pursued they take refuge in the lava fields where they also breed and rear their young in safety. No predator can follow them across the lava and even humans find it difficult to make any progress across the lava which is as hard as broken glass and cut by deep fissures. Shoes and feet are quickly torn and the pursuer soon gives up.

We too stumbled across the lava fields for hours on end and tore our feet. Our helpful ranger showed us the breeding place of a pair of geese, which had been released some years before and had become completely wild again. The nest was well hidden among low shrubs in a shallow depression in the lava. Not far away the gander kept watch. During the incubation period wild geese are among the shyest birds known to man. Gander and goose are faithful to each other and attentive in their parental duties but even the smallest disturbances make them leave the nest. After being disturbed it is always a long time before they return to resume their interrupted incubation. They desert the eggs permanently all too readily.

Almost exterminated by the thoughtlessness of man, the wild geese of Hawaii and Maui were saved by naturalists who took action at the right time. Today they are once again part of the national scene on the lava fields in the interior of these Pacific islands.

In March 1966 I joined a research party for three weeks on the Galapagos Islands. I planned to start the film *The Rare Ones* with a visit to this distant group of islands which has a fauna that is unique in the world. Giant tortoises, marine iguanas, flightless cormorants and Darwin's finches are the characteristic animals of this group of islands. There are also subspecies of other animal groups such as sea-lions, penguins, pigeons, lizards and snakes; these subspecies have evolved in the course of thousands of years and have maintained themselves on these islands undisturbed by outside factors. They have been left undisturbed here by man for a long time.

The research party was under the leadership of the well-known zoologist Dr I. Eibl-Eibesfeldt and was largely promoted by the Charles Darwin Research Station on Santa Cruz. Dr Eibl-Eibesfeldt is a leading expert on the Galapagos Archipelago. He has written a book on this remote island paradise under the title *Galapagos*. Under his experienced leadership we undertook two long voyages through the archipelago on the Research Station's ship *Beagle*.

The first visit was to Duncan Island which has its own species of giant tortoise. Its carapace has a conspicuously marked indentation in the nape region which enables the animal to stretch its neck high upwards when feeding. Unfortunately the population of giant tortoise is very much threatened owing to the introduction of rats on to this island. Numerous small birds, including the various species and genera of finches described by Darwin, live in the bushes. They are all remarkably tame and it is possible to observe them at such close quarters that they can almost be caught in the hand. This trust in man applies to almost all the animals on these islands and it continued to make a deep impression on us throughout our stay.

The expedition to Duncan on the first day was a strenuous but useful preparation for our visit to the next island. The scorching equatorial sun beat down on us mercilessly. Rough blocks of lava were tumbled about on top of each other and thickets of thorny shrubs impeded our progress. We went on to James Island where our attention was focused on the numerous fur-seals, Galapagos penguins and marine iguanas. Perpetually rolling in the swell, the *Beagle* carried us each day a bit farther through the Pacific ocean. We covered hundreds of miles, as some of the islands lie a day's voyage apart. The blazing sun shone out of a blue sky and was only rarely covered by cloud.

On Narborough Island we saw enormous numbers of dragon-like marine iguanas lying out on the rocks swept by the sea swell. Sea-lions gambolled about in the shallow water of the small bays or lay sleeping on the shore. Here too were penguins, pelicans and the flightless cormorants. In Convoy Bay on Indefatigable Island we came across the yellow-green land iguana which is about three feet long and on the small island of Daphne, which rises steeply out of the sea, there were numerous black-and-white boobies with red feet. Their young were almost fully grown.

Finally we visited Hood Island in the south and Tower Island in the north of the archipelago. Red-spotted marine iguanas and numerous boobies inhabited the steep rocky shores of Hood, which were washed by the swell that cascaded over them like fountains. A stone's throw away from our cameras a Galapagos hawk seized a young goat and we watched the bird devour it only six feet away from us.

On Tower Island our interest was focused on the courting frigate birds, red-footed boobies and a shoal of sharks close to the shore. When a female frigate bird flies overhead, the male displays by filling its huge throat sac with air so that it almost bursts. The birds were so little disturbed by our presence that we were able to remove the eggs from under their breasts while they were incubating and examine them at our leisure. It was yet another example of the complete trust shown in man by the wildlife here. This total lack of fear was indeed the dominating impression that we brought back with us from our visit to these distant islands and it is one that we shall always remember.

ANTARCTICA

Through the intervention of IUCN in October 1963, I was invited by the National Science Foundation in Washington to undertake a filming journey in the Antarctic for a whole summer. When I originally planned my film, right from the start it was always my intention to include the animal life of this biotope. I am very grateful for the help given to me by my American friends and by the personnel of the service stations responsible for scientific research on the operation known as 'Deep Freeze', as well as to the US Navy. I should be very happy to think that the films, photographs and observations of the fauna made by Helmut Barth and myself could contribute even in a small way to the intensive efforts of the United States Antarctic Research Programme (USARP).

By international agreement the whole of the fauna of the Antarctic is under protection. And so the 'seventh continent' has become a gigantic wildlife reserve, and the animals living there are the inviolable property of everyone. In this way the world of the South Pole has become the largest animal paradise on earth.

The Antarctic is about as large as the United States and Western Europe together. It is surrounded by ice and even covered with ice which is an average of 9000 feet deep. Unlike conditions at the North Pole this immense ice-cap rests on firm rock. The highest Antarctic mountain is over 15,000 feet high. Nowhere else on the earth is there so much ice as here. Ninety per cent of the ice which today covers parts of our planet is in the Antarctic. If this ice were to melt the world's oceans would rise by about 200 feet—an unimaginable deluge would flood and submerge large areas of the earth.

The flight from New Zealand to the American station at McMurdo on the inner edge of the Ross Sea took eight and a half hours. Immense expanses of ice and high mountains, as yet untrodden by man, slipped away beneath us as we flew on. Then the big transport aeroplane came down to land on a runway of pure ice.

The headquarters of USARP, which control all the current scientific work in the sector administered by the Americans are housed in a comfortable hut. In other places there are representatives of other nations who are trying to investigate the many secrets of the Antarctic world.

Our first visit was to the Weddell seals. A caterpillar-tracked vehicle took us there very quickly. We travelled across ice and crevasses wherever the going was best. There was a certain amount of risk as in places the ice would only just take our weight. We soon found a seal breathing hole, a circular hole in the ice. The animals use these openings in the ice, which they always keep free, for climbing in and out. Although they can remain underwater for 15 to 20 minutes without difficulty, like all mammals, they must come up to breathe air.

Weddell seals are very heavy animals with a weight of 750 to 900 lb. They only live in Antarctic regions. In general they have no fear of man. They have not had any unpleasant experiences with him and, if they are capable of working things out at all, they regard man as one of themselves. Like all seals they enjoy company and one often finds a hundred Weddell seals on an icefield together. Time does not appear to exist for these animals. For days at a time they lie like dead giants on a battlefield, inactive and motionless, letting the sun shine on them. At their hauling-out places, the sound of their unmelodious, mournful voices can be heard incessantly—laments, groans and sighs. They have poor vision and it is thought that these calls help to keep them in touch with each other but their significance has not been fully investigated. Indeed very little is yet known about the habits of Antarctic seals.

Our next expedition was for penguins, 75 miles along the coast to Cape Crozier, a mountain range which falls steeply into the sea. The journey took only a short time as a large helicopter transported us with all our equipment. There is a gigantic colony of Adélie penguins at Cape Crozier. Only two of the approximately 20 species of penguin live in the Antarctic: the small Adélie and the very large emperor penguin. All the other species occur only in the southern parts of the world.

At this season about a quarter of a million pairs of Adélie penguins congregate around the massif of Cape Crozier. They had only recently arrived and some were just starting to mate and collect stones for their nests, others were already at the incubation stage. An indescribable hubbub prevailed in the rookery. There were continual differences of opinion between neighbours as nesting sites became scarcer with every day. Each newcomer struggles to get into the centre of the colony. Sites on the edge of the rookery are not in such demand as there is greater safety in the centre. Penguins are exceptionally sociable birds and there is a great deal of moving about in the colony during the breeding season.

Each female Adélie penguin normally lays two eggs. And with eggs present in the nest, the trials and tribulations also start to increase. Predatory gulls are continually plundering the nests of the inoffensive penguins, as soon as the latter relax their attention for a moment. The marauders maintain an effortless patrol above the nesting sites and nothing escapes them. They notice the slightest sign of an unprotected egg and press home their attack ruthlessly. A pair of predatory gulls work extremely well together.

Unsuccessful and non-breeders usually remain in the water. Day and night the pack-ice is occupied by penguins and it looks rather like a popular seaside bathing resort. When a blizzard is not blowing, the sun shines for 24 hours a day. It is indeed high summer in the Antarctic, even though the temperature never rises above zero and is often 30 or more degrees below. The fact that the bottom is covered with blocks of ice instead of warm sand does not appear to trouble the bathing parties.

The penguins are completely at home in the water; water is their natural element, they find their food there and after being on the ice, they return to it to hunt for fish and other marine animals. All animals in the Antarctic therefore feed only along the edge of the icefields where the water is readily accessible. In the ice-covered interior they would soon starve to death.

One day we had a personal demonstration of the speed at which penguins can travel in the water. We sighted hundreds of them far out at sea, visible only through binoculars. They suddenly turned round and rushed back to the shore, shooting through the water like torpedoes. A leopard seal had arrived beneath them. The leopard seal is the penguin's most dreaded enemy; it is even more dangerous than the predatory gulls. Fear of death re-doubled their efforts and drove them on towards the safety of the shore. As they reached it they leapt out on to the ice, as though shot into the air by invisible springs.

The leopard seal, however, is even faster and we saw it seize a penguin. The penguin struggled and kicked as the leopard seal shook it from side to side, tossed it up high into the air, caught it again with gaping jaws and then dived under with it. The gruesome killing took a few minutes to complete as this greedy predator only eats the flesh of the penguin and the body has to be flayed out of its thick covering of feathers. Man also has to be careful when leopard seals are about.

Signs of the Antarctic summer increased and about this time the ice-breakers of the US Navy arrived on the scene, shattering the peace with the noise of vibrating engines. At this season the big ships are able to come right in and unload their valuable cargoes direct on land. The ice-pack becomes noticeably thinner and the pressure of the heaving sea forces cracks in it in many places. The greatest care had to be taken now in crossing the ice-fields. Transport by the heavy caterpillar trucks was stopped, only light motor sledges and dog sleighs could be used.

We built our camp on an arm of the sea that was still frozen, between high walls of shelf ice. The pack-ice here might have been six to nine feet thick, we did not know. In the light night we heard it crack and groan under us. We could feel the movement of the water beneath the floor of ice but in spite of this we slept well in our warm and comfortable sleeping-bags.

We were now living in the immediate vicinity of a breeding colony of emperor penguins. They had emerged from the sea immediately after our arrival. They greeted us like old friends with lively nods of the head and loud voices. They watched us inquisitively as we erected the tents. They wanted to know what was going on, what kind of a set-up this was. Only animals which had never suffered by an encounter with man could show such blind trust.

There were only about 1000 pairs, few in comparison with the Adélie penguins which are numbered in hundreds of thousands. Emperor penguins are rarer and do not live in such large communities. The first emperor penguin colony was discovered by Edward Wilson, while a member of Captain Scott's first South Pole Expedition. It was midwinter and Wilson could not believe that the emperors incubated during the rigorous Antarctic night. It was not until Scott's Second Expedition in 1911 that he was able to show that it really was so. Cherry Garrard, a member of the expedition, subsequently described this fatiguing and dangerous research journey as 'The Worst Journey in the World'. The second emperor penguin colony was found in 1914, the third in 1915, the fourth in 1948 and the fifth in 1950. In 1951 the total population was estimated at 5000 birds. Only about twenty breeding colonies are known today.

Emperor penguins are the largest representatives of this peculiar family of birds. They are about 48 inches tall and weigh around 75 lb. Their life is spent almost with clockwork precision. They spend ten months of the year, from March to December, on the ice. During this period they mate, incubate and rear their young. The other two months they are in the water, but nobody yet knows where they spend this time. Unlike other penguins, they never go on to ice-free land or rocks.

They are the only birds which instead of incubating their eggs during the summer months, do so in the depths of winter, in the coldest and most inhospitable long nights of the Antarctic. Continuous storms rage over the landscape and temperatures fall to 60 degrees below freezing point. They stand almost motionless, huddled together to conserve heat. They have to avoid every unnecessary movement in order to retain their fat. It is the only source of energy which keeps the birds warm and alive. Under such incredibly harsh conditions it is an astonishing performance.

In March and April they arrive in processions at the breeding site. After mating the female lays the single egg; it weighs about a pound. The male takes it over within the next 24 hours; he rolls it on to the webs of his feet and starts to incubate. There is no nest. The bird stands on the bare ice and carries its whole weight and that of the egg on six, or sometimes only three toes. The period of incubation by the male lasts for about two months. During this period he stands as still as a statue. If one were to photograph him at intervals of one or two weeks the results would be virtually identical.

The female, however, walks 80, 100 or 120 miles across the ice to the open sea. She feeds to satiety, puts on fat and then walks all the way back again through darkness, ice and storm, guided only by her instinct to reach the colony and to relieve the male in the care of the chick. This hazardous journey lasts about two months, the same time as the period of incubation. If something happens to the female on this long trek and she dies by falling into a crevasse for instance or is eaten by a leopard seal, the newly hatched chick is unlikely to survive. From the arrival at the breeding grounds in March or April, the snow falls continuously and apart from feeding the chick when it hatches with a crop secretion, the male is not in a position to nourish the chick.

Many young penguins starve in these circumstances. The mortality among emperor penguin chicks is generally very high and many freeze before they are fledged. Recent investigations have shown that only a quarter of the offspring survive.

If however the female returns safely, she joins the colony and calls to her mate as she searches for him in the dark among the hundreds of males waiting for their partners to arrive. The female then immediately feeds the chick and takes over the care of the young. The male is free to start on the long journey to the sea to make up for lost time in feeding. During the long fasting period, he has become quite thin and his skin, formerly so tight, now hangs loosely around his emaciated body.

This to-ing and fro-ing to the open sea with its abundance of food now goes on between the parents alternately while the young put on weight. The summer returns slowly, the ice-edge begins to break up and the water comes closer to the colony. The parents' route in search of food becomes shorter. At the same time the chick's appetite becomes larger.

We worked in biting frost, which often not only froze up our equipment but also chilled us to the marrow. After some days a helicopter arrived to fetch us and as we broke camp and disappeared into the warmth of the aircraft, the old and young emperor penguins stood by as though to bid us farewell. From the air we saw them waddling about between the high walls of shelf-ice where we had lived with them. We knew that these massive blocks of ice would soon be set free from the mainland to drift away to the sea as icebergs. Perhaps they would carry these self-same birds a bit farther on the next step of their journey, a journey which is still shrouded in mystery as far as man is concerned.

Lying at the foot of Mount McKinley (20,320 feet) in Alaska, the highest mountain in North America, the Mount McKinley National Park extends over some 300 square miles. This unique northern landscape has an unusually rich fauna.

In summer when millions of mosquitoes emerge from the marshes of the low-lying tundra caribou herds numbering several thousand head move into the Mount McKinley National Park. The caribou, as the Indians call the reindeer, move upwards into the higher pastures where they graze on richer vegetation, free from the unwelcome attention of the mosquitoes.

We were also particularly interested in the Dall's sheep in the Mount McKinley National Park. Like the caribou herds these white sheep from Alaska climb higher up into the mountains at the beginning of summer. They are sure-footed and agile. Laden with our equipment, we had difficulty in keeping up with them as they leapt ahead of us.

In Alaska when the reindeer start their summer migration, the grizzly bear follows the tracks of the big herds, searching for weakened animals. It is said that its sense of smell is so keen that it can scent prey on the other side of a mountain.

Right. The glutton or wolverine is bitterly hunted down by the men who look after breeding herds of caribou because it frequently attacks their animals. However, this large and handsome mustelid, in general rather shy, has so far escaped extermination. I was forced to take this picture in the Basle Zoo as we were not successful in photographing it in the wild.

Above and *right*. When the salmon swim upstream to spawn, the large Alaska brown bears make their way to particularly favourable places along the river. Experienced adults will pull an 8 to 10 pound salmon out of the river every five minutes. Like gourmets they are often only after the roe. They let the bodies of the fish slip back into the water, which then become a meal for the young bears farther downstream.

During the summer months 1600 to 1700 walruses assemble on the shingle and boulder beach of a rocky islet in the Bering Strait. This island is the only known place in the northern part of the Western Hemisphere where dense concentrations of these powerful marine mammals are still to be found.

These singular animals, weighing several hundredweights, lie about on top of each other on the narrow beach. There are always some in the water, waiting until there is a free place in which to lie in the sun. They often expose their bodies to the sun for so long that pink sunburn blisters form on the skin.

The American black bear can become very tame under favourable conditions and sometimes it may even be a nuisance. In the National Parks this bear has come to realise that it will not be hunted and approaches humans without any sign of fear.

Left. The Banff and Jasper National Parks lie close together on the east side of the Rocky Mountains. In this area nature has been left undisturbed for generations and the beauty of its profusion is unsurpassed.

Above and *left*. The Rocky Mountain goat is the chamois of the North American mountains. High, inaccessible places form its habitat. It is a superb mountaineer: no cliff is too high, no face too steep for it to negotiate. Like the chamois the Rocky Mountain goat also lives in herds. It is only the aged males that detach themselves and become solitary.

Bighorn sheep are found at lower altitudes in the Rocky Mountains than the Rocky Mountain goats. They live on the grassy slopes between the upper tree limit and the perpetual snow. During spring and summer the females and young separate from the males.

In spring the powerful males in the flocks of bighorn sheep move off and form an exclusive male club. Sometimes they climb very high up into the mountains and only come down to rejoin the rest of the flock when the mating season starts at the beginning of the autumn.

Above and *right*. Not so long ago beavers were quite common in North America but they were hunted for their beautiful pelts to such an extent that numbers are now much reduced. Nowadays beavers are almost entirely restricted to the reserves. They build highly artistic dams in their territories, making use of tree tunks which they fell and cut up with their sharp incisor teeth.

The elk, known as the moose in North America, is the largest living member of the deer family, and the largest specimens live in Alaska and eastern Siberia. Old bulls can reach the size of a horse. Like all deer the elk also sheds its antlers each year and grows a new, larger set within a few months.

The wood buffalo is one of two races of the American bison. In its pure form it now lives only in the north of the continent in Wood Buffalo National Park. The largest National Park in the world, this lies between Great Slave Lake and Lake Athabasca in Canada.

Above and *left*. Around the year 1800 herds of 50 to 60 million 'Indians' buffalo' were still to be seen on the prairies of North America. The white man has reduced these herds of the prairie bison or plains buffalo to pitifully few numbers. The prairie bison is a pure grass-feeder whereas the wood buffalo favours leaves and buds. The cows, calves and young bulls graze together in large groups under the protection of older bulls.

Yellowstone National Park in the United States is the oldest National Park in the world. It was established nearly a hundred years ago. It was from here that the concept of National Parks spread all over the world. There are several thousand hot springs in this park and the geysers are a particular attraction to sightseers.

When the trumpeter swan was put under protection in 1920 there were only 37 individuals left. Since then, their numbers have increased to over 2000 and their ringing call is now frequently heard in the North American reserves.

On the following pages. The most magnificent gorge in the world lies in the middle of the Grand Canyon National Park in Arizona. Here the Colorado River has gouged out the earth to a depth of up to 6000 feet.

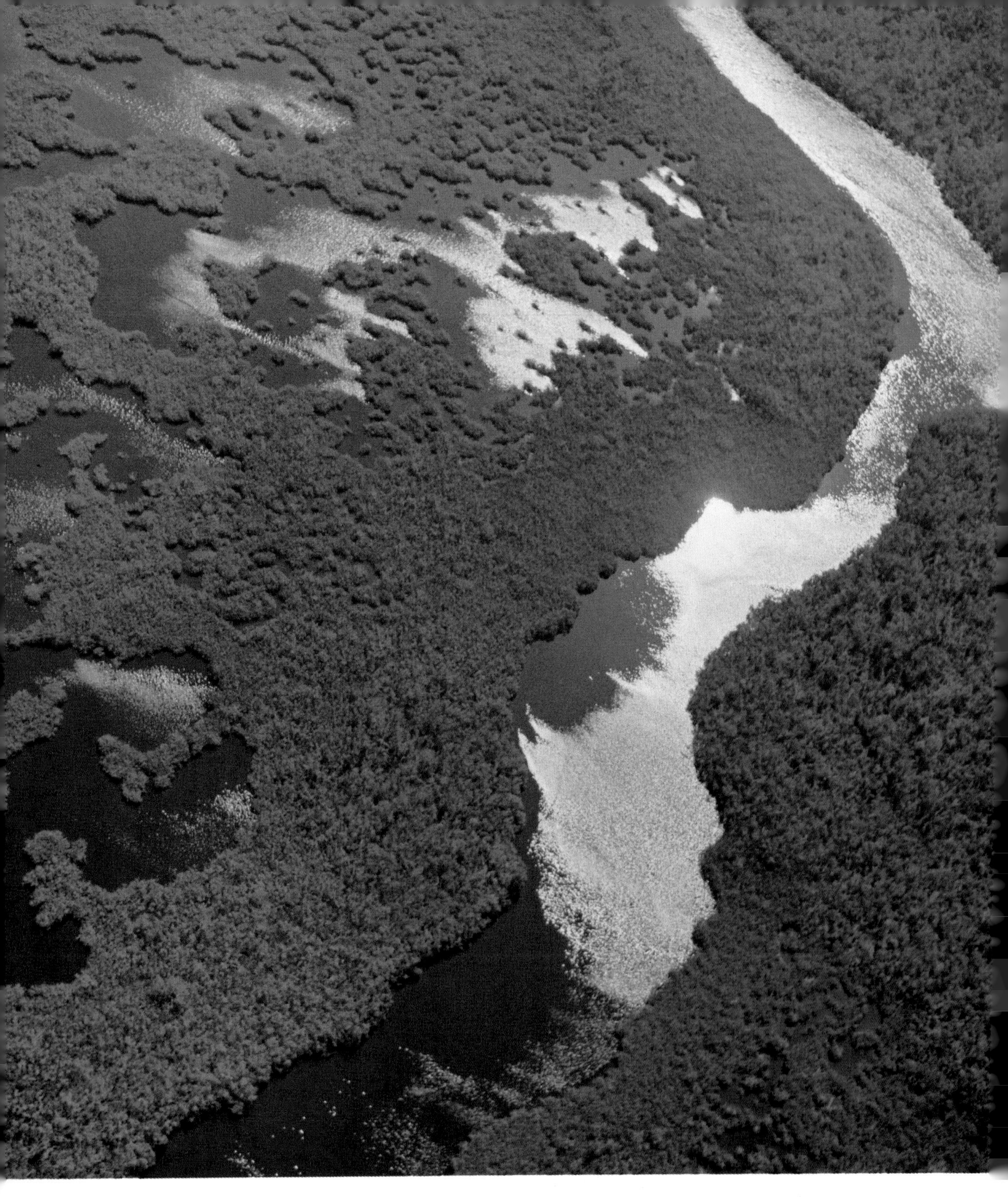

In the Everglades National Park at the southern tip of Florida a characteristic fauna and flora is being protected from the encroachment of man. Luxuriant mangrove swamps and marsh forests, together with a fauna rich in species, give to the area the special charm of a tropical wilderness.

The Everglades National Park has a big population of alligators. These reptiles usually lie idly in the innumerable water-courses, basking motionless in the sun. However, when they are disturbed or if they have sighted prey, they can move with astonishing agility. Outside the protected area, they have long since fallen victim to the hunter's greed for profit.

As well as the alligators, otters also occur in large numbers in the swamps of the Everglades National Park. They eat frogs, crustaceans and birds. However their preference for fish has nearly been the downfall of these exceptionally agile aquatic predators. They have already been completely exterminated in many areas.

Manatees live exclusively in the water because they are unable to drag their heavy body out on to dry land. They look rather like seals, but eat only plants; unlike seals they never eat fish. This picture was taken in the marine aquarium in Miami, because it is almost impossible to photograph manatees under water in the wild.

Whooping cranes are the most closely protected birds in the United States. There are only about fifty of them left. They spend the winter in the Arkansas Wildlife Refuge in the Gulf of Texas, and in spring they fly to the north of Canada where they nest and rear their young.

Left. The "wood ibis" is really a stork, the only one in North America.

About 150 years ago, some 25,000 ne-ne or Hawaiian geese lived on the islands of Haiwaii and Maui. By 1940, these beautiful geese had been reduced to less than a few dozen. Today they are once again to be seen in these islands. The ne-ne has been saved from extinction by breeding it in protected enclosures.

Unlike other geese, water is not essential to the Hawaiian goose or ne-ne. It is largely adapted to the dry volcanic regions of the Hawaiian Islands, where it nests on lava fields which are practically impassable owing to their jagged surface. Crossing the lava is rather like walking on broken glass, and this affords the geese effective protection against pursuit. The ne-ne is the only goose which lives under the tropical sun.

Today giant tortoises only survive on the Galapagos Islands and on the Mascarene Islands and a few other islands in the Indian Ocean. They may reach a weight of 650 pounds and are essentially land animals. Giant tortoises feed on cacti and other plants which they find on these parched islands.

The sea-cliffs of some of the Galapagos Islands are inhabited by marine lizards. These are the only iguanids which go into the sea—to find their food, seaweed. They can drink sea water, because with the help of salt glands they are able to excrete the excess salt. This process can be easily observed: it looks as though the lizards are spitting or sneezing.

Vicunas are the wild humpless camels of the high Andes in South America. At the altitudes between 10,000 and 18,000 feet at which they live the soil only produces very sparse grass. Vicunas have extremely fine wool and during the period of the Inca Empire vicuna wool was reserved for the chiefs. Nowadays these animals are being kept on ranches for their wool, but wild vicunas have become very rare.

The guanaco is another South American camel without a hump. It does not go up so high into the mountains as the vicuna but inhabits the plains. Today the guanaco has disappeared from the greater part of its original range. It is now only found in Patagonia and Tierra del Fuego. The sheep and cattle breeders of South America have almost exterminated the guanaco because it eats seven times as much grass as a sheep.

The spectacled bear lives an extremely secluded life in the cordillera country in South America from Venezuela to southern Peru. It is a solitary animal. To meet a spectacled bear in the wild and to photograph it is most unusual.

Right. The South American condor has a wing span of almost 10 feet and is one of the largest of all the birds capable of flight. It is ruthlessly hunted by sheep farmers because it is said to kill sheep. In fact it does not. As a vulture the condor is exclusively a carrion feeder.

Bull elephant seals, weighing over three tons and up to 21 feet long, are the largest members of the seal family. With the inflated nasal sac and gaping jaws they look just as threatening as they are in reality. But it is easy for sealers to stun an elephant seal with a cudgel and then to thrust a long knife into its heart. In this way elephant seals are slaughtered year after year.

Sea-lions and fur seals have been slaughtered in their thousands for the sake of their skins and oil. For this reason they have completely disappeared from many places. They belong among the eared seals and they are gregarious animals. When the females have produced their young, the colony is seething with excitement.

The Weddell seal is named after the enormous bay, discovered by James Weddell in 1823, which penetrates deep into the mainland of the Antarctic continent. The Weddell seal keeps open a permanent hole for breathing and for climbing out on to the ice. It uses its powerful snout to keep the hole free of ice.

Weddell seals are inhabitants of the Antarctic regions. These large, fat animals are up to 9 feet long and weigh about 940 pounds. On sunny days when there is no wind they lie out on the ice, often in dozens, lolling about and doing nothing.

Adelie penguins live only on the edges of the Antarctic continent. There they live in gigantic rookeries, in which sometimes up to 250,000 pairs nest together. Outside the breeding season they live and feed out at sea, as that is the only place where they do not freeze to death.

The greatest hazards for penguins in the Antarctic are the blizzards which suddenly blow up and often last for days. Many of the young birds fall victim to these. Snow and pieces of ice lodge in their downy plumage and the young often become incapable of shaking them off and keeping themselves warm.

The largest penguin is the emperor penguin. When standing erect at their full height, they are about 46 inches tall. They may weigh as much as 160 pounds. They walk long distances over the ice holding themselves erect. It is only where the terrain is broken up or the going rough that they lower themselves on to breast and belly and move forwards very fast, sliding like tortoises, and using their wings to help them along.

Emperor penguins are much rarer than Adelie penguins. Their nesting grounds are not nearly so densely populated and a colony of 3000 to 4000 pairs would be regarded as large. So far only about twenty breeding colonies have been found. Emperor penguins never walk on ground that is free of ice. They spend ten months of the year on the bare ice, occupied with rearing their young, and the other two months out in the icy sea.

Emperor penguins build no nest, indeed there is no nesting material available. They lay a single egg which weighs about a pound. The egg rests on the feet of the male who covers it with a fold of belly skin and incubates it for a period of two months. During this time the female covers the 80-100 miles to the open sea. After she has eaten enough to satisfy her own needs she fills herself with food for the young and goes back the way she came to relieve the male.

Australasia

AUSTRALIA

In 1959 we travelled to Australia and New Guinea, remaining in this part of the world from April to December. After a few weeks in Australia we went on to New Guinea and stayed on this large tropical island for five months before returning to Australia. This was, in fact, the very first expedition to be devoted to filming scenes for *The Rare Ones*. I took my wife with me and we were also accompanied by Thomas Schelkopf, a young zoology student. Five years later I returned for the third time, flying to eastern Australia from New Zealand in February 1964. Helmut Barth was there during June and July 1954, working on his own once again. My filming project received vigorous support in Australia. The wardens of the various reserves in Queensland, New South Wales and Victoria, and in particular Miss Ina Watson of the Fisheries and Wildlife Department in Melbourne, all gave help and encouragement.

I wanted to include in my film those animals that were particularly characteristic of Australia: various species of kangaroo, the koala, the duck-billed platypus, the spiny anteater, the lesser flying phalanger, the mallee fowl and the lyrebird. Some of these animals have already become rather rare and have had to be pretected in order to preserve them. We filmed them in Mt. Kosciusko State Park, Queen's National Park, Lamington National Park, in the Sherbrooke Sanctuary, in Stony Rises Reserve and in the Sir Colin MacKenzie Sanctuary, a large open zoo where many wild animals live under conditions that approach those in the wild.

All these areas lie on the east side of the continent, extending from the tropical north down to the temperate south. The highest mountains are found on this side of Australia and in contrast to the west, the south and the desert-like interior, the east side has a relatively high rainfall. Running and standing water occurs where rain falls; vegetation is encouraged and a richer and more abundant fauna has developed here than in the dry zones. Nevertheless, the geographical ranges of some Australian animal species are to a certain extent very limited and strictly localised. Many species are highly specialised. They are dependent upon specific food-plants which grow in certain habitats and climate plays an important role. One might almost describe the fauna of Australia as old-fashioned or even residual. It is undoubtedly very ancient. Most of the animals have never left their country of origin and have not changed their habits for thousands of years. For a long time there were no external influences and the Australian species have been isolated to a much greater extent than the animals of other continents. Living on an island which was discovered comparatively late by the white man, they have consequently not been subjected to as much interference as in other parts of the world. The first settlers were indeed astonished by what they found.

When thinking of Australian animals, the kangaroo is always the first to come to mind. Familiar to all, it is also common knowledge that the kangaroo is a marsupial which carries its young around in a pouch on the belly. We know too that it has very long hind-legs and a supporting tail, and that it can make long leaps. Many will say that kangaroos are not really rare or threatened with extinction. They are still so numerous in Australia that they are shot in thousands. Kangaroo meat is even exported to several countries.

It is true that the great red kangaroo is still very abundant and runs no danger of extermination at the present time. Living in the interior of Australia, it is very well adapted for life in the dry bush and desert, and is thus able to withstand long periods of drought. Nevertheless, its survival in periods of severe drought is endangered. Driven by thirst, it makes for the few remaining watering-places which are intended primarily for sheep. It is then subjected to constant persecution by farmers who naturally regard their sheep as much more valuable than wild kangaroos.

The great red kangaroo, however, is not the only species of kangaroo which inhabits this gigantic continent. Australia is the home not only of several kangaroo species but also of a large number of other marsupials of the most varied types. There are well over a hundred species. Marsupials also occur in America but not in any of the other continents. Australia is also the home of the monotremes.

There are not only hopping and jumping marsupials such as kangaroos, wallabies, marsupial mice and others, but also those that are exclusively arboreal and climbing, as well as others that only occur in or near to water. There are plains kangaroos, tree kangaroos, rock wallabies, marsupial 'cats', marsupial 'bears', marsupial 'squirrels', marsupial 'moles', marsupial 'rats' and marsupial 'mice'. The Tasmanian wolf may even still exist. All these include herbivores, carnivores and insectivores. Some are veritable giants, such as the great grey kangaroo and the great red kangaroo, others are tiny dwarfs and they come in all sizes between.

Although barely 200 years have gone by since the arrival of the white man, seven of the original marsupials of Australia and Tasmania have already been exterminated. Other species face the same fate and only strict protective measures can save them from extinction.

One of the marsupials that almost disappeared is the koala. I drove out to Stony Rises Reserve, which lies about 90 miles west of Melbourne, with Ina Watson and Fred Baum to look for these attractive animals. Since koalas were put under protection throughout Australia, they have bred well in this area and have re-established themselves in satisfactory numbers.

We soon came across our first koala in the tall eucalyptus trees growing in open woodland. The little animal sat motionless in the fork of a branch, only twenty to twenty-four feet above the ground. It did not move, even when we walked about under the tree and talked loudly to each other. Koalas are very sluggish animals; they are neither shy nor sensitive to disturbance of any kind. They sleep throughout the day, squatting in the forks of trees and looking like big woolly balls. They only become active in the evening when they move off to browse on eucalyptus leaves. Fred climbed the tree and woke the little animal up. It looked distinctly astonished but not at all frightened. Although it was not accustomed to being disturbed when asleep, it still did not climb away; first it stretched itself repeatedly, yawned and scratched for some minutes, slowly turning its head in all directions. Finally it started to move, taking it at a very leisurely pace, as though performing in slow-motion.

This tolerant attitude to everything going on around it quickly brought trouble to the koala after the arrival of the white man. The settlers soon learnt that this was an easy animal to shoot. It was not the kind of animal to climb or jump out of sight, and all one had to do was to keep shooting at the sitting target until it fell out of the tree. The koala is a marsupial with so little suspicion that even children sometimes kill it—the same children who probably possess a toy bear looking like a koala.

The koala has a very soft and cosy pelt which soon found a value on the market. Hundreds of thousands of koalas were killed and these attractive animals disappeared at an alarming rate from the forests of Australia. If conservation authorities had not called a halt to the endless slaughter at the right time, this marsupial would certainly have been exterminated. The koala is adapted to such a specialised diet that it will starve in the middle of a eucalyptus forest if the correct species of eucalyptus are not present; it feeds exclusively on the leaves. It is for this reason that one scarcely ever sees koalas in zoos outside Australia; obtaining food for them presents considerable difficulties.

The duck-billed platypus has a pelt that is just as soft and coveted as that of the koala. It too would have been in danger of extermination had it not been protected at the right time. The duck-billed platypus is the strangest and most primitive mammal in the world, there is nothing else quite like it. Only the spiny anteater or echidna is closely related and together they form the group known to zoologists as the monotremes. These two primitive animals have something in common in their unusual method of reproduction but their other habits are quite different.

I searched for a long time for the platypus in the slow-flowing and still waters of New South Wales and Victoria. It is completely tied to water where it finds its food and surroundings that suit it. I devoted several days to looking for the platypus but it just did not turn up. I found its burrows in the banks of the streams and discovered its tracks in the mud, I also saw it surface and dive again when I was able to follow its silhouette in shallow water. I even took some pictures but I was not satisfied with them; shots of the animal out of water, sitting on a bank or in the mud, were noticeably lacking. As the platypus is an animal of twilight and the night, it is almost impossible to keep it in view on a bright day for sufficient length of time to get film of it. It has still not been photographed often in the wild.

I therefore accepted the kind invitation of Messrs. Gasking and Mallet of the Sir Colin MacKenzie Sanctuary to photograph the platypus in their open zoo at Healsville near Melbourne. They have two of these remarkable animals in fine condition in a large show tank. Here one can see them well swimming under water. There are only a few platypuses in captivity as it is an exceptionally complicated matter to keep them properly. Their diet raises considerable difficulties because they have enormous appetites. In one night a platypus will eat more than half its own body weight. It burrows in the mud for worms and small aquatic animals which form its diet. The men at the Sir Colin MacKenzie Sanctuary put the animal in the free-flowing stream which runs through the reserve area so that I could film it in natural surroundings. In this way I finally obtained pictures of the duck-billed platypus as I wanted them.

The appearance and method of reproduction of this mammal are completely paradoxical and no parallel has been found in the animal world. It is about the size of a rabbit and, like the otter, beaver and musk rat, it is covered with soft, water-repellent fur. The mouth resembles the bill of a duck and there are webs between the toes on the feet as in a goose. The platypus builds a nest of grass and leaves in a nest chamber in the bank near the water where it lives. Then it lays eggs, normally two, like a bird. These, however, are not hard-shelled as birds' eggs, but have a parchment-like covering as in the eggs of snakes and lizards. These eggs are then incubated by the platypus and the young hatched by body warmth. They might be described as chicks if they were not the young of a mammal. They are reared on the mother's milk. This milk is not suckled by the young from teats as is usual among mammals. The milk of the platypus passes from glands on to the mother's belly where it is licked up by the young. A nest-building, egg-laying, incubating mammal with a duck's bill and goose feet: only the hairy pelt, the tail, similar to that of a beaver, and the four feet mark it out as a tetrapod. On the hind-legs the male platypus has poison spurs, a characteristic which every other mammal except the echidna lacks. Its scientific name, *Ornithorhynchus anatinus*, means 'duck-like bird's bill'.

As with the mammals, the bird fauna of Australia also contains some curious forms. We made considerable efforts to film some of these as for example the mallee fowl building its nest and practising its strange form of incubation, as well as the lyrebird performing its wonderful courtship dance. I spent considerable time and money on the latter as I wanted to film the complete courtship in colour and to record the appropriate sounds of the display at all stages.

In various different years Thomas Schelkopf, Helmut Barth, my wife and I stalked lyrebirds in the Queen's National Park near Sydney and in the Sherbrooke Sanctuary near Melbourne. The search for these birds was always extremely exciting. We made our way through rugged country and tried to locate them, following their shrieks and noisy calls which resounded through the hillsides and the forests; however, we also found it very tiring because lyrebirds are adept at hiding without making any sound at all.

In June, when winter comes to the southern hemisphere, the birds begin their courtship. The sun, after blazing brilliantly for such a long time, almost disappears. It shines weakly for only a few hours a day, lighting up the undergrowth with a yellow haze. In this light it is almost impossible to film in the dense forests. Cloud and rainfall often envelop them for days at a time during the Australian winter.

The lyrebird, so-called because of its lyre-shaped tail, is particularly active at this time of year as its breeding season starts in mid-autumn. During the other months one also sees them frequently but they are comparatively quiet and secretive; the decorative long tail of the male is then seldom unfolded and like the female, it slinks about rarely making any sound. Lyrebirds feed on worms, snails and other small animals, scratching them up laboriously with their large and powerful toes that are adapted for this purpose.

In the breeding season, however, the male is less concerned with eating. With the start of winter its song becomes louder and more frequent, its display more conspicuous as the female is courted. A small mound in a clearing in the forest serves as a stage for this pop-singer of the bird world. One male possesses several of these mounds which it constructs in dense undergrowth, among ferns or grass. About $1\frac{1}{2}$ to 2 square yards of the surface are completely cleared. Neither leaf nor twig is allowed to remain on it. The male devotes a large proportion of the short day to the maintenance of the mound and the remainder to song.

Although as large as a pheasant and like a peacock in its behaviour, the lyrebird in fact belongs among the song birds. Its song however changes constantly; unlike finches, thrushes, nightingales and so on, which inherit their songs from generation to generation, the lyrebird's song is very varied as it practises mimicry of other songsters which live in the same habitat. It also mimics other sounds, such as the humming of a circular saw, the chugging of an engine or the baying of hounds. A remarkably talented mimic, it is the most gifted and versatile songster among the birds. Its repertoire contains at least a dozen different calls of birds and other sounds. When all the dance arenas have been completed, the male visits them one after another. On each one it unfolds the whole splendour of its plumage, spreading the lyrate feathers and raising them above the head while dancing and singing. After a time the male moves to another mound, if it does not succeed in attracting the attention of a female.

Its territory is large and we had a lot of difficulty following the lyrebird around with the camera as it has very sharp eyes. At the slightest suspicion of movement, the male stops displaying and the plumage is lowered and folded again. We could only stalk it with extreme caution and the greatest care was needed in repositioning the camera and sound equipment. The male's devotion to display and song was remarkable. It was always standing on another mound and dancing. An audience was not lacking: a large owl watched the bird's courtship antics as keenly as the wallabies which were close by in the bush. The lyrebird took no notice, regarding them as intruders, and concentrated only on attracting a female lyrebird.

Observed in detail, it is only the tail that is shown off in the display. It is about 30 inches long and the two outer tail feathers, which in the resting position are in the form of a lyre, are widely spread out during the display and swung over its head. Between the outer tail-feathers there is a row of finely branched ornamental feathers which resemble those of the white egret. When in full display, it looks like a large, delicate fan which shakes as the bird moves.

This unique display of the breeding plumage, accompanied by a continuously ringing song, serves but one purpose. It is an expression of the urge to obtain a mate. The male tries to create an impression and endeavours to arouse the female by his stimuli, prancing about and showing off in the grand manner. And when a female puts in an appearance, the male's performance reaches a peak of ecstasy. For days and weeks this courtship goes on with undiminished force. Mating finally takes place somewhere in the bush, among tall ferns, in the plantation—the act of mating has only been witnessed by a few people.

The female lyrebird builds the nest in thick undergrowth, or in the fork of a tree or branches of a bush, and it is not easy to find. We were shown a nest but it was still empty. We knew, however, that one day a single egg would be laid in it, about as large as a duck's egg. The female lyrebird rears only a single chick; the male plays no part in this but goes on dancing and singing, only seeking to create an impression like a typical philanderer. We watched the displaying males throughout the whole of June and July. They were kept very busy because they apparently courted more than one female.

NEW GUINEA

From Australia we travelled on a small and comfortable Chinese ship to New Guinea. We landed at Lae on the north coast of the island. When we arrived it was pouring with rain, a characteristic of this tropical island which we were able to enjoy each day from now on. We were welcomed by missionaries of the Evangelical Lutheran Station of Neuendettelsau in Germany who had lived and worked in New Guinea for many years. It was the missionaries who showed us the way to the highlands and it was due to their kindness that I was able to bring away such valuable film material from this still largely uninhabited and inaccessible island. We originally intended to stay only a few weeks but our visit ran into months. We became so fascinated not only by the birds of paradise but also by the natives that we made a special film on New Guinea. This was shown on BBC Television under the title of *Savage Paradise*.

After Greenland, New Guinea is the largest island in the world. It is the home of the exceptionally beautiful birds of paradise. Forty-three species of these legendary birds are found in New Guinea and a few small neighbouring islands. I felt that my conservation film would not be complete without these beautiful birds and it was on their account that we made the journey to this remote part of the world. Myths and legends about them have arisen from their effortless flight. At one time they were regarded as footless creatures, as messengers from heaven, which moved merely by floating in space and which were also able to hold on to branches with their bills in order to sip dew and nectar. The first explorers called them birds of paradise, since when the name has stuck. They are the most beautiful birds in the world and are constantly in danger of extermination. Their valuable feathers were of great importance to the first sailors who came to New Guinea. Traders still pay high prices for them, even though trading in birds of paradise feathers is strictly forbidden today. Only the inaccessibility of their habitat can protect these birds in the future. The jungles of the coastal areas and the mountain forests where there are no paths provide their best protection. This tropical island is largely inhabited only by savages and there are many places where laws can neither be made nor enforced.

In our search for these legendary birds we made only slow progress through mysterious rain-forests, across deep ravines and over high mountains. There are only a few roads and paths in New Guinea. At the mission stations we always obtained board and lodging, together with interpreters and valuable advice. Small aircraft belonging to the missionaries transported us from one area to another but after landing at each place we had to make our own way on foot. Our progress was much hampered by the heat and the daily showers of rain. We crossed rushing torrents on shaky bridges built by the natives of bamboo and lianas, where a single false step would have meant falling to death.

The mountains rise to over 16,000 feet. The sky was usually heavy with cloud and the sun only appeared for a few hours in the day. In temperate latitudes 8000-12,000 foot mountains would be covered in winter with snow and ice but here the forests are a luxuriant tangle of growth at this height. With such profuse vegetation the distribution of animal life also extends to these altitudes. Animals lurk in cover and on every square yard a merciless struggle for existence takes place, silently for the most part and without any sign of commotion. We constantly saw evidence of the cautiousness and fear shown by one animal after another. The inhabitants of these forests must remain constantly on the alert. It is no place for falling into a deep sleep or for tarrying on the way. An animal must be ready at all times to defend itself or to outwit its enemy.

In the twilight of the rain-forest we heard crowned pigeons giving their singular growls, a sound that has an unearthly quality. The crowned pigeon is the largest of all wild pigeons, almost the size of a duck. Like our pheasants, they move about the undergrowth in small groups. They only fly when pursued or when they go to roost in the trees at night. A generation ago their remarkably beautiful head-feathers, like the feathers of birds of paradise, could be seen adorning the hats of ladies of fashion in the streets of the world's cities—a peculiar caprice of fashion which almost brought about their extermination. Today nature conservation forbids the killing of these species.

Every day we saw different animals as we climbed higher into the mountainous country where there are few paths. In the foliage of a breadfruit tree a cuscus moved forwards as though in slow-motion. Another marsupial climbed from stem to stem in a bamboo thicket: a tree kangaroo. This species does not jump like the plains kangaroos of Australia, but moves by climbing among the trees. Grassy plains are absent in this forested mountain area. These large animals have no enemies, there are no large predators in New Guinea.

We went on, mile after mile, penetrating deeper into the mysterious mountains. Only the natives are familiar with the few secret paths which run through the darkness of the mountain forests but, as they move quietly along them, they listen carefully for the loud sounds which constantly emanate from the jungle. The lives of the natives are dominated by a belief in spirits but the ghostly cries which they hear are not those of unearthly demons but the calls of a bird of paradise, one of the long-tailed sickle-bills. These birds live along the mountain slopes at an altitude of 3500 to 4500 feet. The long-tail, the superb bird of paradise and Princess Stephanie's bird of paradise also live here.

Our native guides were continually stopping as we penetrated deeper into the dark forests, but we were dependent on them as without them our undertaking would have been doomed to failure. They alone were able to interpret the signs of nature which were strange to us. When they stopped and showed doubt or actual fear, we only had to shake our heads and laugh, and this was sufficient to calm them down and get them moving again.

Mountain forests with plenty of undergrowth form the habitat of the smaller species of birds of paradise. These seldom come out into the light of the sun but spend their lives in the half-light. They do not remain long on any one branch. Their small wings 'whir' loudly and one usually hears them before they come into view. It is as though they are driven to conceal their magical beauty from the eyes of man. Their restlessness is only allayed temporarily while they feed. Our only opportunities to film them came when they paused to feed and we had to work fast.

The courtship display of Duke Rudolph's bird of paradise looks like the antics of a clown. It holds itself upside down, an engaging position which is rare among the birds of paradise. Their attractive plumage is of heavenly beauty and their song sounds like a plaintive sobbing as it rings through the forests.

The little king bird of paradise and the fantastically adorned King of Saxony bird of paradise are decidedly secretive in their behaviour. The little king is no larger than a sparrow and has a fiery red plumage. The King of Saxony bird of paradise has two feathers on the back of the head which glisten like enamel plates. These are about 16 inches long and are particularly coveted by the natives as nasal adornments.

Duke Rudolph's bird of paradise, King of Saxony's bird of paradise, Augusta Victoria's bird of paradise, Princess Stephanie's bird of paradise—what odd names for birds. They remind us that a part of New Guinea was once a German colony and the birds were named by their discoverers in honour of the rulers of the country at that time.

In a remote valley of the Jimi River, we found the lesser bird of paradise at an altitude of about 6000 feet after weeks of searching. The dance arena of the *gey gurri*, as it is called by the natives of the central highlands, was at the top of a forest tree that towered above all the others. The dancing display, typical of this species, took place in the tree. I believe that we are among the first to have recorded on film and sound this spectacle of the steamy mountain forests of New Guinea.

The courtship display started soon after sunrise. It was introduced by the plucking and throwing down of small twigs. The top part of the dance tree was already completely denuded. The birds remained in the same tree, following the natural rhythm of their display in a limited area of the branches while waiting for the arrival of receptive females. Only short pauses interrupted the ceremony before it continued again with renewed fervour. Hours went by and it was noon when the birds gradually moved off and disappeared into the surrounding forest.

Not every native is allowed to kill this golden-yellow bird. Only the owner of the land on which the dance tree grows is allowed to kill it by shooting with bow and arrow. However much he covets the plumes for adornment, no native would disregard this unwritten law. The birds are repeatedly shot at during their courtship display. Nothing is so treasured by the children of this wilderness as the plumes of birds of paradise. They have great value as barter and are the equivalent of pure gold to the natives. The trading jargon of the island can be translated thus: one large gold-lip shell, one fat pig, one beautiful woman is worth so-and-so many birds of paradise skins. This is why these birds have had such a high market value.

The ornithologist Fred Shaw-Meyer of Nondugl gave me repeated help in my search for birds of paradise and I regard him as the best authority on these species. He wrote to me about their habitat and behaviour, and he also told me in which altitude zone I should find them. I had already succeeded in taking pictures of eleven different species of birds of paradise when one day an opportunity presented itself to complete the dozen. It happened thus.

We were walking through a rain-forest one morning, led by the natives from one of the villages in the highlands, when they brought us to a halt in front of a casuarina tree to which they proudly drew our attention. We stood and looked at the casuarina. This was the favourite courtship arena of the red-plumed bird of the paradise (*P. raggiana*). The native landowner had erected a small hut only a few yards away from the dance tree. From this hut he was able to satisfy his requirements for personal adornment. The owner of the hut took me inside and we both squatted close together in the small hide. The lens of my camera pointed over his naked shoulder to the peep-hole. A bird was already giving its dancing display and the Papuan, bursting with eagerness, was already taking aim with his arrow. It was only with great difficulty that I was able to restrain him from shooting until I had had time to film the display. Unnoticed by the lovesick birds we waited for the dancing display to reach its climax so that I could film it at the right moment. The birds were distributed, each one on its own branch, over the whole of the top part of the casuarina. A very old male in brilliant plumage led the display.

This male was the principal dancer and, like the lurking Papuan, the master of the tree in the rain-forest. The red bird tumbled in ecstasy from twig to twig, while the younger birds followed his example, dancing like marionettes. He moved a little lower down in the branches for a short rest where he was dangerously near to our hide. I could scarcely restrain my native companion any longer; at heart a hunter, his arrow was ready, the string taut. The red bird started to dance again, his calls came louder and his display was even more passionate than before. A female who came close to him brought him to a peak of rapture.

The first arrow streaked past him. The bird scarcely faltered and went on hopping and singing. The sun glinted on his red adornment plumes. The bird became aware of us too late and fell to the ground, pierced by an arrow. The Papuan wanted new feathers to adorn his curly head at the forthcoming feast and now he would be able to attend it, splendidly adorned in traditional style.

Neither calendar nor clock has any place in the natives' way of life and there are no fixed feast days. They simply assemble together when the village pigs are sufficiently large and fat and a Lucullan banquet can be prepared. The beat of the drums and the sound of mystical singing rises to a crescendo. Clusters of birds of paradise feathers gleam on the men's heads as multi-coloured head-dresses; they are also fixed in their noses and ears. We are able to recognise individual feathers as belonging to the species which they originally adorned. Many birds of paradise have lost their lives on account of this traditional adornment of the natives which includes caps of cassowary feathers and parrot wings, head-bands of beetles, and collars of clams and human teeth. There are also wigs of human hair, matted and painted in gaudy colours; these are made of curly hair shorn from the heads perhaps of their long-suffering women or from the decapitated heads of dead enemies. In the hurly-burly of the dance, they all crowd together, forming a phalanx across the arena—the epitome of primitive power. They carry their weapons in the dance and are ready to use them if overwhelmed by the excitement of the massed performance.

What are these men thinking about as they let themselves go in passionate abandon? What goes on inside their primitive minds? We do not know but can only marvel at this unique spectacle, and make use of our modern equipment to record as much as possible of it on film. How much longer will these primitive people continue to adorn themselves with birds of paradise feathers? How much longer, indeed, will they continue to populate this tropical island which to them is still the Land of Spirits?

NEW ZEALAND

On the return journey from the Antarctic we visited New Zealand in December 1963 and January–February 1964. This small island realm, set apart from the world at large must surely captivate every traveller by its scenic beauty and by the friendliness of the people. At all events, I was greatly impressed by New Zealand and not least on account of its interesting animal life which is unique.

One finds almost all kinds of terrain in New Zealand. There is forest country with subtropical and temperate vegetation; there are grassy plains, lovely hilly country, dreamlike fjords and mountains covered with ice and snow. There are many solitary islands, extinct and still active volcanoes, hot springs and geysers, rushing streams and rivers, and fantastically beautiful lakes.

In these islands so richly endowed by nature there is still plenty of room. There are less than three million people distributed throughout the country including the Maoris, the original inhabitants. Unfortunately the European immigrants, who settled in New Zealand since 1769, have radically changed the original appearance of the landscape in many places. They have wantonly cut down the luxuriant rain-forests, burnt them to the ground and taken the land into cultivation. Today they graze their domestic animals on most of the areas which have been denuded of their natural vegetation by such violent measures. Where dense forests once grew, millions of sheep now graze all over the place. Wild animals from all sorts of countries have been introduced into the original landscape. Deer from Scotland, chamois from Austria, tahr from the Himalaya, wapiti and geese from Canada, opossums and swans from Australia, and numerous small birds from Europe—all these alien species now live alongside the indigenous animals of New Zealand. The results of this irresponsible introduction of foreign game are catastrophic. The fertile soil has been trodden and loosened by the rapidly increasing animal populations and is being washed into the sea by rain. The green mountain slopes have become desolate, the grazing grounds have been eaten bare and the forests destroyed. The introduced species dominate the endemic fauna which is now reduced either to sad remnants or to total extermination.

A halt must be called to the uncontrolled felling of the forests and to the arbitrary introduction of foreign animals, if the natural balance is not going to totter still farther. The New Zealand nature conservation movement has tackled the problem vigorously. Within the space of a short time they have established several extensive areas for the protection of animals, plants and scenery and have thus managed to prevent further damage at this late stage. Today New Zealand has over ten National Parks and many smaller protected areas and scenic spots. One fifteenth of the country is under protection.

Mr R. Cleland, Supervisor of the National Parks, and Mr K. H. Miers, Director of the Fish and Wildlife Division in Wellington granted me the equivalent of a free pass which enabled me to enter all the protected areas and I was able to work in them without restrictions. Messrs. Nicholls, Burke,

Schofield, Croft, Meisy, Walker, Sharpe, Fox and Japson did everything possible to ensure that rare and threatened species in various National Parks and Reserves were accessible for filming.

Stephen's Island lies in Cook Strait, between North and South Island. A fisherman took us there and the lighthouse keeper winched us up on to land in a huge cradle. The sea around this rocky island is so choppy that one cannot approach the cliffs in a boat. We landed, in this fashion, on the island of the tuataras, one of the few localities where this rare reptile is found. It only occurs on Stephen's Island and on a few neighbouring islands. These reptiles are classified in a special group, the Rhynchocephalia; their skull has two bony arches, which are absent in the true lizards and the snakes, although still present in the crocodilians.

The tuatara is a truly primitive animal and one can rightly call it a living fossil. The herpetologist Uta Hick described it thus: 'It is a survival from the Mesozoic period. It is the only survivor of an animal group which was already in existence when the long extinct dinosaurs were still young.' I had never had the chance to film such a primitive reptile as this and I took particular care to treat it with the respect due to a species of such ancient lineage.

Tuatara is the original Maori name for this reptile which has a third eye, the pineal eye, which can be seen through the top of the head in the young, but is obscured by thickened skin in the adult. Over its nape and back runs a row of easily visible, flexible horny plates. Although these plates look like a series of prickly spines, they are quite soft to touch. Tuataras are capable of attaining a good age; they do not become sexually mature until they are 20 years or more. The eggs, which are buried in the ground, do not hatch for about twelve months. An adult has a length of about 25 inches and weighs approximately two pounds.

Normally the tuatara digs a burrow in the soil where it rests underground during the day and in front of which it also suns itself when not disturbed. Sometimes, however, they take possession of the nesting holes of the small petrels which breed in thousands on Stephen's Island. They show no hesitation in driving out the occupant of the burrow and taking it over for themselves. In doing so they destroy the petrel's eggs and eat the young. We frequently found the downy chicks of the petrel with heads bitten off. But normally the tuatara feeds on the large crickets, which live on the island and sometimes a burrow is shared peaceably with a petrel.

Stephen's Island is also the home of a rare frog. A small area of boulders of only about 60 square yards is the sole habitat of this little animal, of which the closest relatives occur in North America. The lighthouse keeper assured me that only fifteen people had ever found this frog. During the last war, thousands of soldiers, who were serving on the island, searched repeatedly for five years for it without success. Naturally we also went to look for it but we had better luck. Helmut Barth discovered it on the second day and he is thus the sixteenth man to have found the rarest frog in the world! Externally it scarcely differs from the other members of its family. Only the webs on its feet are very much reduced; webs cannot be of any use to it on Stephen Island as there is neither standing nor running water there.

In search of the kiwi, the national bird of the New Zealanders, we went to the damp rain-forests where there were many tree-ferns. The New Zealanders like to call themselves 'kiwis' and one finds this bird depicted everywhere as a trademark.

The kiwi is a very difficult bird to film as it is active only at dusk or after dusk. We were only able to take short sequences when it suddenly emerged in front of us or remained briefly in a well-lit area before disappearing again. It is completely flightless. It has only tiny wing stumps and no tail. But it has very powerful legs, on which it can run astonishingly fast. When pursued it always seeks a dark hiding-place, a tree-trunk, a hole in the ground or somewhere similar. It is a primitive type of bird. There were already kiwis living in New Zealand when moas were still there. The latter are now extinct but the kiwi still survives. Its plumage does not consist of the usual bird feathers. It looks much more like a long-haired animal with a tattered coat which seems to wrap right round the bird's body. The Maoris put a high value on the pliant, soft feathers and made them into cloaks and coverings.

As a flightless bird the kiwi has to seek its food on the ground; it feeds mainly on worms and so it constantly probes the soft earth with its long bill, like a snipe. As it feeds chiefly after dark, it possesses a very keen sense of smell. It seeks its food by smell, like a hedgehog. For this purpose the nostrils of a kiwi are situated far forward at the tip of the bill and not at the base as in other birds.

The kiwi is protected throughout the whole of New Zealand. More and more of its habitat is being destroyed as the forests are cut down. Also the introduced cats and other small carnivores find it easy to catch this harmless earth-bound bird.

Mount Cook National Park on the eastern side of South Island is one of the large protected areas. Here the impressive scenery of mountains, covered with snow and ice, together with the flora and fauna of the whole area, are protected from the onslaught of man. Mount Cook (12,349 feet), the highest mountain in New Zealand, towers above all the other big mountains.

This is where we filmed the kea, a parrot the size of a raven. Unfortunately the kea is ruthlessly hunted everywhere outside the protected area. The sheep-farmers pay high premiums for its shooting. They firmly believe that it kills sheep and eats their flesh, although not a single scrap of evidence exists to support their claim that the kea is a killer of sheep. This type of misrepresentation of the habits of various species has already brought about the extermination of many kinds of animal. It is extremely difficult to convince the farmers to the contrary. Because the kea has been seen at the carcasses of sheep, it is dubbed a killer and sentenced to death. The kea will eat the flesh of sheep from time to time and perhaps pluck wool from the fleece to line its nest, but the sheep-farmers will not admit that the sheep was already dead before the kea arrived on the scene.

Fjordland National Park, the largest wildlife reserve on either Island, lies right in the southern part of the New Zealand Alps. It covers an area of about 5800 square miles and is one of the largest areas in the world where wild life and natural scenery are protected. Fjordland National Park is larger than all the other New Zealand reserves put together. Here completely undisturbed forests, many unclimbed mountains, unnamed and unharnessed rivers, lovely lakes and picturesque fjords, deep gorges and peaceful sea bays, show clearly how beautiful and harmonious nature can be if left by man in its original condition. A seaplane of the National Parks Administration took us right into the middle of this beautiful wilderness. The water on which our aircraft landed was ice-cold. We ferried our film equipment over to the shores of a small lake of fabulous beauty which was framed by trees of virgin forest. On the edge of the shore there was a simple hut in which we took up quarters with a young forestry assistant and our own helpers.

The birds that we were looking for in this remote area are among the rarest and indeed the least photographed in the world. In New Zealand, apart from the tuatara and the little frog, our attention was focused only on the birds. There have never been any strictly indigenous mammals in New Zealand, if one excludes two species of bat. These were the moa-hunters of about 1200 years ago. They were followed by the Maoris, Polynesian seafarers, who arrived here long before the appearance of the white man. New Zealand was already separated from the mainland before the age of mammals. It became isolated as an island and had no further connection with the continents on which the mammals later developed.

Round this small lake there lives a bird which has already made a name for itself as a much discussed species in ornithological circles throughout the world. It is the takahe or *Notornis*, as it is referred to in professional circles. The colour of this bird is very unusual; its plumage is bright cobalt blue and its bill coral-red. It is about the size of a duck. It is astonishing that a bird with such striking coloration should have been able to remain hidden for so long that for fifty years it was considered to be extinct. Although quite common previously, from about the turn of the last century the takahe was not seen again in New Zealand. From then on its name was erased from the list of living species. Then in 1949 there suddenly came the surprising news that this long-lost bird had been found again. Dr Orbell, an ornithologist from Invercargill, in New Zealand, who in common with many others did not believe that this rail had really disappeared, found it again at a small lake after a long and intensive search. It was in his honour that the lake—the same lake where we landed in the seaplane—was named Lake Orbell.

'You'll be lucky if you find it,' declared the nature conservation people in Wellington. 'You must look for collections of droppings and then its nest will not be far away. It has the habit of leaving its excrement close to the nesting site,' they explained.

We followed their advice and made a careful search of the area. On the third day we had the luck to find not only the bird but also a nest with one egg. The takahes were in the vicinity; they moved silently from one grass clump to the next, constantly re-appearing and disappearing again. They were not particularly alarmed, only suspicious and we had the feeling that we were being closely watched.

We built a hide. We waited behind bushes and clumps of grass for it. We set up two cameras at separate places and eventually managed to film these secretive birds. We also put out our microphone and succeeded in recording their loud calls which echoed from the mountain slopes which enclose the lake. Our work at Lake Orbell was favoured by beautiful, sunny weather; we were especially fortunate in this as there is a high rainfall in this mountain area, up to 250 inches in the year.

The takahe is mainly vegetarian in its diet. It favours the flowering heads and stem bases of large grasses. It pulls off the panicles like geese and fowl do, but it also eats the soft bases of the stalks in a way that is unusual for a rail. It draws the stalk out of the sheath, holds it like a parrot between its long toes and then bites it off piece by piece. It throws away the hard middle part of the stem. Its long and large toes allow the bird to walk unhindered on mud and floating plants. It is particularly exciting to be confronted by a bird which was once said to be extinct and we did not spare the film but exposed many feet on the takahe. The weather then broke and the small aircraft flew in over the mountains to fetch us, taking us safely back to Te Anan, the charming place at the entrance to the Fjordland National Park.

Living in the same reserve area is another rare species, perhaps the rarest bird in the world, the kakapo or owl parrot. For several years it has only been seen in a small side valley deep in the mountains. Even the New Zealand experts do not know exactly how many of them still exist.

'There are still eight kakapos for certain in this isolated valley,' said the experts who try to determine the relic population of this species from year to year. Optimists among them believe there might still be twenty. They added: 'It is only because the deer, which eat the food-plant of the kakapo, have not yet reached this area that a few pairs can still survive,' and I can still hear the bitterness in their voices as they spoke of the detested red deer.

The kakapo in fact looks rather like a tawny owl and is about the same size. Like the kiwi and the takahe it is a bird which has almost completely abandoned flight. For thousands of years it did not need to fly as it had neither enemies nor food competitors and was not pursued in any way. Today the deer are a serious threat to its survival as they eat away its food-plant.

The kakapo, like the kiwi, is also a bird of the twilight and night. It is uncommonly difficult to photograph and we were happy to have achieved at least a few usable film sequences and a couple of still photographs. These were all made with the help of artificial light, as this retiring bird spends the day in the darkness of its hiding-places. At night it slinks quietly from cover to cover like a cat, nibbling a fern frond or a grass stem here and there. The half-eaten vegetation is the only sign left behind which serves as an indication of the presence of this nocturnal bird.

No one can say how long the rare kakapo will continue to exist in its solitary locality in the mountain valley in the Fjordland National Park of New Zealand. The New Zealand conservationists are doing everything possible to preserve it. If they do not succeed in protecting it from the deer which are gaining the upper hand, then the last kakapo will succumb in its own country to competition from the alien intruders.

The still and slow-flowing waters of eastern Australia and Tasmania form the habitat of the duck-billed platypus. It makes a burrow in a sloping bank and lies hidden underground during the day.

The duck-billed platypus is surely the most remarkable mammal in the world. They have webbed feet and a bill like a duck; they build a nest, lay eggs and hatch them out. But the young are fed on milk from the mother.

It is only on the island continent of Australia that such a primitive mammal as the spiny anteater or echidna could survive as a species for over 150 millions years. This mammal also lays eggs but hatches them out in a skin pouch on the belly.

As a result of reckless hunting by sheep farmers in central Australia, the great grey kangaroo became so rare that it has been given protection in certain areas. The great red kangaroo is still comparatively abundant in central Australia.

Right. The koala, like the kangaroo, is a marsupial. It is very easy to hunt and kill because during the day it sits in a tree for hours at a time and is not easily disturbed.

During courtship the male lyrebird displays its tail feathers; the lyre-like shape of the tail gives the bird its name. The lyrebird is a remarkably skilled mimic and can imitate the strange cries of animals. Although it is as large as a pheasant and resembles a peacock during its courtship display, in fact it belongs among the song-birds.

Left. Leadbeater's opossum is an arboreal marsupial with protruding eyes, which only becomes active at night; it resembles the European fat dormouse. Leadbeater's opossum was at one time reckoned to be already extinct, but a few years ago it was seen again near Melbourne.

The strikingly coloured takahe, a rail about the size of a duck, astonishingly enough managed to live hidden for half a century in among the tall grasses which fringe Lake Orbell and in the forests on the mountain slopes around the lake. It disappeared without trace from the turn of the century and it was not until 1948 that the New Zealand naturalist Dr. Orbell rediscovered it here.

Left. The area round the idyllic Lake Orbell in the Fiordland National Park in New Zealand is the only place in which some 50 pairs of takahe still occur today.

The kiwi, the national bird of New Zealand, is completely flightless and about the size of a domestic fowl. Like a hedgehog it uses its sense of smell in searching for food. The nostrils are positioned far forwards on the bill, which it pokes into the soil seeking for worms and insects.

Those parts of the primeval forests of New Zealand which man has still left standing are now protected; they provide a habitat for the last representatives of a bird fauna that was once very rich in species. Precipitation is high and the rain-forests grow luxuriantly. It is only here that the original bird fauna of New Zealand can survive.

The kakapo or owl parrot is one of the rarest birds in the world. It lives in a confined and secluded valley in the Fiordland National Park; its numbers scarcely exceed a dozen. It is almost incapable of flight. As it has no enemies, it has no need to fly.

Right. The population of the kea parrot is seriously threatened unless the bird is soon declared a protected species throughout the whole of New Zealand. It is only safe within the national parks, because sheep farmers believe it—mistakenly—to be a killer of sheep.

On the Otago Peninsula on the eastern side of the South Island of New Zealand for decades there has been a small colony of royal albatrosses. The single chick which a pair of royal albatrosses rear every two to three years has to be fed by its parents for nine months before it is fledged. Albatrosses return to land only during the breeding season, the remainder of their lives being spent out in the oceans of the world.

Wild ducks usually live on slow-flowing or comparatively still waters. The blue duck of New Zealand, however, prefers rushing streams which come down from the mountains. They dive in the fast-running water for their food and nest on the banks. Blue ducks usually live in pairs; they do not congregate into large flocks like other ducks.

Two very rare animals occur on a few small islands in the Cook Strait, which separates the two main islands of New Zealand. These are a small frog and a lizard-like reptile. Only the seclusion of these islands has so far saved them from extinction. The rare frog lives in the boulder scree shown here, which is about as large as a football field.

The scientific name for this frog is Leiopelma. It is about 1½ inches long and it has no webs between the toes. It could not make use of them as there is no water on the small island. This amphibian relies on moisture from the soil, plants and dew.

The tuatara of New Zealand has been described as a living fossil. It is the only surviving member of a group which lived about 170 million years ago. The tuatara, which is about 24 inches long, sometimes enters the nesting burrows of petrels and chooses them as a refuge.

Right. New Guinea is the largest island in the world after Greenland. In this 'Land of the Spirits', the dense rain-forests are inhabited by Papuans who worship spirits. Deep gorges divide up the mountainous terrain which supports a remarkable fauna. There are still many parts of it which have not yet been explored.

Crowned pigeons live in the undergrowth of tropical forests in New Guinea. Their deep growling calls have an unearthly quality as they resound through the jungle and it is hardly surprising that the Papuans believe these noises to be made by spirits. Crowned pigeons are not yet protected and have almost been exterminated for the sake of their attractive head feathers.

Right. In the densely forested island of New Guinea there are no open plains and the kangaroos have become arboreal. Instead of leaping across open country, as in Australia, the tree kangaroos live in the trees and bushes, clinging and climbing among the branches.

Among the many species of birds in New Guinea the multicoloured birds of paradise take pride of place. The little king bird of paradise is one of the smallest of these beautiful birds, it is no larger than a finch. It would have come near to extermination, on account of the decorative value of its brilliant plumage, if it had not been protected.

The lesser bird of paradise is one of the larger members of this group. Only the males have the beautiful ornamental plumes. They use these during courtship display, spreading their brilliantly coloured plumage, hopping and dancing in the trees in front of the females. No white man is allowed to hunt birds of paradise; only the natives are permitted to kill them with bows and arrows.

The feathers of the legendary birds of paradise play an important role in the life of the natives of New Guinea. They are used as adornment in ceremonial dances. These multicoloured feathers mean as much to the Papuans as money. They reckon that one large bivalve shell, one fat pig, one pretty girl are worth so many bird of paradise skins.

Asia

locomotives whose brakes have failed, which I found quite alarming, but our riding elephants stood firm like a barrier of armoured shields. We had been allotted the best riding elephants in Kaziranga and they stood their ground, refusing to give way by even an inch. Although such charges are usually only sham attacks, it has been known for riding elephants to run off with their riders when seriously attacked by rhinos.

We frequently got down from the elephants and filmed from the ground. Here the camera had a steadier position than on the back of an elephant where it was inevitably subjected to vibration and movement. We never knew whether the rhino intended to attack or whether it was merely inquisitive, and it was of considerable advantage not to have to take flight when the rhino came to within fifteen to eighteen feet of the camera. Filming under an elephant's belly is scarcely a familiar position for a camera-man but it was reassuring to have the massive body towering above us.

There are also some wild elephants remaining in the Kaziranga Reserve. We came across them and filmed them just as we did the wild water buffalos, swamp deer, the wild boars, the numerous egrets, storks and pelicans. We also found the tracks of a tiger which had ripped open a newly born rhino calf. The enraged mother must have driven the tiger off before we arrived.

From Kaziranga we flew back to Calcutta and Bombay, then on to Keshod in Gujarat State. From Keshod it is not far to the Gir Forest Reserve where the last remaining lions on the continent of Asia live; their numbers are estimated at about 280. These big cats are continuously controlled and watched by the State Forestry Department which also administers the lions' protected area. It is not difficult to get a sight of the lions in this area, although the terrain is covered with dense bushy forest and is nothing like as easy to see across as the plains and savannahs of Africa. But the shikaris, who are part of the staff of Gir Forest, are first-class hunters and they know the favourite spots of the lions. They know where they like to rest during the heat of the day, where they go to drink in the late afternoon and where they prefer to hunt.

In the Land-Rover which brought us out to the area where the lions were, a goat was frequently on board with us, as well as the skilful shikaris. The goat had an important part to play on our filming expedition as it was our bait. Its bleating would attract the attention of the big cats and draw them towards us; for the most part it was vociferous but when it stopped bleating, one of the hunters tweaked its ear. It seemed a bizarre idea that the so-called king of beasts could be lured by the bleat of such a humble animal but it certainly worked successfully.

Although there is plenty of larger game in the Gir Forest, such as deer, boars, nilgai and wild peacocks, the lions often attack the domesticated animals of the farmers who have settled there. The lowing of cattle and the bleating of goats are consequently familiar sounds to the lion. Furthermore it is easier for a lion to bring down a domesticated animal than the many faster and more wary wild animals. Such damage is however made good by the forest authorities so that the lions can be preserved. This is an unparalleled example of conservation at work, on bold and imaginative lines, in a country which undoubtedly has more important problems to solve.

To the north-west of Gir Forest, the last remaining Indian wild asses live in the Little Rann of

Kutch. Everywhere in India, rare animals are protected by the Forestry Department and this applies also to the Little Rann which is situated not far from the Pakistani border.

We had to drive far out into the brackish-water lake of the Little Rann, which at this time was completely dried out, before we found the wild asses. They looked small and rather indistinct as they stood in the shimmering heat on the treeless horizon. There was a herd of about thirty in the distance but we drew near quite fast as the floor of the dried out lake was as hard as cement. As we approached the asses started to move off, going farther out into the shimmering expanse of the lake basin. They appeared to be floating over the ground, their shapes reflected as in a mirage. As we chased after them, it developed into a race between animal and machine, the asses galloping away as fast as they could. All our photographs had to be taken through the side windows or windscreen of the vehicle, travelling at a speed of 25 to 35 miles per hour. Sometimes we managed to gain on them, sometimes they drew away. The wild asses withdrew deeper and deeper into their strange domain, in which there is unlimited space but not a single blade of grass. No one can follow them for long when they retreat into this area, and we soon realised, from the stuttering of the over-heated engine, that in the long run the asses were bound to win.

JAPAN

From the blistering heat of India the aeroplane quickly brought us into cooler regions again. When we stepped out of the aeroplane in Tokyo we were met by a cold blast of wind. It was February and winter-time in Japan, just as it had been in Germany when we had set out on our expedition four weeks earlier. We were greeted with great kindness by people from the Nature Conservation Society of Japan. Dr Tamura, Mr Ishigami, Dr Miyawaki, Mrs Otsuki and others had already got everything ready for my filming in the island realm of Japan and it all worked like clockwork.

We first travelled down to the southern island of Kyushu with Dr Miyawaki as interpreter. In an area that is decidedly cold but usually free of snow, hundreds of white-necked cranes and hooded cranes overwinter every year. We left the train at the small town of Izumi where we were greeted at the railway station by the mayor, his assistant and a German priest; our reception almost amounted to a festive ceremony.

The next morning we were taken into the reserve of the white-necked cranes. Two wardens, who were as friendly as they were helpful, had already got everything ready for a long session in a prepared hide. There was even a small charcoal stove burning in the hut in front of which the cranes were fed. It was extremely cold but the heat from the small stove enabled us to remain there the whole day in comparative comfort and we were able to take comparatively good pictures of these rare birds. On the following day we filmed hooded cranes in their hundreds; we also took more photographs of the white-necked cranes just as they were preparing to set off on the long journey to their breeding places on the mainland of China and Manchuria.

To my surprise and pleasure the people of Izumi arrange a ceremonial farewell feast in honour

name of orang utan means. I was able to film, photograph and watch them in their natural habitat the whole day long. Although there were no fully mature animals, the orang utan lived in complete freedom on Bako and gave me good opportunities to record all those aspects of behaviour which are peculiar to this large anthropoid ape. I was constantly presented with ideas of what kind of an animal an orang really is and of how they behave as real 'men of the jungle' when they do not have to eke out their existence behind the bars of a cage.

Armed with a stick a male approached us on one occasion and seriously threatened to strike with it. He climbed from tree to tree above us and swung from branch to branch like an acrobat. He showed us how to drink water out of canna plants and how one can extract hidden insect larvae from stems using fingers and a small stick. We found the sleeping nests of the orangs which they make afresh every evening. We also saw how they shield themselves on the ground with branches and palm leaves from the oppressive heat in the rain-forest. The hot and humid atmosphere of the tropical jungle appears to suit them best. They undoubtedly feel well in this climate where we were continually bathed in sweat.

It is to be sincerely hoped that the Bako National Park will continue as a safe refuge for this threatened species and that these remarkable anthropoid apes which are subjected to so much persecution will be able to live here, free from any form of disturbance.

INDONESIA

From Sarawak we went on to Indonesia. Hans Klein, the Cultural Attaché of the German Embassy in Djakarta, like Harold J. Coolidge in Washington, had procured entry for us into those areas which for a long time appeared to be unattainable. After negotiations with Indonesian police, military and conservation authorities which took up a lot of time, we were finally able to proceed on the long journey eastwards through the chain of the Sunda Islands. Armed with a written 'open-sesame' from the Commander-in-Chief of the Army we started out on our expedition: by air, motor car and boat we moved from island to island, making gradual progress through east Java, Bali and Lombok to Sumbawa. From there on, the forestry authorities gave us as much help as they possibly could. Fuel and transport, such as we pampered Europeans know it, were extremely scarce in this country. Even when I reached Bima, the easternmost town in Sumbawa, it was some days before I could make the last crossing to the tiny island of Komodo, the home of the dragons. Unfortunately, Helmut Barth was forced to remain behind in Sumbawa as he was suffering from an attack of paratyphoid.

It was fifteen days after our departure from Djakarta that I was able to make the final stage of this long and complicated journey through the islands. Mr Abdul Kahir, the Governor of East Sumbawa, was kind enough to put his boat at our disposal for this sea voyage. His was the only small boat in this little town which was in working order. On board, apart from the Governor and his personal staff, there were six soldiers in full field kit with machine-guns and rifles, three armed policemen in uniform and a member of the secret police. I learnt to my astonishment that they were all in the party for my personal protection, including an interpreter and a forestry assistant assigned to me by the forestry authorities; there were 26 persons in all. The small boat that set out for the island of the *boja daras* or Komodo dragons was swarming with people. The voyage took two days and passed without incident.

When we arrived on Komodo none of my retinue gave a thought either to myself or to my project. The first three days were spent in festivities which consisted of much feasting and drinking. For the few wretchedly poor people who lived on this small and god-forsaken island our presence was a most unusual event. It was only when the festivities were completed that I was able to break away and proceed with the search for the large lizards, which after all was the reason why I had come to one of the most remote islands in the world.

The thought of attempting to film with all these people hanging around my neck was appalling. I managed to persuade the six war-like soldiers that they would do far better to remain behind instead of setting out with me into the unknown to look for the dangerous dragons. According to the custom of the country I had to feed them; however, the official travel rations which I had obtained in Sumbawa were scarcely sufficient for myself alone. I was not so successful with the three uniformed policemen who insisted on carrying out their orders to accompany me to the place which I chose as the most suitable for a base camp. It lay in a small bay, about three miles from the little village of Komodo. However, when night came and the supply of food was inadequate, they were persuaded to return to the others.

This left the detective, the interpreter, the forestry assistant and a villager who knew the locality. The latter was an essential companion if I was to find the dragons. The detective was extremely stubborn and it was not easy to deflect him from his duty. On the second morning I explained to him through the interpreter that the valuable boxes of film and equipment ought not to be left unprotected in the camp and that he was precisely the right man for this job. By this strategy I managed to avoid taking him with me during the actual filming when he would only have got in the way.

After we had gone about 2½ miles inland on our first reconnaissance, a dragon crossed our path in a dried-out river bed. It was not long before we noticed a wild pig snuffling and munching round a dead Timor deer. The carcass was already starting to decompose, spreading the smell which the dragons like so much and which attracts them from great distances. I agreed with my guide that we should make an attempt to film at this spot. A small hide was quickly erected about ten yards away from the dead deer. The guide and the interpreter were sent back with instructions to return in the evening.

After waiting for two hours a Komodo dragon came straight down the dry river bed and approached the carcass. After some licking it began to feed without delay. It was somewhat larger than the first one we had seen. I estimated its length at about six feet. When it had eaten enough, it disappeared with its belly full and the wild pig approached again without delay. It had been waiting all the time in the bush for this moment. But it was not left in peace for long. Another dragon, a bit larger than the first two, arrived on the scene. Its arrival was sufficient to drive off the pig again. Soon after a fourth dragon appeared and then a fifth. A greedy munching began.

I was able to film these giant lizards tearing and eating their food without difficulty and I took no

departure of the Dutch. The high price paid for the horn attracts them just as irresistibly as all poachers in other countries where rhinos still survive. The protection laws exist only on paper and the people who should see that they are enforced are well away from the scene of action. They sit in Djakarta and Bogor and do not even know how to get to the reserve. So the slaughter of these rare animals continues unchecked.

We found an old dilapidated watch-tower in this fabulously beautiful wilderness of rain-forest and made our quarters there. It stood on the edge of an artificially created clearing, which had become practically overgrown again. Behind it the green wall of forest rose implacably, secretive in its impenetrable darkness. An enchanting tropical world extended all around; in our wildest dreams we could not have imagined a lovelier place. There was not another human being for miles and miles, communications with the outside world did not exist and there was not the slightest sign of civilisation anywhere. This was nature completely untouched. The innumerable voices of the rain-forest are never hushed by day or night and the abundant vegetation bears witness to the inexhaustibility of life. Udjong Kulon is an indescribable tropical paradise; nowhere else have I seen a more beautiful wilderness, not in the African rain-forest nor in the mountain jungle of New Guinea, not even on the Amazon nor in any other place near the equator.

For two weeks we made strenuous efforts to find the Javan rhinoceros. A native guide piloted us through jungle and swamp, leading us through pools and streams. We pressed on under a dense canopy of leaves through which scarcely a single ray of sunlight penetrated. We built hides in the trees from which we mounted watch for days and nights at a time. We glided in a canoe up and down narrow streams of crystal-clear water and when the boat could go no further, we waded through the boggy tributaries. Each day we found fresh tracks of the rhinos in the mud on the river banks and on the soft forest floor. We heard the heavy animals breaking through the undergrowth and we could smell the sweat on their bodies at very close quarters. But we never saw them.

Our spirits flagged as time went by and the day we were due to be fetched drew nearer and nearer. We filmed monkeys, wild peafowl, Timor deer, flying foxes, wild banteng and other inhabitants of this wildlife reserve. We also continued to film the beauty of the tropical vegetation and the efforts of our column to move forwards in this wonderful forest. It would not have surprised me if one day Adam and Eve had popped up in person in front of us.

We then decided to split up into different groups. While I went on watching alone at night, perched high in the trees, and paddled along the little river by day, Helmut Barth went by water to the far distant eastern side of the reserve, taking with him our guide and a young assistant. There, on the last afternoon, he finally succeeded in getting within camera range of the rhinoceroses which had eluded us for such a long time. His guide discovered an adult and a young one in the dense undergrowth; they were only a few yards away with the rain-forest all around but he had to risk everything on this last chance.

He stood in front of the rhino for ten minutes. The guide and the porter had already climbed up a tree as they were frightened of the huge animal. However, Helmut stood his ground fearlessly and filmed as well as he could in the poor light. During this short period he was able to take about 200 feet of film of this rare animal. And at the end he even managed to get a colour photograph. This unique encounter with the Javan rhinoceros came to an abrupt end. They disappeared as fast as they had appeared, the rain-forest of Udjong Kulon swallowing them up as they moved on.

Naturally we are proud of these 200 feet of film; they are the first to be taken of this animal that is so close to extinction. The single colour photograph is also the first of its kind. These pictorial documents are of special value because the Javan rhinoceros cannot be seen in any zoo in the world; and if they are exterminated at Udjong Kulon this species will be lost for ever. One cannot help wondering who will be the next person to meet and photograph these animals in their last refuge.

A short time after this fortuitous meeting with the long sought rhino, a naval vessel appeared in the small bay; the light was just going. Two hours later we were on board. We sailed for Djakarta, and the rain-forest of Udjong Kulon sank slowly into the tropical night.

MALAYA

Soon afterwards we flew on to Malaya. Dr Elliot McClure was waiting for us at the airport in Kuala Lumpur and escorted us to the place where we were to do our filming: the mountain forests north of Kuala Lumpur. Some time earlier Elliot had erected a roomy platform in one of the very tall trees which he used for his own observation work. It was built a hundred and fifty feet above the ground in the fork of a branch and the tree extended above it for a further sixty feet. He believed that from this platform we would be able to film gibbons and siamangs without much difficulty. It certainly gave a wonderful view over the whole valley and the opposite mountain range. As far as the eye could see there was only forest, tall and luxuriant tropical forest.

I first heard the gibbons calling while we were lifting the heavy camera equipment up into position. The forest reverberated with their remarkably melodious voices. No other mammal has such a powerful and musical range at its disposal as the gibbon. In between we could hear the calls of the argus pheasants and of many other birds.

Within a week we had taken sufficient film of the wild monkeys. They were the brown and black white-handed gibbons which haunt the mountain forests around here and give a full-scale display of their climbing and acrobatic abilities. They swing through the branches like flying spirits, allowing themselves to fall deliberately, only to swing themselves up again, effortlessly and weightlessly. The black siamangs do not follow the gibbons. They hunt in small groups in the tops of the trees, passing through the 'walls' of rain-forest, now here now there, singing in a chorus which carries far and wide.

From the mountain forests near Kuala Lumpur we then drove over to the east coast of Malaya. According to Elliot, it was at this time of the year that the big leathery turtles lay their eggs near Trengganu on the sandy shores of the South China Sea. They only do this at night during high spring tides and I was advised by friends to take floodlights and batteries with me, although it was not easy to get hold of this auxiliary film equipment.

Today the area of western Malaysia has been pushed into the political arena. Indonesian partisans are infiltrating in increasing numbers into the region where the Sumatran rhinoceros lives. They slink about in this habitat and Malayan soldiers try to capture these guerilla fighters. As in parts of Indo-China there is shooting, burning, plundering and poaching. These military operations constitute a very serious threat to an animal that is already very rare. All in all, the chances of survival of the Sumatran rhinos, the smallest species of rhinoceros in the world, seem rather slight.

Fujiyama, the sacred mountain of the Japanese, is the most beautiful and symmetrical volcanic cone in the world. With a height of some 12,380 feet it is the highest mountain in Japan and is visible as a landmark from a great distance. The countryside around the mountain forms the Fuji-Hakone-Izu National Park, which is one of the most frequently visited nature reserves in Japan.

The valley of the River Akan in the Japanese Akan National Park on Hokkaido is the home of a fascinating bird. Thirty or more Manchurian cranes assemble in a meadow behind a small farmhouse and spend the whole winter there. Through regular feeding the cranes here have become really tame. As the sun rises higher and higher in February these large birds—almost the height of a man—start their dignified and graceful dancing display. Many of them fly over to the mainland of Asia to breed.

For many years the Manchurian crane was lost to Japan as a breeding species but by intensive protection and preservation measures, Japanese nature conservationists have recently succeeded in restoring its status to that of a resident. Cranes are sacred in Japan; the esteem and reverence which they enjoy were naturally a considerable help in establishing protective measures. Nevertheless the Manchurian crane is still one of the rarest species of crane. At present there are not more than 130 individuals in the whole world.

While we were riding on our domesticated elephants, we met some wild ones which stared inquisitively at their tame cousins, trumpted several times and then moved off. In India, elephants like rhinos are relatively safe from persecution only in protected areas.

Left. In the Kaziranga Reserve in Assam we moved through a thick screen of grass, growing 18 to 24 feet high, on the back of a well-trained and experienced riding elephant. We were looking for the great Indian rhinoceros.

There are still five species of rhinoceros living in the world today: two species of African, the Sumatran, the Javan and the great Indian rhinoceros (illustrated here). In contrast to both African species and to the Sumatran rhinoceros, the Javan and Indian rhinos have only one horn. Outside the reserve areas this one-horned species was exterminated long ago.

The powerful Indian rhinoceros is covered with very thick skin which looks like armour plating. It has a truly prehistoric appearance. Like all the rhinoceroses the Indian rhino is completely vegetarian, and as with all pachyderms in the tropics, it likes to bathe frequently or at least to wallow in the mud.

The last lions in India live in the Gir Forest Reserve on the Kathiawar Peninsula. Even in pre-Christian times the Maharajahs used to keep lions here for hunting purposes and efforts were made to have an adequate supply of them permanently available. Today it is estimated that there are about 280 of these asiatic lions.

The lion is the strongest of all the carnivores. It is capable of pulling down and killing prey that is double its own size, as for example the Cape buffalo. Apart from man the lion has no enemies. When left alone, as in the National Parks, it can still live in peace.

In the Gir Forest Reserve in India, we tracked nilgai as well as lions. These are the only large antelopes in Asia. The bulls attain the height of cattle. During the rutting season rival bulls make a spectacular sight as they test their strength. They lower themselves on to their knees and strike at each other with their horns and push with their foreheads, until finally one gives way.

On the Little Rann of Kutch, in the extreme north-west of India, close to the Pakistan frontier, during the dry season the rare Indian wild asses find a last refuge from pursuit by man. They galloped away in front of our motor-car at a speed of 30 m.p.h., disappearing into the shimmering distance of the vast, dried-up area of brackish water basin. Mr E. P. Gee, the principal authority on these animals, reckons the total population of this wild ass at 800 head.

Orang-utans are confined to extensive tropical forest areas, where they live in family groups. They are arboreal but they can also move quite well on the ground. They are dangerous when cornered.

Left. Orang-utans are the large apes of Asia, occurring now only in Borneo and Sumatra. Today orang-utans are the most seriously threatened of the anthropoid apes. The young are caught in an unlawful and gruesome manner, by first shooting the mothers.

Komodo dragons live only on the small island of Komodo, the neighbouring islet of Rindja and in the western part of the island of Flores. They are the largest land lizards which still exist and can attain a length of over 9 feet. The Malayans call them 'boja dara' which means land crocodile.

Komodo dragons are carnivorous. With great skill they catch deer, wild pigs, birds and other animals, which they overpower and tear apart. They also take carrion which they scent from long distances. We watched some fifteen Komodo dragons feeding on this Timor deer which they devoured completely within three days.

The rain-forest of Udjong Kulon on the extreme south-western tip of Java is the sole refuge of the last 25 Javan rhinoceroses. We followed their tracks in this fabulously beautiful tropical jungle, in which we felt like dwarfs. Udjong Kulon was originally declared a National Park by the Dutch and the Indonesian conservation authorities now regard it as their most valuable nature reserve.

Like the other species of rhinoceros, the Javan rhinoceros is continually threatened by poachers. They kill it wantonly in order to get the rhino horn, which is still much in demand as an aphrodisiac throughout Asia and particularly in China. In the female the horn is very small or sometimes absent, as is clearly shown in this photograph. But the horn of aged males may be up to 6 inches long.

Banteng, wild cattle of South-East Asia, have become very rare on the Island of Sunda. Formerly Banteng were distributed throughout many countries of South-East Asia, whence they have long since disappeared. A herd of about 150 head live in various groups in the Udjung Kulon National Park, together with the few Javan rhinoceroses which have managed to survive there.

The Malayan tapir is also becoming increasingly uncommon in the forest country of eastern Asia. It represents a very ancient form of mammal. Tapirs only exist in eastern Asia and in South America, the former being marked strikingly with black and white, the latter plain grey-brown. They attain the size of a pony. The elongated, trunk-like upper lip, with which they pluck their leafy diet, is characteristic.

The deep ravines in the mountain forests of the Malayan Peninsula are the home of many tropical animals and plants. Long stretches of this mountain jungle have no roads or paths and are largely untouched. One can only penetrate deep into these areas by water.

Gibbons haunt the rain-forests of Malaya, swinging and climbing amongst the trees like acrobats. One usually hears them before they come into view. No other mammal possesses such a varied and melodious voice. The forests often echo with the song of the brown and black white-handed gibbon.

The leathery turtle is the largest living turtle and it may weigh up to 1500 pounds. The female lays her 80-120 eggs in a pit which she digs laboriously with the help of her hind-legs. But the eggs are usually collected by the Malays before the female can cover them with sand.

Left. When a leathery turtle moves over land it leaves behind a track 6 feet broad, which resembles that of a tractor. A stretch of beach about seven miles long, near Kuala Trengganu on the east coast of the Malayan Peninsula, is one of the few places where these turtles still lay their eggs regularly.

The Sumatran rhinoceros is the smallest of the five living species of rhinoceroses. Like the two African species it has two horns. It still occurs in isolated pockets in a few areas of Malaya, in neighbouring Burma, in Thailand and in Sumatra. We tried our luck on the Slim River in eastern Malaya and soon found fresh tracks. We had set our heart on photographing the animal, but we never found it.

Africa

SOUTH AFRICA

It took me three expeditions to the dark continent to become reasonably familiar with the more important wildlife reserves in Africa and to film the rare and threatened species which live there. Each expedition took several months; I travelled through the whole of the Union of South Africa and large areas of East Africa.

It was December 1960 when Helmut Barth and I first set foot on African soil in Johannesburg. At the offices of the South African National Parks Board in Pretoria, Mr R. Knobel, Director of National Parks Administration, drew up a detailed itinerary with me for visiting the different reserves in the Union, which lie far apart from each other. In the newly established Willem Pretorius Reserve in the Orange Free State we filmed our first wild animals in Africa: white-tailed gnus. Earlier, the Boers and their descendants had decimated these animals to such an extent that a mere handful of them survived. The surviving population scattered in all directions and for a long time the animals managed to eke out a precarious existence in wild areas and on remote farm land; they were subsequently assembled by man in the reserve in the Orange Free State in order to preserve them. Today only about 800 white-tailed gnus still survive.

Black wildebeest was the name given by the Boers to the white-tailed gnu and this term is particularly appropriate. We saw them in the distance in the reserve and while we were still a long way off they galloped away ahead of us over the wide grassy plain. We had great difficulty following these large antelopes. None of the other wild animals behaved so warily when it came to filming them. They were so wild and impetuous that we were even pleased at achieving distant shots. In behaviour they resemble horses more closely than antelopes. Their general shape is distinctly reminiscent of a horse except that they have cleft hooves and a cow-like head with horns. We chased them for several days and then one morning we outwitted them at a water-hole where we had spent the night. They were obviously thirsty and came quite close. For a few minutes they remained quite still and we were at last able to film them in a less restless mood. However, they soon detected us and as nervous as ever they fled, leaving behind a huge cloud of dust.

We then drove on a straight road through the hot dried-up Karroo Desert 600 miles southwards to Cape Town. This journey was almost torture to us. There seemed no end to the monotony. For long stretches we saw only sheep; large wild animals disappeared from these areas a long time ago. The drive along the Garden route was more pleasant. There was an alternation of green fields, vineyards and orchards. Fruit and wine were available in friendly villages. In the small ancient town of Swellendam, one of the early Boer settlements, I called on the mayor, Mr Rieth; he was an elderly man who was a South African to his fingertips. He was very friendly and took us straight to the bontebok reserve, which is only 2½ square miles in area and the smallest national park in South Africa.

In 1931 there were only 17 bontebok still surviving. Before very long the government established this small reserve in order to preserve the bonteboks which were in serious danger of being exterminated as a species. Today the population of bontebok has increased to over 800 and it is no longer the rarest antelope in the world. We spent three days and nights out in the reserve. Each day these uncommonly marked antelopes stood scarcely a stone's throw from our motor-car, in which we spent the night. It was comparatively easy to get pictures of them because they were not particularly shy and usually kept in our vicinity. Every morning Mr Rieth brought us good South African beer instead of coffee. He knew that we came from Munich and intended that the beer should be a special treat. We much appreciated his gesture and accepted the beer with alacrity.

The Addo Elephant National Park, which is only about 20 square miles, is not far from Port Elizabeth. It is one of the few wildlife reserves that is completely enclosed, being encircled by a unique fence which withstands even the most powerful Addo Elephant. This fence is made of old tramlines from Port Elizabeth which support very thick cables from disused lifts, making a strong but springy fence. Mr Marais, the Chief Game Warden of the Addo Elephant National Park, took considerable trouble to bring his few elephants within camera-range. In 1960, when we were there, only 29 of these pachyderms still lived in the reserve. They were the remnants of the most southerly form of elephant in Africa, which once numbered thousands. Known as Cape elephants by zoologists, they differ from those occurring farther north in being somewhat smaller. It is believed that a few more may be living a secluded life in the tropical forests of Knysna, an area which we had passed a few days earlier when driving along good roads. These animals however have not been seen for years and only occasional tracks bear witness to their presence.

The campaign against this form of elephant is a typical example of the systematic persecution of a wild animal population. It is a particularly tragic chapter in the story of wildlife extermination by the white man. In 1922 there were still about 120 to 130 Cape elephants living in the Addo bush country, an extensive and almost impenetrable area of rain-forest. However, they caused damage in the neighbouring plantations of the settlers who continued to encroach on the bush and consequently official circles decided that all the elephants should be shot. A skilled hunter was employed and in this fairly restricted hunting area he shot 100 elephants in a period of eleven months. When, however, he brought down sixteen elephants in a record time of only half a minute, public opinion changed and became opposed to any further slaughter. Only about a dozen Cape elephants survived and it is from this remnant population that the herd now living in Addo Elephant National Park is gradually being reconstituted.

When the reserve was established the game warden at the time, Mr Armstrong, decided to protect the few remaining animals by enclosing them completely. By doing so, the humans and their plantations would also be saved from further damage. After much trouble and many attempts he finally managed to construct the fence with the tramlines and cables already mentioned. With a bit of goodwill this would have been possible earlier and thus the gruesome shooting of so many animals could have been prevented.

On our first afternoon a group of eleven Addo elephants came out of the bush in brilliant sunshine and passed along in front of the thorn scrub where we could see them, as though giving us a formal parade of welcome. 'A rare occurrence', said Mr Marais. 'You are in luck, because normally they do not come out into the clearings until dusk, where we sometimes feed them. As a result of being hunted for years, they are still continually on the alert and when they see man they become bad-tempered and aggressive.'

They formed a long procession as they walked slowly past us on the other side of the fence. One of them had lost the tip of its trunk. 'It tore it in a wire-noose trying to free itself,' explained Mr Marais. 'Some planter must have set the wire-noose many years ago when the elephants were still being hunted. That elephant must now be regarded as particularly dangerous because elephants have good memories and do not forget if man has done something harmful to them.'

The elephants then disappeared again, still in procession. It was almost as though they had made a point of showing themselves so that they could be included in the film of the world's threatened animals. After the tragic massacre to which they were subjected and from which they escaped as though by a miracle, I felt that they were certainly entitled to a place in my film.

A few days later at Doornhoeck near Cradock, Farmer Noel Micheau and his charming wife gave us just as hospitable a welcome as we had received in Mr Marais's elephant paradise. This private estate lies close beside the state Mountain Zebra National Park and here Noel Micheau preserves a few dozen offspring of the last mountain zebras which escaped extermination by the Boers. Today there are not more than 80 Cape mountain zebras in the wild.

We spent some days stalking the mountain zebras in the Micheau estate. The clatter and rattle of stones became a familiar sound as the zebras galloped fast over the gravelly slopes of the hilly terrain. The hunt was interesting even if somewhat exhausting on account of the effort of coping with the heavy film equipment. We could only approach them by easy stages. The coloured boy, a capable servant of the Micheaus, knew their habits and exactly how to approach them. We hid in the bush with our cameras ready and he managed to bring them closer to us, working on his own. We parted from Mr Micheau with many expressions of our gratitude to him and received the modest rejoinder that it had been a pleasure. I believe that the Cape mountain zebra has not been given such extensive coverage on film before.

Our journey proceeded through the native reserve of Transkei, an extensive stretch of land in which everything is preserved for the coloured population. We were aiming for the reserves of Hluhluwe and Umfolozi in Natal. In the Hluhluwe Reserve we filmed buffalo, black rhinoceros and the rare nyala antelope. The latter received our special attention.

As the sun was going down, the nyala herd appeared in the bush where we lay in wait as directed by Mr Dean, the Chief Game Warden. A troop of baboons and a sounder of warthogs accompanied them. Even the shy antelopes appeared to feel more secure under the watchful eyes of the monkeys. Completely silent, as though moving on rubber-soled hooves, these secretive antelopes of the forest stepped out along the edge of the swampy pool, one after another, testing the ground. They repeatedly broke through the soft earth and thereby startled themselves by their own clumsiness. They were exceptionally wary and each one appeared to be a bundle of nerves. They drank for a long time, with outstretched necks, their big ears continually on the alert. Finally the leading bull arrived; females and young respectfully made way for him. It was an enchanting sight. Fortunately the baboons had not noticed us. Had they done so their alarm calls would have immediately scared the nyalas away. These crepuscular antelopes are rarely seen and scarcely ever in sunlight suitable for filming.

Some days later our luck held in the Umfolozi Sanctuary, one of the few refuges of the white rhinoceros. Colonel Vincent in Pietermaritzburg recommended his Chief Game Warden Players to us and with his help we were able to make rapid progress. Even on our very first stalking expedition through the reserve area we got a sight of the white rhinoceroses. We saw ten of them standing peacefully in a swampy hollow, grazing together by a small pool. It was like a scene from prehistory. As we started to set up the telephoto camera at a distance of about 100 yards, Players signalled to us and invited us to go up closer to the rhinos with him. The wind was favourable and the animals did not notice our approach. Soon there were only 15 to 20 yards separating us. We were standing completely unprotected in front of these powerful animals, hidden from them only by a natural screen of grass about three feet high, without a tree in the vicinity in which we could have taken refuge in an emergency.

Then they went for a bathe. They moved into the water one after the other, calmly and without any sign of haste. I was so excited that I could no longer count how many of them were already lying down in the water, how many were stuck in the mud on the banks, or how many were still standing in the shade of the bushes which fringed the pond. I filmed while Helmut took still photographs. In a herd of white rhinoceros there is plenty of activity and every aspect of this unique spectacle was worth recording.

Then I suddenly felt the wind on the back of my neck. Simultaneously all the rhinos stood up and came out on land. Rhinoceroses have poor vision but their hearing is good and their sense of smell excellent. With loud rumbling noises they came even closer to us, trampling on everything. In spite of their clumsy shape their agility astounded me. They could easily have overrun us and trampled us underfoot—each of these animals weighs two tons. Players lifted up his hands and shouted something at them. He knew his animals, their habits, their weaknesses and naturally also their strength, but he was also quite certain that in this situation there was nothing to be afraid of. The animals appeared surprised but in no way frightened. All wild animals take special guard when young are present but as there was none in this group there was no reason for them to attack. Black rhinos would probably have charged but white rhinos are not so aggressive.

The whole herd then moved off. We followed them in the Land-Rover and overtook them; we were able to film them again before they hurried off. We spent four days among these huge animals of which there are now only about 4000 in existence. Whenever we encountered them they were in open country with scattered bushes and undergrowth. We often stood only a few yards from them, even closer than on the first occasion at the pool, but Players urged caution on two occasions only: once when a mother with a calf showed no sign of giving way to us and the other occasion was when two bulls were fighting for the favours of a cow. After the fight, we were able to film the victor mating with the cow.

We travelled on through Swaziland to the largest national park in South Africa, the world-renowned Kruger National Park where we spent over two weeks. Dr Brynard had give us free access to all parts, including those which at that time were not accessible to other visitors. From Pretorius Kop we drove through Skukuza to Letaba, Oliphant's River and Shingwitzi, 150 miles to the north and back again.

Every day we came into contact with animals of all kinds; almost all the African big game occurs in the Kruger National Park which is 7500 square miles in area. During the dry season they can be found in large numbers at the water-holes. At one of these places, the Leu Pan, the Park authorities built an observation tower for us. From this we were able to work in complete peace without disturbing the animals and without being in any danger ourselves. Impala, roan and sassaby antelope, kudu, water-buck, brindled gnu, zebras, klipspringer, warthog, giraffe, elephant, buffalo, hippopotamus, baboons and other monkeys, many kinds of birds and, of course, lions and leopards—all these came our way day after day. We exposed several rolls of film in this densely populated animal paradise. Only the rare sable antelopes remained invisible until the last afternoon. Finally we caught sight of them in the tree savannah, coal-black and with sabre-like horns. Shortly afterwards we succeeded in filming them.

We then travelled westwards, up to the border of south-west Africa. By this time we were pretty tired and rather run down after our long journey through the South African nature reserves. Also I was suffering from another attack of malaria, a legacy from New Guinea. However Mr Knobel strongly recommended a visit to the Kalahari Gemsbok National Park and so we decided to push on.

Beyond Kuruman we were forced to take roads which were in the worst possible condition. Our car sank deeper and deeper into the sand the nearer we came to the Kalahari Desert. We were often completely stuck and only got free again after a great deal of trouble. After three adventurous days we finally reached the 'entrance' to the remote park; this is a completely dried-out river bed on the edge of which stands the ranger's house.

The Kalahari Gemsbok National Park was established for the protection and conservation of the gemsbok or South African oryx, an antelope with long pointed horns which has become very scarce. The present total population is about 1000, perhaps even 1200, but it was formerly much more widely distributed. Here, too, things are no different from what they are in the north, the south and the east of this continent: everywhere the European has settled he has brought death and extermination to the animal world.

The ranger drove us at breath-taking speed over the red dunes. We crossed the high crests of the sand-hills, which divide up the desert like giant waves, by putting on sudden bursts of speed. The oryx fled before us as we breasted the dunes and disappeared behind another crest where they paused for a brief rest. There is no cover in this bare terrain except for a few miserable bushes and the oryx obviously felt they were hidden from view when standing in a dip behind a crest. They only stood still for a few minutes, however, and we had to take our pictures during this short period.

Springbok continually crossed our path. Bushmen, looking as primitive as the desert itself, crept after them with bow and poison arrows. They too are protected in the Kalahari Gemsbok National Park just as the oryx and the other animals. The park offers a last asylum to these primitive people, a small paradise for one of the oldest human races of Africa. Here they can hunt with bow and arrows and obtain the modest essentials for their simple way of life. They do this in the old traditional way, as their ancestors did hundreds of years ago, long before the white settler came and drove them back into this sun-drenched, waterless waste. During the greater part of the year man and animals can only satisfy their requirements for water by obtaining moisture from the juices of tuberous plants.

The bushmen showed us how to hunt with poison arrows and we were able to film these primitive hunters bringing down a springbok in record time. They creep up to the wild herds like cats; then the arrow speeds from the bowstring. The stricken antelope leaps high into the air and soon dies from the action of the poison. The bushmen then squeeze the green stomach juices from the paunch, and drink this fluid which has a high vitamin content. While we were filming them they talked to each other, making peculiar clicking sounds; they were probably discussing us or speaking about the successful hunt. They only hunt to supply themselves with food. A native population has never been known to exterminate an animal species yet. It is only the foreign intruder who goes mad with his modern weapons in an immoderate and irresponsible way, either for profit or for the sheer pleasure of killing.

EAST AFRICA

In February 1961 we left South Africa and flew to the eastern part of the continent. Our first stop was Nairobi. This bustling but beautiful capital city was the point of departure for most of our safaris in the National Parks of Kenya, Tanzania and Uganda. The best known nature reserves in these three East African states are Nairobi National Park, Tsavo National Park, Amboseli Game Reserve, Ngorongoro Crater Reserve, Meru Game Reserve, Manyara National Park, Serengeti National Park, Queen Elizabeth National Park and Murchison Falls National Park. In the course of the year we visited all of these reserves and went in search of the rare animals living in them. In South Africa I had tended to concentrate on individual animals species, whereas here in East Africa I was more keen on filming big herds. Nowhere else in the world today can one find such enormous congregations of big game of various species as in the wild life reserves of East Africa. I visualised shots of these huge herds of animals as providing a particularly impressive closing sequence for my entire film.

During my first expedition I did not see any herds of sufficient size for my purpose as the time of year was not suitable. This first tour in East Africa, therefore, served more as a preliminary reconnaissance in which I was able to get to know a world full of animals that was still new to me. One cannot hurry through these reserves and it takes more than one expedition to get the feel of the place and to sort out the endless opportunities which these areas offer to a maker of wildlife films.

In September 1963 I flew for the second time to East Africa. During this journey I was accompanied by my wife who had already been with me in Australia, New Guinea, the United States and Canada. I got to know new areas such as Tsavo National Park, the Uaso Nyiro Reserve and Lake Magadi. As well as seeing a number of species which we had already filmed, we were always coming across species that were new to us. The animal life of Africa with its wealth of species is still almost inexhaustible even today. I believe that one could spend a lifetime and still not manage to find and film everything that lives there. For an animal photographer elephants, rhinos, hippopotamus, buffalo, zebras, gnus, giraffes, lions and leopards are wonderful subjects. They repeatedly appear in different surroundings and there always seems to be some fresh aspect of behaviour to film. One of the things which impressed us most was the way in which the animals reacted to our presence on their own home ground: they seemed to be quite undisturbed and to have regained a sense of security in the reserve areas.

During my second African visit I added several species to my film, including the gerenuk, the reticulated giraffe, Grévy's zebra, the Cape hunting dog and a fantastic assembly of flamingoes.

The gerenuk's characteristic method of feeding makes a particularly charming sight. When browsing it stands on its hind legs and rests its front hooves on the branches of the bush as it nibbles the leaves and buds. The long neck, which resembles that of the giraffe, enables the gerenuk to browse high up in the foliage. This slender animal can remain balanced in this position at the same bush for several minutes at a time without becoming tired. No other ungulate shows such elegance and adroitness when feeding as the gerenuk. Previously I had often tried to film them in this unique pose but they had always run a long way off; they can leap and run very fast.

I filmed the reticulated giraffe in the Uaso Nyiro Reserve in northern Kenya. It has a more restricted distribution than the other giraffes of Africa. White lines form a delicate network over the whole of its large body. When standing motionless against the background of the bush, it is very difficult to spot a reticulated giraffe; the patterning on its body provides excellent camouflage. Giraffes are inquisitive and a herd of seventeen reticulated giraffes rapidly gathered around while I was filming the animal standing closest to me. Then when they started to move, it seemed as though the whole landscape had come alive. They sprang out of the bushes all around me and when they reached open country they lapsed into their typical method of progression. Giraffes are amblers, the legs on one side of the body are both moved forward simultaneously, which helps them to attain great speeds. Even a car finds it difficult to overtake a fleeing giraffe.

In the Uaso Nyiro Reserve I also found Grévy's zebras in considerable numbers. This species is distinguished from the other zebras by the stripes and the form of the body; it looks more like an ass than a horse, and has striking goblet-shaped ears. They live in herds of up to twenty animals in open country. There was no cover at all where we found them and as we walked straight towards them, they did not run away but gazed inquisitively at us as we advanced slowly. My friend Wolfgang Bell of Dar-es-Salaam and I went closer and closer, taking film shots of these handsomely striped animals every few yards; we got to within about fifty yards of them before they started to trot slowly away and even then they soon stopped again and kept looking back at us. They appeared to be surprised that we did not follow them any farther.

One morning we were returning tired and hungry after a reconnaissance trip through the Nairobi National Park. Even our guide, Kilonso, no longer showed the typical alertness of an African game warden when taking someone out with him on safari. Some vultures in the sky, however, suddenly made him aware that there was something going on. They were circling high in the sky and then gradually losing height. I turned the car across country, following the hand signals made by our guide. We soon discovered a large pack of Cape hunting dogs. Most of them lay sleeping in the grass while five youngsters romped about among the adults. They allowed us to approach them in the car to within about twenty yards without getting up. One of them occasionally looked across at us briefly but had we stepped out of the car, they would all have been off. These animals are not accustomed to humans walking on foot and it is only possible to approach them in a car without alarming them or, indeed, being frightened oneself.

The Cape hunting dogs had full bellies; they had eaten a gnu and the remains were still lying in the grass. The vultures which Kilonso had noticed circling in the sky were attracted to these remains. I had always been on the lookout for hunting dogs but had never been able to locate them. Now I had a whole pack spread out in front of me, including youngsters playing quite happily.

Cape hunting dogs are sociable animals. They usually hunt in packs according to a well-defined plan, which one is tempted to regard as a tactically planned campaign. Once they have selected their prey by sight, they do not kill it as quickly and painlessly as lions and leopards. They chase it to the point of exhaustion and slowly overpower the tired animal. Then the pack feeds to satiety. All Cape hunting dogs have the same colours, but in spite of this the actual patterning is very variable and no two animals are exactly the same in external appearance. Only the tip of the tail is white in every individual. Like wolves these wild dogs are restless wanderers, they are here today but by the morrow they may be dozens of miles away. So I was glad, therefore, to have them in view on this occasion in such large numbers and for such a long time.

On Lake Magadi, one of the salt and soda lakes in the Rift Valley, we found the largest assembly of flamingoes that I have ever seen in my life. There are only a few places in the world where one can see these elegant birds in such numbers—possibly still in India, South America and the West Indies. We could only estimate the numbers approximately in this vast assembly, an exact count would have been virtually impossible. There must have been hundreds of thousands of birds.

We arrived at Lake Magadi in the middle of the day when the temperature was at its maximum. The heat was almost unbearable as we left the car. There was a little shade, provided by some bushes about the height of a man but it was totally inadequate. The glaring rays of the sun glittered over the wide, shallow basin of the lake which was covered with a hard crust of soda in many places. The light colour of the shores and the mudflats glistening with salt helped to reflect the heat. Wherever the eye rested on the lake there were flamingoes standing or walking about, so densely packed that there was scarcely a foot's breadth between them. There were also thousands on the wing, and their pinkish-red plumage made bands of colour in the sky like flying banners. There was constant activity, birds coming and going all the time. In this 'city of flamingoes' one could no longer distinguish individual voices, the calls mingled into a single murmur which came in waves of sound across the glittering landscape.

The water of a flamingo lake must contain an incredibly rich food supply for the birds; how otherwise could it satisfy the hundreds of thousands that are there every day? In the mud of the saline water there live tiny invertebrate animals and blue-green algae which the flamingoes eat. They continually stamp and trample in the shallow water and in this way loosen the food which they take from the water, scooping it up in their bills. The finer particles of food are caught in the hair-like lamellae on the inside of the bill which serve as a sieve, the water being expelled by muscular movements of the tongue and throat.

The drinking water required by flamingoes must be fresh. Although we were in the vicinity, thirst made them forget all shyness. It seems that in the heat of midday they find it more important to slake their thirst than to feed. They collected in their thousands at a shallow channel in which fresh spring water flowed into the lake from the slopes of the shore. We made use of some cover provided by tall elephant grass in a small hollow to creep a bit closer. There was not a breath of air moving across the bay and the heat was almost stifling. The film equipment was so hot to touch that I could handle it only with a handkerchief. We managed to remain in the hollow for half an hour but were then driven out by the fierce heat. On the way back we found a completely fresh spoor of a lion in the sand which had not been there previously. Had the lion been following us or had it also wanted to get to the fresh water for a drink? We decided not to investigate any further but to beat a hasty retreat as thirsty lions can turn unpleasant.

My third journey to East Africa took place in the period March to May 1965. Once again Peter Höser was my companion. We worked first in Kenya, then in Tanzania and flew back later to Uganda. There I wanted to pay a visit to the Murchison Falls National Park, with which I was still unfamiliar. During this journey I was looking principally for large herds of game which I eventually found in the numbers I wanted.

It was a very hot day in March when we drove from Nairobi to the Tsavo National Park. Mr Mervyn Cowie, Director of National Parks in Kenya, had already warned the park authorities that we were coming. Two hundred miles of the poorly surfaced road from Nairobi to Mombasa lay ahead of us. Although our equipment was placed on the upholstered rear seat of the Land-Rover, we did not dare to drive fast. We reached Voi late in the afternoon and turned off the main road here; two hours later we were at Aruba Lodge in the eastern part of the Tsavo National Park. This park is one of the three largest protected areas in the world and is well-known for the wealth of its big game. A particularly large number of elephants live here; their population is estimated at 16,000 head. No African reserve has as many pachyderms as this National Park.

A large dam has been constructed in front of the comfortable lodge. It was built as a freshwater reservoir. During the dry season many elephants come to this lake every day to drink. However the rainy season was just starting, rain had already fallen in the neighbourhood when we arrived and we had no time to lose if we were to film the large herds of elephants before they moved off.

Next morning we had everything ready. We did not have to wait long before the first group of elephants appeared at the lake. While I was still filming them a second group moved down into the water and then a third. By the time that half an hour had gone by, there were 65 elephants assembled at the water, an unforgettable sight. They soon moved off, and this was the last big elephant herd to appear at the Aruba Dam for this season. During the following days only individual stragglers came to the lake. All around the rains set in. The clouds released downpours of bluish-black rain, or so it looked, which cascaded down on the parched land and blotted out the horizon. Overnight the elephants had moved off, re-distributing themselves in the boundless space of the National Park, which is more than 7500 square miles in area. They would soon find water and fresh grazing everywhere.

We also filmed a large herd of buffaloes which came to drink and a flock of white storks which were probably on their return journey to their European nesting sites; we also took sequences of pelicans and other aquatic birds which are not driven away from this inviting spot during the rainy season. Later, we were able to film another family group of elephants at a small watering place near the Mudanda Rock and we also filmed a herd of eland.

We spent a few days in the Amboseli Game Reserve where Kilimanjaro reveals its most beautiful aspect. Although I had seen Kilimanjaro before, its summit had always been enveloped in cloud; it is the highest mountain in Africa (19,340 feet) and the peak is perpetually covered in snow. On this occasion I was able to see it in all its glory, with elephants and rhinoceroses in the foreground.

We drove through Arusha to the Manyara National Park. We only stayed two days, just long enough to be able to film some of the lions which habitually rest there in trees; I had not met this unusual type of behaviour in these big cats before. As we climbed up the slopes to the Ngorongoro Crater it was pouring with rain. The highest point of the crater edge is about 8000 feet above sea level; a fresh wind blew in our faces. When we arrived at the top the cloud cover parted and the sun shone all over the wide basin of the crater which is 2500 square miles in area and one of the largest volcanic craters in the world. It is full of wild animals of all kinds. The sun also shone as we drove on into the Serengeti National Park. One can leave the rainy season behind quite fast in East Africa and find the sunshine which is nearly always present in these regions.

Mr J. S. Owen, Director of National Parks in Tanzania had informed the authorities in Seronera, the Park's headquarters, that we were coming and the staff did all they could to help us. The annual migration of the herds of gnu, in search of fresh pasture, was in full swing when we arrived. The movements of the migrating herds extended for several hundred miles. We followed them on the ground and also by air, and Mr Turner repeatedly piloted his little Cessna to places where the plains were dotted with gnus, migrating and resting. They were brindled gnus, which are still much more common than the white-tailed gnus of South Africa. It was an extraordinary sight. Thousands and thousands moved forwards beneath us, tens of thousands or probably even hundreds of thousands. '367,000 animals in search of a home,' writes Professor Bernhard Grzimek in one of his books, and by this he meant the gnus, the zebras, the Thomson's and Grant's gazelles, hartebeest, giraffes, rhinos, buffaloes, lions, leopards and many others which live in the Serengeti National Park.

Before flying on to Uganda we spent a few more days in the Nairobi National Park. This small wildlife reserve lying close to the gates of Nairobi provides a home for numerous animal species. It was the cheetah that I was particularly interested in. I had never been able to film these spotted big cats and so we did everything possible to find them on this occasion. Mervyn Cowie and Mr Dennes, the Chief Game warden, kindly sent out their most experienced ranger to look for them, and a report soon came in that a female with three young cubs had been sighted in Section 18.

We went in search of them and spent the whole day trying to find them without success. It was as though they had vanished into thin air. The next day it was raining. In spite of this we again drove off with our keen-sighted ranger in search of the cheetahs. About noon he spotted them behind a small rock in the middle of the savannah. They were lying indolently in the grass, a big handsome female and three half-grown young. The cheetahs were soaking wet and when they shook themselves drops of water flew off their fur like a fine spray. It was obvious that, like the true cats, they definitely disliked the rain. Peter drove the Land-Rover slowly backwards towards the cheetahs while I filmed them through the rear window. The animals appeared to take little notice of our approach. Then a few feeble rays of sunshine broke through the cloud cover, and I got to work with the camera.

We stayed near them for three hours. Then they slowly got up and walked one behind the other over a small hill, the mother leading the way with her nose raised in the air. Perhaps they were driven by hunger to move on. There is no lack of prey in the Nairobi National Park. Food is plentiful in nature reserves, though the animals have to find it for themselves.

The cheetah, also known as the hunting leopard because it can be easily tamed and used for hunting, is an inhabitant of open plains and savannah country. When hunting its prey it is able to accelerate to a speed of 55 to 65 m.p.h. in a few seconds, and can run much faster. But it cannot keep up this speed for long and when it sees that it cannot overtake the animal on which it has fixed its eye—perhaps a gazelle or a reedbuck—it will quickly abandon the chase and wait for a more suitable opportunity. The cheetah is the fastest mammal in the world. Unfortunately it is hunted for its beautifully spotted skin wherever there are no protection laws to prevent it from being killed. Like the leopard, it is now seriously threatened. If the demand for spotted fur-coats from big cats does not fall off soon, before very long one will only be able to see the cheetah in reserves and in zoos. It has already been almost exterminated in the wild.

We lost no time in flying on to Uganda from Nairobi. The flight over Lake Victoria and the mountains which rise to over 9000 feet is quite short. When the plane comes down to land at Entebbe it is almost as though it is aiming to dive into the water.

In Kampala, Mr Katete, the Director of National Parks in Uganda and Mr L. D. Tennent, Chief Game Warden in Entebbe, both helped me greatly with their generous assistance. We drove to Murchison Falls National Park which is different from most of the East African wildlife paradises as the Victoria Nile, part of which is included in the reserve area, gives it a special character.

We travelled up and down the big river in search of animals in a spacious launch which Mr Onslow of the Park administration put at our disposal. These wonderful trips were extremely successful. It was as though one had been transported into a veritable tropical paradise as the boat glided by the banks, lingered under spreading trees which fringe the river, or entered small bays. Everywhere was teeming with wildlife and none of the animals took flight at our intrusion. They had long since learnt that the boats passing by, holding motionless humans, constituted no danger. Here nobody hunted them and every living creature felt secure.

Large numbers of hippopotamus lay in the water. When the boat came too close to them they dived without a sound; they soon surfaced again, puffing and blowing. Elephants stood on the banks, buffaloes and waterbuck grazed close by. On the sandbanks or on trees and bushes stood African fish eagles, goliath herons, open-bill storks and saddle-bill storks, pelicans, African skimmers, marabous, cormorants, bee-eaters and others. Colobus monkeys leapt through the trees, from which came the calls of many birds.

Most impressive of all, however, were the numerous crocodiles which were to be seen everywhere, as the boat glided past. Singly, in pairs and even in dozens, they rested on the land and on the sandbanks in the middle of the river, which in many places is up to 900 feet wide. Like stranded tree-trunks they lay motionless on the mud, in among reeds or foliage, lapped by the water, half covered by grasses or even right out in the open, revealed in all their dangerous magnitude. They looked even more menacing when they opened their mouths wide, showing their formidable rows of teeth, and remained for minutes on end in this position without moving a muscle. Only the bluish third eyelid—the nictitating membrane—which they sometimes drew across the eye showed that these huge armoured reptiles were still alive. But this position is deceptive. According to a legend that goes back to Herodotus a crocodile with its jaws open is said to be inviting small birds to enter its mouth, to pick leeches from the soft skin of the jaws or remove scraps of meat from between the teeth. To us this seems an odd invitation and although it makes a nice little story, it has never been confirmed by serious naturalists, although many have tried to do so.

Crocodiles several feet in length are by no means harmless reptiles. They should always be treated with respect; many people have been attacked by them and badly lacerated or even killed. The idea of falling out of the boat into the midst of these lurking monsters was a terrifying thought. There is no other place in the world today where there are so many crocodiles as on the Victoria Nile below Murchison Falls. It is a crocodile's version of Utopia. The high cliff over which the river flows, forced through a channel that is only about twenty feet wide at the place of the falls, provides an insurmountable barrier for all fish; they remain trapped in the gorge below in their thousands and the crocodiles have only to open their mouths when they are hungry.

The final stage of our expedition was spent in the vast papyrus swamps on the north shores of Lake Victoria. With the help of game rangers and fishermen we went in search of the shoebill, a rare bird that is very difficult to find. Lake Victoria is the largest lake in Africa; its waters alone cover an area of 24,000 square miles, but the swamps and reed-beds along the edges extend much farther and are well-nigh impenetrable. Myriads of mosquitoes, huge numbers of crocodiles and bottomless swamps prevent entry into this completely unknown world.

First we made an air reconnaissance. Flying in a small aeroplane, we circled over the wooded islands which are dotted about in the many square miles of the swamp area. On three occasions we put up shoebills. We marked the places at which they had gone into the reeds as well as we could, which was not easy in view of the monotonous nature of the swampy country beneath us. We then took to a narrow flat punt and attempted to reach the places where, according to our reckoning, the birds should be. In spite of a good crew we made but slow progress in this confusion of reeds, water-lilies and mud; the papyrus swamps are full of animals which live undisturbed year in year out.

After a lot of wearisome poling, the punt stuck fast. It took us hours before we were once again out of this green, swampy hell. During the night the mosquitoes almost devoured us, there was no thought of sleep. They seemed to know just how to get under the mosquito nets without being noticed and we fought a losing battle with them for hours.

The boat journey gradually took on the character of a completely hopeless undertaking. Our spirits flagged and the willingness of the fishermen showed signs of diminishing. Urged on by Pat Martin and Lawrence Tennent, we carried on and tried to follow out our original plans. At last we were confronted by an odd-looking bird with a big head and a large, somewhat misshapen bill to which the shoebill owes its name. It is sometimes known as the shoe-billed stork or the whale-headed stork.

It moved slowly ahead of us. The shoebill is unfamiliar with man as its habitat is seldom penetrated by humans; in fact, we found that it was not particularly shy. At the next hillock it stood quite still, only about 20 yards from us. It prefers islands of 'floating' vegetation and avoids the deep water which offers it no firm footing and which teems with crocodiles. The shoebill is thought by some authorities to be related to the storks. It likes to stand for hours at a time on the same grassy islet and sun itself. When it shakes its feathers one can hear the rustle from a distance. The shoebill needs to be constantly on the alert and to keep an eye on its surroundings. This is why it prefers elevated ground.

Many years ago the Swedish animal photographer Bengt Berg wrote a book about this species in which he referred to it under its Arabic name: *abu markub*. He found it farther north in the Sudan; these immeasurable swamps extend right up to the Sudan. Since then very little has been published on this peculiar bird.

The shoebill virtually protects itself by its retiring habits and its restriction to inaccessible swamps. It has never been photographed at the nest and we still do not know exactly where and when it nests; it probably builds in dense reed thickets or possibly even in trees, like storks and egrets. The fishermen firmly declared that they had once found a tree-nest on one of the wooded islands.

There can be no shortage of suitable food as the water was alive with fish and frogs all over the place. The shoebill scoops them out with its great bill when they come close to the surface. There appears to be an abundance of food throughout the year not only for the shoebill but for all the other animals living in this habitat. There are thousands of pools and as far as the shoebill is concerned, when it has exhausted one pool it has only to move on a short distance to the next. We could not help envying the ease with which the shoebill moved around in its habitat. Our progress in the boat was very slow despite all our efforts.

Having spent seven years searching for rare and threatened animals all over the world, I reckon that the most unpleasant and exacting expedition of them all was to the mosquito-ridden and crocodile-infested swamps of Lake Victoria.

Among the national parks and nature reserves of Africa those in Tanzania, Kenya and Uganda take pride of place. Almost all the species of large African game are represented in them. Kilimanjaro, Africa's highest mountain (19,340 feet), forms a remarkable backcloth to some of the reserves.

The lion has as much the right to live in all the African wildlife reserves as the numerous species of antelope, zebra, buffalo and elephant. If the lion and other carnivores were not present, the herds would multiply without check.

The lion is an inhabitant of plains and savannahs. It lives in groups known as prides and usually remains on the ground but when necessary it is a very accomplished climber. One sometimes finds them resting in trees in the Manyara National Park in Tanzania.

Cheetahs are the rarest of the three African 'large cats'. They can only use their teeth as weapons because their claws are blunt and non-retractable. Due to their long legs they are very swift and can cover up to a hundred yards in five seconds.

Left. Whereas the lion only climbs exceptionally, leopards prefer to use tall trees to rest in as they feel safer here than in the grass. Their black-spotted skin merges against the background of moving foliage and up a tree they are often perfectly camouflaged in the play of light and shadow.

Cape hunting dogs are wild dogs which live and hunt together in packs. Each animal differs from the next in the pattern of spots on its coat but they all have a white tip to the tail. They are very fast hunters and cover large distances at speed.

Colobus monkeys, which belong among the leaf-monkeys, are also known as guerezas. Their tail is rather short and their thumbs are reduced to small stumps. Towards the end of the last century their beautiful black and white pelts were much in demand, and they were hunted ruthlessly.

Above and *right*. The vast and almost inaccessible papyrus swamps around Lake Victoria and northwards to the Sudan are the habitat of the rare shoebill. This bird with the misshapen bill lives in the seclusion of the swamps where protection is not necessary as there are no paths. Even today we do not know whether the shoebill nests in trees or in the swamp, for it has never been seen at its nest.

The Victoria Nile below the Murchison Falls in the Murchison Falls National Park is a haven for water-loving animals of all kinds. The river offers them water in inexhaustible quantities, and there is a constant supply of fresh grass and bushes growing along the banks. This is a true animal paradise.

Attracted by the immense quantities of fish for which the Murchison Falls act as an impassable barrier, thousands of crocodiles of all sizes live in the warm waters of the Victoria Nile and on the mud and gravel banks. They are protected by conservation measures inside the Murchison Falls National Park and today there is no other place in the world where so many crocodiles live together.

There are only 4000 head of white or square-lipped rhinoceros remaining alive in Africa. Like the black rhino this species also has two horns. The horns are not supported by any part of the bony skeleton, but consist of long horny filaments firmly fused together and anchored only in the skin.

Left. The black rhinoceros is the commoner of the two African species of rhinoceros but even its population is steadily decreasing. Outside the reserves these animals are mercilessly hunted by big game poachers because the powdered horn is still in great demand, especially in China, as an aphrodisiac.

The Arabian oryx is one of the rarest mammals in the world. At the most there are a hundred of them still living. A few years ago a number were caught and transported to Arizona to prevent them being completely exterminated.

Right. The gemsbok is not yet threatened to the same extent as the Arabian oryx. Together with the springbok, it is safe from being hunted in the Kalahari Gemsbok National Park.

Nowadays Cape mountain zebras live wild only in South African reserves or on the farms of a few animal-loving landowners. At one time herds of these animals ran into hundreds of thousands but there are probably less than a hundred now remaining. If these remnants of the mountain zebra had not been given protection, they would have been exterminated just like the related quagga.

The multicoloured bontebok is another species which was protected just in time before it was completely exterminated. Only seventeen animals survived slaughter by the Boers. Since then they have bred successfully in small South African reserves and on private farms. Bontebok belong among the antelopes with lyre-shaped horns, which vary in form between a lyre and a half-moon.

The eland is the largest of the many species of antelope in Africa. A fully-grown bull will develop to the size of a large ox. Attempts to tame this antelope have been very successful; the cows even allow themselves to be milked. But its natural habitat is shrinking rapidly as man takes more and more land for his own purposes and the population of wild eland has already been considerably reduced.

The sable antelope bull, with its pitch-black body and contrasting white facial markings and its pointed sabre-like horns curving backwards, is one of the most handsome antelopes of Africa. They look like black devils against the drab background of bush country where they usually live. They are shy and alert, moving off very fast when approached.

Zebras can be regarded as the wild horses of Africa. They do not occur in any other part of the world. It is an unforgettable experience to watch a herd of these remarkable striped animals at comparatively close quarters. A few years ago it was estimated that on the big plains of the Serengeti National Park and on the neighbouring Mara Plains in Tanzania there were still about 170,000 head of Boehm's zebra.

Grevy's zebra is the largest of the zebras. It is rarer than Boehm's zebra and does not live in such large herds. Grevy's zebras prefer semi-open country with scattered bushes and trees. They are closely marked with narrow stripes and their ears are much larger than those of other species.

Giraffes, such as the Masai giraffes shown here, may measure up to 18 feet to the crown of the head. The head and neck alone of this tallest living mammal measures about 7-8 feet. Nowadays giraffes can be found from the southern edge of the Sahara to South Africa, wherever man has left them a suitable habitat.

The patterning on the body, neck and head of the reticulated giraffe is a handsome network of white lines. All the giraffes are sociable animals. In spite of their size they are extremely skillful at making themselves invisible among the trees. Giraffes like camels are amblers. The two legs on one side of the body are moved forward simultaneously. This gives them a peculiar gait and they may break into a fast gallop if pursued.

The gerenuk has a longer neck than the other species of gazelle. It is a supremely elegant and slenderly built mammal. When browsing it stands on its hind-legs and supports itself by resting the fore-legs on the branches of the bush on which it is feeding. It can remain in this singular position for a long time. Gerenuks need very little water; they often do not drink for weeks at a time.

In the nyala antelope the males and females differ greatly in colouration, and the females are hornless and significantly smaller than the males. Nyalas are forest antelopes. They remain hidden in thickets and do not willingly come out into open country. They can only be seen and photographed at watering places in the forest in the early morning or in the evening.

Hippopotamuses like to spend the day lazing in the water, half-submerged as in this picture, which also shows cattle egrets in the background. In the evening they come out on land to feed throughout the night. These heavily built animals require so much food that they are capable of eating whole areas bare, thus doing considerable damage.

Left. In the salt lakes of the Rift Valley in East Africa hundreds of thousands of flamingoes assemble for the breeding season. The shallow lakes are eminently suitable as nesting sites for the flamingoes, which obtain food for their young from the water.

The Cape buffaloes of Africa live in herds like most wild cattle. They move through the plains and savannahs in groups of several hundred head—cows, calves and bulls all keeping together. Only the very old bulls become solitary. Buffaloes can be very dangerous and even lions and leopards avoid them.

When the dry season starts in Africa and many rivers dry up, the wild animals such as these impala congregate at the remaining water-holes. These places are then more vital to wild life than their feeding grounds. There is a constant procession to the water throughout the day, large herds of the same species keeping together as they come down to drink and then moving on again, to make room for another species to get to the water.

Of the many proboscideans which at one time inhabited the earth, only two remain: the Indian and the African elephant. Like the Indian, the African species has been continually reduced in numbers, by increasing settlement and cultivation of the land as well as by legal and illegal hunting. Nowadays large herds are only to be found in the African nature reserves.

The African elephant, which weighs five tons, is the largest land mammal in the world. The daily food requirement of an adult elephant is at least 130 pounds of leaves, grass, roots, twigs and bark as well as about 40 gallons of water. It is therefore understandable that an extensive area, with the necessary food and water, is essential to the life of a herd of elephants. Africa is now the only place which can offer a habitat on this scale.

The perpetual struggle for space in our overpopulated world, in which man can wrest a living, has left us with very few places where we can still experience the wonder of nature in all its beauty. Today the future survival of many wild animals can only be assured in reserves and protected areas. It should be the concern of all mankind to regard these last refuges as a precious heritage and to make sure that they are preserved for future generations.

Description of the species illustrated

Adélie Penguin

Pygoscelis adeliae pp. 116, 117

The Adélie penguin is the true penguin of Antarctica. It gets its name from Adélie Land on the Antarctic continent where this species was first discovered.

The range of distribution of the Adélie penguin extends round the coasts of Antarctica. The penguins spend the long winter in the open pack-ice. As the winter slowly comes to an end, in September and October, the adult birds make for the land, returning to the traditional breeding grounds which are known as rookeries. After landing they still have a good distance to travel on foot. They have to cover up to 60 miles over rough going because at this time the ice still extends far out from the mainland. If the birds were to lay their eggs on the sea-ice the brood would sink into the water during the spring thaw. In the endless expanse of snow the penguins find the exact place where they bred the previous year. Even when the nest-sites are still covered by a thick layer of snow, they are able to find the precise spot.

Tens of thousands of Adélie penguins congregate in the rookeries. Some observers give even higher figures and make reference to millions. The population of each colony consists of four classes of individuals: the old, experienced breeding birds, birds which are breeding for the first time (aged 3–4 years), immature 2–3 year old non-breeders which make a half-hearted attempt at display and nest-building, and a few yearling non-breeders which generally spend most of the time in the pack-ice but wander into the rookery from time to time.

The first weeks in the colony are spent in courtship display, in finding mates and in numerous fights. The best places in the centre of the rookery belong to the old pairs, the young ones having to be content with sites on the periphery. Then a proper nest is built. In these regions the only nesting materials available are flint pebbles. The female lays two eggs after which she goes to sea to feed, leaving the male to take the first spell of incubation, for nearly three weeks. The male has had no food since his arrival and goes through a period of starvation which lasts until the end of the first spell of incubation; during this period he loses about 40 per cent of his body weight. The female then returns to the nest and the partners relieve each other twice in the course of the 35-day period of incubation.

When the young hatch they have a fine, silky covering of down which is soon replaced by a second plumage of thicker, woolly down. So long as the young remain small, the male or female stays the whole time on watch, guarding them. When they are large enough to be on their own they soon leave the nest. A large number of young of the same age then gather together in a kind of kindergarten or crèche.

About a week before the young become independent, the crèches break up and they go to sea independently of the adults when about 9 weeks old. The young penguins do not have to go so far to reach the sea as their parents did when they arrived at the breeding-sites because in the meantime the sea-ice has melted in the summer temperature.

(See also emperor penguin)

ALBATROSS see Royal Albatross

Alligators and Crocodiles

Alligatoridae, Crocodylidae pp. 99, 227

The crocodilians exceed all other reptiles in size and weight. Giant forms such as the American crocodile may grow to a length of 23 feet. Nevertheless they are not as large as some of their ancestors which often had a skull of 6 feet in length. The first crocodilians appeared in the Triassic Period, that is, about 175 million years ago. Nowadays there are still about 25 living species. They are classified in three families: the true crocodiles, the alligators and the garials.

The crocodiles and the alligators, to which the caymans also belong, have fewer than 22 teeth in each jaw. In contrast to the alligators, the fourth tooth of the lower jaw of the crocodiles is enlarged and visible because it lies in an indentation of the upper jaw.

Crocodilians are circumtropical in distribution. The garial is found in the rivers of India and farther east. The alligators, which are exclusively inhabitants of fresh water, are distributed in North, Central and South America. Only a single species is found outside this range, in China. Crocodiles live in the tropics and subtropics of the whole world. Most of them are in fresh water, but a few are also found in brackish and sea water.

When the traveller drifts quietly in a boat down one of the large rivers of Africa or South America, he sees these enormous animals basking on the mud-banks in the sun, often with widely gaping jaws. At first sight they appear to be very clumsy, but they get up on to their legs with surprising agility, glide into the water and disappear into the depths with astonishing speed. After some time they come up again cautiously, with only the nostrils and the eyes appearing above the surface of the water. All the crocodilians are strong swimmers. They are driven through the water by the powerful laterally compressed tail, the limbs being held close to the body. A flap of mucosal skin closes the throat so closely that a crocodile can open its mouth underwater to catch prey. The internal nostrils open behind this flap valve, thus enabling the crocodile to breathe with only the slightly raised external openings of the nose showing above the water surface. These openings are closed when the animal is under water.

Crocodiles are greedy eaters. They feed on fish, terrapins, birds and mammals. Crocodiles will lurk underwater and suddenly seize an animal drinking at the water's edge and drag it down so that it drowns. Crocodilians never chew their prey. Large animals are cut into pieces with the help of the shear-like jaws, sometimes after a period of decomposition. Large pieces of prey are sometimes torn apart by several crocodiles twisting and turning their bodies in opposite directions.

Since tropical rivers usually have cloudy water it is only rarely that one observes the approach of a crocodile. I remember hearing of a poor woman on the Magdalena River in Colombia standing in the water to wash her hands, who was suddenly seized by a cayman, drawn underwater and drowned. Thus some crocodiles also become man-eaters, sometimes by accident.

It is known that crocodilians can reach a great age. In captivity some have been known to live for more than fifty years. The damage they do, however, is small and bears little relation to the sustained slaughter of crocodiles and alligators. Long stretches of the Nile have been completely cleared of crocodiles by hunters. The Nile crocodile only occurs now in large numbers in the big national parks such as the Murchison Falls National Park in Uganda. The Mississippi alligator can be seen in the Florida Everglades lying beneath swamp cypresses luxuriantly bedecked with tillandsias.

Many years ago I kept a fruitless watch for crocodiles on the mud-banks of the Cuanza in Angola; in the space of six years about 4,000 crocodiles had been shot or caught by three hunters at a small place called Dondo. The skins were sold for manufacture into shoes, handbags and similar articles. It is high time that a determined effort should be made to get crocodiles protected in many areas of the tropics.

Alpine Ibex
Capra ibex ibex p. 27

The continued survival of alpine ibex was very seriously threatened during the last century. At a time when the species had been practically exterminated it was saved by the efforts of one man, and numbers were subsequently raised to a safer level.

This is a hardy species which lives in the highest mountains where it is an agile climber. At one time it held a prominent place in folklore medicine. Great healing powers were attributed to parts of its body: in particular to the stomach stones, also known as bezoars, and to the ossified heart septa. The bezoars are masses of hair matted together to form bodies that are as hard as rock. The cud-chewing stomach is unable to digest these horny structures but the constant working of the stomach muscles results in the formation of rounded bodies which rub against each other so that they become smooth and polished. The heart septum is a cartilaginous or bony strengthening of the dividing wall between the front and back chambers of the heart. Bezoars and hardened heart septa are found in many ungulates and are therefore not peculiar to the alpine ibex. In folklore, however, the allegedly miraculous powers attributed to the relevant parts of the alpine ibex made this species a much valued animal.

For centuries a bitter war was waged on the one hand between the gamekeepers who tried to protect their animals and the poachers who on the other hand were determined to get hold of an alpine ibex at all costs. This war claimed so many victims that at the beginning of the 18th century Johann Ernst, the Archbishop of Salzburg, publicly ordered that all the ibex should be shot; this happened only after he had spent years trying in vain to preserve and increase the stock of ibex on his land. Under his successor there were no alpine ibex to be found and in this way the population of the eastern Alps, which formed a separate subspecies, disappeared beyond recall.

The population of alpine ibex in the western Alps would have met the same fate if King Victor Emmanuel II of Italy had not placed the last 50 of them under strict protection in his large wildlife reserve in the Aosta valley. Thanks to this measure the western population was saved and it became possible to raise their numbers by breeding. Gradually it was accepted that the organs of the ibex had no special healing powers and so the main reason for their pursuit lapsed. When King Victor Emmanuel III presented the Gran Paradiso Reserve in the Aosta valley to the Italian people there were already some thousands of alpine ibex living there.

The ibex of Aosta were the original source of all those which have been put into breeding enclosures; animals were later reintroduced into Switzerland, Austria, Germany, the High Tatras of Czechoslovakia on the border between Jugoslavia and Austria, where they still exist. Today the total population is well over 6000 head, and so the alpine ibex has been saved for the future.

There is scarcely any other animal to compare with the alpine ibex for hardiness and agility. It has frequently been chosen as an emblem for badges and crests. The embodiment of endurance, combining strength with beauty, it would have been a tragedy if this species had vanished for ever from the alpine scene.

Andean Condor
Vultur gryphus p. 111

The Andean condor of South America has the largest wing span of the family of the New World vultures and it is larger than any of the Old World vultures. Its wing span measures 115–125 inches but its weight is no greater than that of the king vulture which has a wing span of only about 100 inches.

The range of the Andean condor extends from Venezuela and Colombia to Cape Horn. It occurs from sea level up to the steppes of the mountain ranges. The population of condors is not immediately threatened today in the sparsely settled expanses of the high Andes; it is not encountered everywhere in this vast area and in general it is not common. But such large birds are seldom common, because there is basically never enough food. They require plenty of space to meet the food requirements for themselves and their families. Like the other vultures the condor is also a carrion-feeder. When searching for food it soars overhead on widely spread wings, spying out the land, often for long spells at a time and then drops down as soon as it spots something.

Condors have been known to strike weak or sickly animals over a precipice with their wings but such an occurrence is extremely rare. Normally they hunt only for carrion. Although a powerful looking bird, the condor is not able to strike an animal with its talons as an eagle does. A glance at its feet, which are almost like those of a fowl, makes it apparent that they are not adapted for grasping; they lack the sharp, curved claws with which an eagle seizes and kills its prey. The claws of the condor are short and flat, it can only use the foot in order to hold small prey on the ground while the beak tears it up.

It is not surprising that such a large and impressive looking bird has played a role in the age-old myths and legends of the people of the Andes. Today the condor appears in the coat of arms of the South American states of Colombia, Ecuador, Peru, Bolivia and Chile. Nevertheless in some countries the cattle-breeders have succeeded in getting high rewards paid for condors that are shot. Stories of condors which have allegedly killed young cattle are fabricated or greatly exaggerated.

ANTELOPES see Bontebok; Eland; Impala: Nilgai; Nyala; Oryx; Sable Antelope

APES see Orang Utan

Bald Ibis

Geronticus eremita pp. 42, 43

The bald ibis or waldrapp only breeds today in a few scattered colonies in Morocco and in the Near East. It is nowhere abundant and everywhere in danger. From its appearance one would be unlikely to guess that it was formerly a European breeding species. A long time ago it was present in Austria, Switzerland and even in a few places in the Danube Valley in south Germany but it became extinct in central Europe in the seventeenth century.

A description appeared in 1555 in Conrad Gesner's *Historia Animalium* of a strange black bird with red legs and a long red bill, which he called Waldrapp or Klausrabe. His description was later held to be fictitious in spite of the fact that he had made some precise points about the bird which were correct for this species. It was not until 1897 that three well known ornithologists found out that Gesner's bird was identical with the bald ibis, newly discovered 275 years later in North Africa.

Some years ago Professor Tratz of Salzburg gathered together all the information about this bird that he could find from official documents and old papers. These showed that in the sixteenth century this bird was still living in Austria and the neighbouring countries, but it disappeared in the course of the 17th century. Its nesting habits were much the same then as today; it nested on cliff faces either in areas of human settlements or in their immediate vicinity, particularly in Graz and Salzburg. From the 16th century documents relating to regulations, it appears that the contemporary rulers had already laid down strict orders for the preservation of the waldrapp. The bird was apparently persecuted continuously by the population and also shot on its breeding cliffs. The regulations were evidently not very effective.

If the disappearance of the bald ibis from its European range could not be attributed to climatic reasons, it is possible that the ceaseless persecution at the breeding colonies should be held responsible. It appears that the majority of the young were taken from the nest every year. Changes in the landscape due to the spread of civilisation and the immoderate use of highly poisonous insecticides, which virtually decimate the insect population, could scarcely have exerted any influence at that time.

Today, on the other hand, these factors may shortly be disastrous in their effect. Dr H. Kumerloeve, the acknowledged expert on the bald ibis colony at Birecik on the Upper Euphrates which was the most significant population a few years ago, has emphasized the seriousness of the position. In 1911 the colony had approximately 1000 pairs; in 1957 there were 600–800 pairs. In recent years, however, the colony has decreased still further for unknown reasons, and now stands at less than 100 pairs. It is not clear whether the birds have found another nesting site or whether they have died. The discovery of at least 200 dead bald ibis in the year 1957/58, reported by Dr Kumerloeve, gives rise to the worst fears.

The bald ibis, unlike its relatives the glossy ibis and the sacred ibis, is not a swamp bird but seeks the greater part of its food, which consists of beetles and grasshoppers or locusts, on plains and in dry country. This lays the birds open to the dangers of taking insects poisoned with DDT and other preparations. As these substances are widely used in the Near East, this might account for the decline in population as reported from Birecik.

Banteng

Bibos sondaicus p. 194

The greatest number of wild cattle species occurs in Asia, which is the original home of these impressive ungulates. Even the bison of North America, the wisent and auroch of Europe, and the Cape buffalo of Africa, came originally from Asia. Today the following species of wild cattle can still be found in Asia: the yak, the wild water buffalo or arni, the anoa, the gaur, the kouprey and the banteng.

Of these the banteng is the most brightly coloured. The red-brown cows and the brownish-black bulls have white feet and white stockings on the hind legs which contrast sharply with the rest of the body. They make an attractive picture against the green background of their forest and jungle habitat.

Bantengs live in small herds consisting of a bull, with two or three dozen cows, young animals and calves, while old bulls often become solitary. Banteng are not aggressive and if caught as calves or juveniles they can easily be tamed and even crossed with domestic cattle.

The distribution of the banteng extends from Manipur and Mandalay in northern Burma southwards to the northern edge of the Malay Peninsula and on through Siam, Cochin China, Cambodia, Laos, South Annam and Tonkin. The species also occurs in Borneo and Java. Until recently they also lived as wild animals in Bali but were exterminated by the deforestation and cultivation practised by the fast-increasing human population; however, before this happened they had already been incorporated into the stocks of domestic cattle. This probably occurred also in Java. The domesticated forms are known as Bali cattle. These have also been introduced into other parts of Malaysia, and have again become wild in, for example, Bali and Lombok.

The banteng has a number of subspecies. Those from the mainland are different from specimens from Java and Borneo, which each form a separate subspecies. The mainland banteng has been exterminated in many parts of its range, the Borneo banteng only occurs still in North Borneo and the Java banteng only on the Udjong Kulon Peninsula in the extreme west of Java, where the Javan Rhinoceros reserve is also situated. There is a second population of bantengs in the Tjikupeh Reserve in western Java.

The entire responsibility for the reduction in the population of the banteng rests with man, due to his habits of hunting and of uprooting forests to make room for cultivating the land. These large, powerful cattle have only a few natural enemies. Now and again a tiger may take a calf or a pack of wild dogs will worry an animal to death. It is true that in the countries where it occurs the banteng enjoys some degree of protection from hunting, which is restricted to certain areas, and it is completely protected in the reserve areas. Unfortunately however these measures are often only on paper. The vast majority of the people either do not know of their existence or disregard them in characteristic oriental fashion. So the future of the banteng is not exactly rosy.

Barbary Ape

Simia sylvanus p. 39

Among the many subjects of the British Crown there are a few dozen which are quite different from any others in the British Commonwealth. These are the Barbary apes which live in the 2 square miles of the Crown Colony of Gibraltar.

Tradition says that the Rock of Gibraltar will only remain in British hands so long as the Barbary apes continue to live there. Even today nobody knows whether the British brought these monkeys over from the opposite coast of north Africa when they captured the Rock in 1704. It is possible that long before this the monkeys had already been introduced by the Phœnicians, Carthaginians, Greeks, Romans, Moors or Corsairs; they may even belong among those groups of animals which were living on both shores of the Mediterranean before the Ice Age, when the Strait still did not exist.

Whenever the ape population of Gibraltar has seriously declined, the British Government has taken the trouble to preserve them and to increase their numbers. The last time this happened was in 1942 when the number had sunk to seven. Winston Churchill then personally ordered the number to be increased. In 1950 Parliament decided to increase the daily allowance by a penny from three pence to four pence. This money was used to buy extra food for the animals as they were not able to find enough to eat on the Rock itself.

The Barbary ape is the only representative of the macaques in Africa. The other macaque species such as the toque, bonnet, rhesus, pig-tailed, kra, moor, and Japanese monkeys are all Asiatic. The large gap between the present distribution of the above species and that of the Barbary ape arose during the Ice Age. At present the latter are distributed locally in Morocco and Algeria.

The privileged status accorded to Barbary apes in Gibraltar is not repeated in the rest of its range. On the contrary the apes are continually hunted because they are capable of causing serious damage in orchards and vegetable gardens. As omnivorous social animals they live in troops which may number several dozen. Add to this the simian drive for destruction and one can understand that the human population grudges the apes a share of their food.

A troop of Barbary apes spends the night for preference on steep cliffs, which the leopard, their principal natural enemy, is unlikely to climb. Although leopards have been almost completely exterminated in north Africa, the habit persists. The apes wander off in search of food in the morning, hunting for locusts, beetles, butterflies, and other insects, lizards and small mammals: they are also not averse to the eggs of ground-nesting species. Their diet includes fruits, roots, tubers, buds, young leaves, fresh herbs, grain, seeds and so on. They cannot be described as fastidious feeders.

Each troop is dominated by a powerful male who controls the females and their young. There is a strict ranking order which is observed by the subordinates; only the young have freedom to play about. Fully grown males will start fights with the leading male when they want to get at his wives. In these battles for supremacy, the fight becomes a matter of life or death when the young rival is roughly equal in strength to the old male. On Gibraltar the leading ape, who always holds power for a few years, is given a name. The animals are known to the public by their names and elderly inhabitants of the Crown Colony can recite the sequence of names of the dictators back to the turn of the last century.

The female produces only one young after a gestation period of about 7 months. The young animal is lovingly nursed and carried around by the mother. It clings firmly to her fur. After a few weeks it starts to leave the mother's body for short periods at a time and to make its first attempts at walking. Proficiency increases rapidly and the more nimble the young become, the more they indulge in play and mischievous tricks. They first become sexually mature in the third or fourth year and may easily live for 15 years. In captivity some have lived for over 20 years and one has even been known to live for 27 years.

BEARS see Black Bear; Brown Bear; Polar Bear; Spectacled Bear

Beaver

Castor fiber pp. 88, 89

The beaver is the largest European rodent, and indeed one of the largest rodents in the world. The length from head to rump is 30–38 inches, the tail is about 11 inches long and it weighs 55–65 lb. Only the coypu and the porcupines reach this size, and only the capybara exceeds it. Among the rodents the beaver is classified in a separate family. It is not generally known that today there are still beavers living in the wild in Germany: in the water-meadows of the Elbe and Mulde between Magdeburg, Wittenburg and Dessau a population of about 100 animals still survives under strict protection.

At one time the beaver was common throughout central Europe but by the middle of the last century it was exterminated everywhere; it was hunted on the one hand for the value of its wonderfully soft, thick and water-repellent fur, and on the other for the secretion of the testicular gland near the anus which was alleged to have healing properties. In addition the Roman Church classified it as fish which could be eaten on fast-days. Fishermen also accused it of taking fish and treated it as vermin. Apart from the rightly valued fur, there was a general lack of knowledge at that time concerning the real habits of the beaver and its structural anatomy which unfortunately worked to its disadvantage. In addition there came the ever increasing spread of cultivation. The water-meadow areas were destroyed by the drainage of marshes and swamps and the alterations to rivers and streams, and so the beaver lost its habitat.

The beaver is a rodent specially adapted to a diet of soft wood. In a single year an adult requires a good 4 tons or 7–8 cubic yards of timber with its bark, in addition to its intake of soft marsh and water plants. The beaver only finds this diet of willow, poplar, alder and so on in damp, swampy areas. To live in such places it has to be able to swim and dive well. The fur is water-repellent, the ears are small and both ears and nostrils can be closed under water; it has webs between the toes and a broad, flat tail as a steering organ. The beaver was formerly held to be a fish on account of the surface of the naked tail resembling fish-scales. It was also convenient to regard it as a fish because its flesh could be eaten on fast-days. The beaver qualifies as a master-builder in aquatic sites. It makes a home or lodge in the water by building dams with approach channels to the lodge; it dams up pools which provide adequate space for swimming and for diving when in danger, and also for entering the lodge from under water. The water around its lodge must also remain deep enough to hold a large winter store of soft wood, without this becoming frozen in. The beaver does not hibernate but during the winter it dives down under the ice to fetch food from its store.

Beavers are monogamous and lead a model family life according to human standards. In May, after a gestation period of about 105 days, the female gives birth to 3 or 4 young which can see, are fully furred and capable of moving about on their own. The young enter the water when two weeks old, are suckled for two months, take their first solid food at six weeks and are tended by the parents for about two years. They then wander away in search of a mate and establish new families and colonies.

In Eurasia the beaver is only found in small numbers in the Rhône delta, on the Elbe, near Magdeburg, and in a few colonies in Norway, Sweden, Russia, Siberia and Mongolia. In North

America, where they were widely distributed, they have been brought to the brink of extinction by the demands of the fur trade.

Today the beaver is protected everywhere and it can be trapped again, to some extent, for the fur trade without endangering the population.

BIGHORN SHEEP see Wild Sheep

BIRDS OF PARADISE see Lesser Bird of Paradise; Little King Bird of Paradise

Bison

Bison bison pp. 91–93

The bison or North American buffalo and the wisent or European bison are two closely related species of wild cattle which first became separated from each other towards the end of the Ice Age. Asiatic in origin, they were once distributed throughout the temperate zone of the Old World. They reached North America over the land bridge that is now covered by the waters of the Bering Strait, and colonised it as far south as central Mexico. In this vast area a number of forms evolved, including giant plains dwellers from which only the wisent and the North American bison survived the Ice Age. Although the wisent remains restricted to Europe and the bison to North America, they are so closely related that even today they can be crossed with each other.

They are almost identical as regards the structure of the skull, and strictly speaking are to be regarded as subspecies of a single species.

In North America the bison occurs in two forms, the wood buffalo and the plains buffalo just as in the wisent there is a plains race and a more lightly built mountain form in the Caucasus.

On the average the bison is about 6 feet tall at the withers and weighs up to 1900 lb. The bulls are always about ¼ to ⅓ larger and heavier than the cows.

The habitat of the plains buffalo is grassy prairie and parkland broken up by large meadows; the wood buffalo as the name implies lives in open woodland or forests.

Plains buffalo feed almost exclusively on grass and herbs. They graze mainly in the morning and evening, but on light nights throughout the night. At one time seasonal migrations took place, the herds travelling hundreds of miles in search of new pastures. Nowadays, with their habitat restricted, this is no longer possible. Wood buffalo have always been comparatively stationary. They feed mainly on the buds, bark and twigs of trees and bushes.

The mating season of the plains buffalo is July and August, according to the latitude, and August and September for the wood buffalo. After a gestation period of nine months the cow gives birth, somewhat apart from the herd, to a single calf (rarely two) which she takes back to the herd after a few days. The calf is suckled for about a year. Bison usually become sexually mature in the third, more rarely in the second, year. They may live to an age of 25 years or more.

The bison, also known as the Indians' buffalo, formed the basis of life for almost all the tribes of North American Indians. As they only took the surplus from a population of 40 to 60 million animals, they did not endanger the species as a whole. It was not until the arrival of the white man, and in particular the building of the transcontinental railway, that this apparently inexhaustible supply was reduced to a mere hundred head. In the 'nineties of the last century resolute idealists saved this pitiful remnant which, under conditions of full protection, has now increased again to about 30,000 animals. From now on restricted hunting can be allowed in order to prevent overgrazing of the reserve areas.

(See also Wisent)

Black Bear

Ursus americanus p. 83

In North America, in addition to the brown bear there is a second species of bear, the black bear or baribal. It is smaller, lighter and more slender than the brown bear and somewhat built up towards the rear. It attains a height of 27–35 inches at the shoulders and a weight of 400 to 600 lb.

The silhouette of the black bear makes it immediately recognisable. Compared with the brown bear, it has a comparatively narrow and pointed head, with only a weak bridge to the nose which is always cinnamon coloured, and the neck is less heavy. Its general colouring is black, from which it gets its name, and there is often a white spot on the breast; however it is not always black and a second colour, cinnamon, is quite common. This second colour is frequently seen in the western part of the range, particularly in the Rocky Mountains and such animals are known as cinnamon bears. There are also chocolate-brown specimens which occur mainly in the coastal areas of British Columbia, whitish-yellow ones are sometimes found on Gribble Island in British Columbia, and there are bluish-white bears in southern Alaska and northern British Columbia.

Formerly the black bear was found from north Mexico to central Alaska and from Florida into northern Labrador. It occurred in all areas where mature forest and parkland offered sufficient food, from the sea coasts up to the tree-limit on mountains. Today in the USA it has almost completely disappeared from the foot of the Rockies to the east coast. It is still holding out in the more extensive forest areas (particularly in the Alleghenies) and also from the Mississippi estuary area to Florida.

In one sense civilisation and densely populated settlements have driven the bear out of some areas, nevertheless it cannot be said to avoid humans. Providing man leaves it alone and the neighbouring countryside offers it sufficient food supply, together with quiet places where it can withdraw undisturbed for the winter, the black bear is able to tolerate the presence of man.

Like the brown bear, the black bear is an omnivore. During the spring and summer months it eats more grass, herbs, roots, tubers, berries, bark and other plant material than flesh. The bear takes up residence in its winter quarters in September or October, according to the latitude. When it re-emerges it barks conifers in order to get at sappy fibres; trees that are ringed in this manner will die. The bear's requirements for flesh, or more properly protein, are met more often by taking a quantity of small animals than by killing large animals. For instance, ground-dwelling rodents, young game, birds' eggs, young birds, insects including larvae, ants, nests of bees and bumblebees, fish and so on, all form part of its diet. Large animals can only be overcome when they are not fully active. Carrion is in no way despised by the bears.

The black bear is normally solitary. The mating season takes place in June–July but the embryo does not begin to develop properly in the female until December; it is born at the end of January or beginning of February in the winter quarters. At birth the black-haired cubs are only the size of a rat; they are born blind, and do not open their eyes until they are about 40 days old. At two months they weigh about 5 lb. and leave the lair accompanied by the female. They look like playful teddy bears at this stage. The female continues to look after them during the following winter and does not mate again until the succeeding summer. As the litter usually contains two to three cubs, rarely four, the number of offspring produced by a female bear between the third and fifteenth year of her life is not particularly high. However the bear is a powerful carnivore which has practically no enemies, apart from man, and it manages quite well. In the wild they live for 18 years at the most but one has been known to live in captivity to the age of 24 years.

Black Stork

Ciconia nigra p. 31

The white stork is familiar to the public at least in name, but few people know that there is a second stork in Europe: the black stork. Apart from the underparts which are white, its plumage is a metallic iridescent blackish-green.

The black stork has never achieved the popularity of the white stork because, in general, it shuns man and seeks the seclusion of large forests. Originally it was distributed throughout the forest belt from central and southern Europe to the eastern coasts of Asia but its present distribution in Europe is rather patchy. In Germany, for instance, in the few areas where it still occurs, the black stork is now regarded as one of the rarest species. Nesting sites are kept secret by the forestry authorities and the few experts who know where pairs are breeding, in an effort to prevent disturbance by importunate photographers and to provide complete protection during the breeding season. In Poland, however, the population of black storks is reported to be on the increase; conditions favouring it appear to have improved whereas in Germany these are deteriorating steadily.

In parts of eastern Europe and Asia the black stork is still relatively common. This statement, however, must be viewed in the context of the conditions which are necessary to this species which is solitary in its habits. The local density can never be high because each pair requires a large territory to itself.

The black stork is a bird of the forest. The nest is built in one of the oldest and tallest trees, either deciduous or coniferous, with widely spreading branches and a large crown. This type of nest-site appears to suit the birds' requirements completely. Nowadays in Germany, however, trees of this type scarcely exist in the dense forests and pairs are forced to accept smaller trees if they are to remain for the breeding season.

The black stork is a migratory species which winters in Africa. It belongs among the few European species which have colonized their winter quarters, remaining there to breed regularly, at least in a few isolated places.

The black stork seeks its food in waters which are rich in fish either in the forest or in the vicinity. It likes shallow water in which it can wade. Fish forms the basis of its diet. In Germany's polluted countryside, one may well wonder where it is possible to find rivers or lakes in the forest which still have an abundant supply of fish. The black stork is regarded in Germany as symbolic of the solitude of the forest. The only chance of retaining it as a breeding species is to give it effective and complete protection in the few areas which still appear to suit it.

Blue Duck

Hymenolaimus malacorhynchus p. 151

It is only in a few places in the world that there are ducks capable of living in wild mountain streams and rushing rivers; there are torrent ducks in the Andes in South America and two rare species in New Guinea and New Zealand.

The blue duck of New Zealand is a highly peculiar water bird, which to an expert on ducks appears at first sight to be completely out of the ordinary. The plumage is leaden-grey with chestnut-brown spots on the throat and underparts. As in all the ducks of mountain streams, the tail is rather long and is carried erect when swimming, even in quite young ducklings. On each side of the tip of the bill there is a small fold of skin which is thought to be used in sucking algae off stones, although little is known about this.

This duck is not very gregarious and apparently lives for the greater part of the year in pairs. Early on the individual pairs divide up the stream or river between themselves and each of the pairs claims several miles of water for itself. On the broader lower reaches, which are sometimes colonised right down to the coast, more food is available and the pairs are less widely spaced. Blue ducks dive right into the middle of the foaming torrent without being washed away by the current; even the downy ducklings will seek out such turbulent waters.

Their food consists mainly of aquatic insects which are caught by diving, but food is also sucked up from the surface and from rocks sticking up out of the water. Even a narrow forest stream, winding between rocks and tree roots, provides a habitat for this duck; it also lives on broad rivers provided the water is clear, fast-running and the banks are wooded. They normally nest amongst rocks in the water but occasionally nests are found under dense bushes or in the shelter of overhanging branches, but the nest is never far from the banks because the blue duck moves awkwardly on land.

As in all birds living in fast-running waters, the call is a shrill whistle which can be heard even above the roar of the torrent.

The misfortune of the blue duck is that it is neither shy nor wary. Man has been able to kill it easily and does so abundantly. The unfledged young are particularly vulnerable to the dogs of settlers which wander about. As a result, the blue duck has become exceedingly rare and every single encounter with it is regarded as worthy of recording. The bird-lovers of New Zealand keep a record of all observations in their annals.

Bontebok

Damaliscus pygargus p. 233

The wildebeestes and the hartebeestes are among the most striking in appearance of the antelopes of Africa. They are distributed in numerous subspecies all over the countryside of Africa with the exception of the rain-forest areas. Both groups are found alongside each other in many areas. They are rather similar in appearance—about the size of a red deer—and within each group many of the members can only be distinguished from each other by a real expert. Their habits are also very similar.

The hartebeestes have horns which vary in shape between a lyre and a half-moon; these are carried by both sexes. In this group the head is somewhat shorter that the noticeably larger one of the wildebeestes or gnus but like these they have a sloping back, a medium-length tail which ends in a tuft, and a hide colour which varies between pale and dark brown.

The hartebeestes live on open plains and in savannah country with scattered bushes. They also occur in dry semi-desert and in damp grassy jungle in the flooded lowlands. They are gregarious, moving about in small to large family groups consisting of a male and several females with their young. There are also herds containing only females or only males.

In the dry season hartebeestes congregate into herds of several hundreds. Associations of antelopes, zebras and ostriches are not unusual. The groups often set up individual watch posts on termite mounds or other vantage points. Normally the animals drink in the morning and evening but they can do without water for days at a time. The breeding period varies somewhat according to the season in the different areas. At this time the males fight strenuously for the females. After a gestation period of 7–8 months usually only one calf is born. In the wild they live for about 12–15 years; a life span of 17 years has been recorded in captivity.

The hartebeestes can be divided into two groups: the true hartebeestes which have a shoulder height of 42–48 inches and the more attractive bastard hartebeestes which stand 32–42 inches high at the shoulders. To the latter group belong the bontebok and blesbok. In the bontebok the body is red-brown and black, and there is a sharply contrasting pattern on the head, legs and body. The blesbok is more drab in appearance. The flashing white blaze on the front of the face, which gives the blesbok its name, adorns both species but the bontebok also has white patches on the legs and underparts, as well as a prominent white patch on the rump.

The bontebok used to live only in a narrowly restricted area in the southernmost part of Cape Province, the blesbok in eastern Cape Province. With the settlement of Cape Colony by the whites both species were largely exterminated and disappeared completely from the wild. They would have disappeared altogether if in the last century generous-hearted farmers had not taken them under their wing and looked after them on their farms.

Today the blesbok is strictly protected on certain large private farms and in reserve areas at Winburg and Kroonstad in Orange Free State and at Pretoria in Transvaal; it has already increased to over 1000 head. There are also several in zoos.

The bontebok suffered even more severely and at one time there were only 17 animals left. They were then put under strict protection and from 1931 to today they have increased to 700.

They live partly in the Bontebok National Park at Bredarsdorp and partly on private farms in the Bredarsdorp, Swellendam and Albany areas. Individual animals are already living wild in the Swellendam area.

Brown Bear

Ursus arctos pp. 76, 77, 79

The brown bear as it exists today is of recent origin. It originated in the course of the Ice Age contemporaneously with the cave bear, a separate species which died out towards the end of the Ice Age.

The structure of its cheek-teeth allows the brown bear to live on a vegetarian as well as an animal diet. This enables it to survive in widely varying habitats, from the arctic tundra to primeval forests and on high mountain tundra. It is not surprising, therefore, that before it was persecuted by man in the last century, it had a very wide distribution which extended over the whole temperate and northern parts of the Old and New Worlds. Today in western Europe it has been reduced to small relict populations in the Pyrenees, southern Alps and the Abruzzi. As a result of strict protection, however, numbers are present from southern Poland to northern Greece, Rumania and Bulgaria. Small populations also still exist in Scandinavia. From eastern Poland and western Russia it is widely distributed eastwards in Asia Minor, Syria, Persia, Afghanistan and from there eastwards through Tibet to Mongolia. In North America it has disappeared from the whole of the USA and also from western Canada—except in the national parks along the Rocky Mountains where bears are protected.

Within this vast range the brown bear occurs in forms which vary between small and large. The smallest representatives are the relics in west and central Europe and those in Syria; the largest are the Kamchatka, the Alaska and the Kodiak bears. The largest Alaska bears live on the Alaska and Kenai Peninsulas and the adjacent islands of Unimak, Kodiak, Afognak, Shuyak and Montagu. An adult bear can reach a shoulder height of 4½ feet, a total body length of about 8 feet and a weight of over 1500 lb. It is in fact the largest land carnivore in the world. The grizzly bear, in which mostly grey tones predominate in the fur, lives mainly in the region of the big North American mountains.

The brown bear is by nature a phlegmatic loafer; it wanders about in search of food and its large territory covers several square miles. In spring when the bear comes out of its winter quarters, it first eats some grass and herbs, in order to clean out its digestive tract and to obtain vitamins. Then it takes the carcasses sticking up out of the snow, thus eating carrion. Later it also searches for nests and young birds of ground-nesting species or for young game. It also likes to go fishing. It is well known that the Alaska bear can live for weeks on salmon, which move up the rivers at spawning time. In other regions brown bears fatten up on hares, ground squirrels and marmots. In the summer they feed for weeks only on berries, but later they take wild fruits, acorns, chestnuts, beech mast and other tree seeds; they also dig for juicy roots, bulbs and tubers—not to mention bees' nests with honey and grubs. They are usually too clumsy to kill healthy game but will take calves, kids, young boars and other young animals; they also take large animals that are injured or sick. Where domestic animals are put out to graze in forests, brown bears will also kill these; they then frequently develop into raiders, killing fully grown cattle and horses. A 700-lb. grizzly can quite easily kill a 900 lb. bison.

In the autumn the bear looks for a winter lair, a natural hole in the earth or among rock crevices; it may dig a hole for itself. The lair is lined with grass, leaves and moss. The bear sleeps throughout the winter months, but does not hibernate in the strict sense of the term. It then lives on its fat. The female usually produces her cubs in January, normally two to four, but occasionally more, after a gestation period of 180 to 250 days. The cubs are very small at birth, roughly the size of a rat and weighing only 1–1½ lb.; they are sparsely covered with fur and are blind and helpless. By the end of the first year they weigh about 180 lb. They remain with the mother in the winter lair until April. By this time they are already very active, like playful teddy bears with a white patch or ring on the neck which begins to disappear in six months. The parents tend the young for a good two years, so mating only takes place every third year. The normal life span of a bear is 25 to 30 years.

BUFFALO see Cape Buffalo; Bison

BUSTARD see Great Bustard

Cape Buffalo

Syncerus caffer p. 244

At the present time the following different kinds of wild cattle still occur: banteng, gaur, kouprey, yak, wisent and bison, anoa, water buffalo and Cape buffalo. Banteng, gaur and kouprey are three closely related forms from southern Asia. The yak is most closely related to the extinct auroch and to the domesticated cattle descended from it. Bison and wisent are so similar to each other that they can be regarded as subspecies of a single species.

The three forms of buffalo, namely anoa, water buffalo and Cape buffalo, form a group apart from all the others. Of these, the smallest and most primitive species is the anoa which is restricted to Celebes and the neighbouring islands. On the other hand, the wild water buffalo was formerly much more widely distributed than it is today. It used to be found from north Africa through Mesopotamia, India and south-east Asia, Malaya, Sumatra, Java, Borneo to central China and the Philippines. Its occurrence in Mesopotamia and north Africa linked up with the Cape buffalo which is now found only south of the Sahara although in the post-glacial age, when there were still rivers in the Sahara, it lived in forests on the plains. The water buffalo was finally exterminated from north Africa during the last decade. The close relationship between Asiatic and African buffaloes is thus irrefutably confirmed and is further supported by their similarity in form and behaviour.

When considering the African buffaloes one tends to think only of the large black buffaloes with powerful horns from the plains of east and south Africa, but the small red buffaloes with weakly developed horns from the rain forests should not be forgotten. Between the two extremes there is a continuous series of transitions in size, horn shape and coat colour, so that it is not possible to separate the eastern and western forms into different species. Furthermore the similarity between a dark dwarf buffalo of the west African forests and the Mindoro buffalo or tamarau, the Philippine form of water buffalo, is so great that even an expert finds it difficult to distinguish between them. The west African red or dwarf buffalo stands about 42 inches high at the shoulders and weighs only about 500 lb. The Cape buffalo of east and south Africa, on the other hand, attains a height of 65 inches at the shoulders and weighs over 2000 lb. This considerable difference in form is also borne out in their habits. The dwarf buffalo lives in pairs or small groups in dense forest or swamp; it is secretive in its habits, like an okapi. The Cape buffalo lives in large herds out on the open plains; it reveals its swamp origin, however, as it likes to wallow and get into the shade of the bush. The breeding season is somewhat variable within its range, but in the plains the calves are usually born at the end of the dry season or the beginning of the wet season. The gestation period is 10–11 months, and the calves are suckled for at least six months. The young become sexually mature at 1½ to 2½ years. The longevity is about 20–25 years.

In some areas the Cape buffalo has suffered as a result of human settlement. In South Africa it only has a refuge in the Addo Bush Reserve and in the Kruger National Park, in South West Africa only in the extreme north. Elsewhere its status is in no way threatened; it is moderate in its food requirements and reproduces very fast if it is left undisturbed.

Cape Hunting Dog

Lycaon pictus p. 222

Among the wild dogs of the Old World there are two species, classified in one genus; the Cape hunting dog of Africa and the Indian wild dog in Asia. The Cape hunting dog occurs throughout Africa south of the Sahara except in the forest regions. Both species live in family groups or in packs of several family groups. They hunt fast game and do not kill with a lethal bite but bring down their prey and eventually kill it by biting and tearing at the flanks. They do not have any hierarchical order and food is not jealously guarded. All members of the pack are allowed to benefit from the kill.

The Cape hunting dog has fur attractively marked with whitish-yellow and black patches, whereas the Indian wild dog is duller with greyish white or yellow to dark fox-red fur. No two hunting dogs have exactly the same pattern of markings. Within its total range the species becomes paler towards the south; thus black predominates in the north-east and yellow in the south-west. However the colour phases pass almost imperceptibly from one to the other, so that it is questionable whether the four species which have been distinguished for some time are in fact valid. A Cape hunting dog has a body length of about 40 inches, a tail length of 12–15 inches, a shoulder height of 27–28 inches and a weight of 50–60 lb.

These animals have comparatively fixed times for hunting, namely the early morning and late afternoon; during the heat of the day they rest among bushes, grassy tussocks or in holes in the ground. Before the hunt they become restless, and they emerge from their individual sheltering places, greet each other by licking noses (the bitches also lick their nipples) and they run around each other, gambolling in the grass. Then most of them trot off in a loose group, while a few remain behind to guard the puppies. Regardless of the direction of the wind, they approach an antelope or gazelle which they have sighted from a distance. Each dog that is in the vicinity of prey chases it at full speed. This often brings the prey into the range of another member of the pack which then joins in. Sooner or later the prey is brought down even if an individual in the pack is not able to maintain the speed of the victim it has selected long enough to keep up with it and bring it down. Generally speaking their endurance is not particularly great and they tend to run in short bursts, conserving their energy, and then intercept it with another attack. The prey dies within a few seconds from the numerous bites, with which the members of the pack tear it to pieces; these are roughly the size of a palm of the hand and are ripped from the sides and entrails, then swallowed whole. When each dog has eaten its fill, the remains of the carcass are left lying around. They trot back to their starting point and regurgitate a large part of the fresh meat to the other members of the pack which have remained on guard and to the puppies. The hunt usually lasts for about 1 to 2 hours. If there is sufficient game in the vicinity the whole procedure may be completed within half an hour.

In northern and southern Africa mating takes place in late winter, but in the full tropics it does not appear to be restricted to any particular period. The bitches have a gestation period of 63–80 days and give birth to 2–12 puppies in an aardvark or warthog hole, lined with grass. The young are able to see at 14 days and from then on they run about and also eat meat; it is at least six months, however, before they take a full part in hunting. When the young are taken into captivity and reared by man they become tame and dependent.

A pack requires one to two medium-sized prey animals each day. To get them the game is only disturbed very briefly because apart from the actual animal which is selected, the remainder are only slightly disturbed and are probably not upset by what takes place. As Cape hunting dogs only remain in an area where there is plenty of game, they remove only the excess and must therefore be reckoned among the population regulators of the fast-breeding ungulates.

CARIBOU see Reindeer

Cattle Egret

Ardeola ibis p. 243

In many areas of the tropical parts of Africa and south-east Asia one of the most striking birds is a small graceful egret: the cattle egret. Its neck is relatively short and thick; its spear-like bill is moderately long.

One meets cattle egrets principally among the herds of large domesticated animals or of wild animals. Flocks of these brilliant white egrets accompany the herds of large species of mammal such as rhinos and hippos, and smaller species including gazelles. At short range buff plumes can be seen on the head, chest and the back of the cattle egret but outside the breeding season the buff areas are very indistinct. The birds walk about at the feet of the large mammals, snapping up grasshoppers and beetles as they are disturbed by the feet of the grazing animals. The egrets also make use of the animals as lookouts and resting places. The quadrupeds are not worried by the egrets perching on their backs and carry them around quite happily. Occasionally they derive benefit from the sentinels on their backs as, for example, when the keen-sighted egret warns of the distant approach of an enemy by extending its neck.

The cattle egret is one of the few bird species which has significantly extended its range in recent times. Originally it was only found in large areas of Africa and southern Asia. The northern limit of its range extended to a few places on the European coasts of the Mediterranean; for example there is an old-established breeding site in Spain. In the years 1911 and 1912 cattle egrets were suddenly observed in South America, in British Guiana. These birds had definitely not escaped from captivity. One must accept the fact that they reached the New World on a trans-oceanic flight from Africa, probably driven by storms.

A number of American species, even small song birds, are repeatedly driven across the Atlantic to Europe in this way, and a smaller number of European birds reach America travelling in the reverse direction. Owing to the existence of a wide network of experienced ornithologists who report such cases, the claim that birds cross the Atlantic is nowadays regarded as well-authenticated. Such accidental migrations very seldom result in a firm colonisation. No American species has succeeded in doing this in Europe. The cattle egret, however, succeeded in colonising America. Evidently a whole flock must have made a landfall at the same time in a place which was strange to them but they seem to have found a suitable habitat in the cattle-breeding areas. This first wave of immigration was apparently not very successful. It was not until 1930 that the egrets appeared again in British Guiana and quickly spread in the succeeding 25 years over central America, up to the north-east of the United States, to Newfoundland and down to Bolivia in South America. Many places have been closely colonised but the density of distribution is variable over this huge area.

The cattle egret is evidently somewhat restless and outside the breeding season small flocks of them turn up in places which are not really within their range.

Cheetah

Acinonyx jubatus p. 221

The cheetah could be described as a 'dog-cat' as it is a combination of two quite different types of carnivore, the dog that hunts by chasing its prey and the cat that lurks in wait; as such, it is something of a paradox. It is not, of course, any kind of hybrid between a wild dog and a wild cat species but is a true cat. From its size (shoulder height of 27–30 inches, weight about 120 lb.) it can be described as a large cat.

From the evolutionary viewpoint the cheetah must have branched off quite early on because the earliest cheetah remains, which date back to the beginning of the Ice Age, show scarcely any difference from the present-day type. The cheetah is a cat which has largely given up stalking its prey and taken to chasing it. Looking critically at a cheetah today one can see that it is more obviously adapted for its special hunting technique than any other quadruped; it has disproportionately long slender legs, scarcely retractible stumpy claws, a deep chest, long and narrow loins and a long rudder-like tail. Paced on a greyhound track a cheetah can cover about 100 yards in 5 seconds, that is, twice as fast as any human runner and faster than a greyhound. It is a wonderful sight to see a cheetah hunting at full speed, scarcely touching the ground between ten-yard leaps, extending its rangy body, increasing its stride and accelerating fast.

With such a speed the cheetah is the terror of gazelles, for the fastest of all the ungulates are its natural prey and it occurs only where there are antelopes.

It is an inhabitant of the bushy and grassy plains and semi-deserts from Turkestan to Arabia, from northern India to northern Mesopotamia and in many parts of Africa. When the cheetah starts a hunt, it behaves at first rather like a cat, using every bit of cover and crawling along with its belly to the ground as it gets as near as possible to a herd of gazelles. Then this lurking and procumbent cat, nervously twitching the tip of its tail, changes in a flash to a predator on the chase; it suddenly leaps up and with lightning speed pursues the gazelles which immediately take flight. The cheetah picks out one animal in the herd, overhauls it in a few seconds, springs at it, bringing it down, and then bites it through the throat.

Cheetahs live in pairs with their cubs until these are fully grown and have learnt how to hunt properly. Each litter has 2–5 cubs which are born, after a gestation period of about three months, in a sheltered spot among bushes or rocks. The young have an ashy-grey fur with small spots, a yellow-brown belly and pale grey head and nape, and a characteristic long pale grey dorsal mane which is gradually lost with the change of colour to the adult coat which is yellow-brown with black spots. In tropical areas litters may be found the whole year through, in subtropical areas in the spring and summer.

A wild-caught cheetah can be tamed quite quickly. For this reason the cheetah has a long history of association with man as a sporting animal; in south-west Asia, for instance, it has been used to hunt antelopes for three thousand years. This fact and its spotted coat are why it is sometimes called the hunting leopard, although it is not at all closely related to the leopard. In spite of such a long history of association with man, it has never become a truly domesticated animal. It was bred in captivity at the Philadelphia Zoo in 1956, but the young died soon afterwards. The first successful breeding and rearing took place in the Krefeld Zoo in Germany in 1960.

Although the cheetah does not attack man, this unique animal type has regrettably already been entirely exterminated throughout the whole of India, north Africa and in southern Africa as well as in the rest of south-west Asia; it is also seriously threatened in east Africa. The juvenile mortality is rather high; unknown diseases and other factors which are not yet fully understood also play a part. The cheetah is sensitive to environmental changes and only complete protection together with the establishment of sufficiently large, undisturbed habitats will make it possible to save this species from early extinction.

Colobus Monkey

Colobus sp. p. 223

In addition to the higher primates (anthropoid apes and gibbons) and the better known Old World monkeys such as the guenons, mangabeys, macaques and baboons there is also the subfamily of leaf-monkeys containing at least 20 species. To it belong the colobus monkeys of Africa and the langurs and proboscis monkey of south Asia.

A distinctive feature of the leaf-monkeys is that, like the kangaroos among the marsupials, they are browsers. As their group name implies they are essentially leaf-eaters. Their stomach, similar to the ruminant stomach of the ungulates, is capable of taking in and breaking down pounds of plant food. The stomach which is three times the size of that of the baboon is not just a simple sack, but is a tripartite structure with an enlarged front portion for the initial reception of the leaf mass and two other compartments with lateral diverticula. These are especially well developed in the end portion in order to break down the food still further. Also the molar teeth with double transverse ridges are particularly suitable for a forward and backward chewing movement for grinding the leaves to a mush. Their diet limits these monkeys to dense stands of trees so that they are only found in forest regions, usually in fact in rain-forest. They pluck large masses of leaves in the top canopy where they sit digesting their food for hours.

The colobus monkeys have their thumbs reduced to small stumps, whereas their Asiatic relatives only show this to a lesser extent. The scientific name *Colobus* is derived from the Greek word 'colobos' meaning mutilated.

The colobus monkeys occur in Africa in the rain-forests from the west to the east coast, from Sierra Leone to the Congo and north Angola and from Abyssinia to Nyasaland (Malawi). They can be separated into three distinct species on the basis of coloration and the type of hair.

The green colobus monkey lives in the forests of Sierra Leone and Liberia. It is the smallest member of the group, with a body length of about 18 inches and a tail of 22 inches. It is olive-green-brown and has no special hair adornment except a comb on the crown of the head. It is the most primitive of the whole genus: it lives in different types of forest from swampy to dry forest where it occurs in pairs; occasionally it searches for food on the ground and the structure of its stomach is not highly specialised. The red colobus monkey has a much wider range and is distributed in nine subspecies from Sierra Leone eastwards across the Congo basin to East Africa and Zanzibar.

It is a most attractive monkey with its orange to brownish-black coloration which is divided into darker upperparts and paler underparts. As hair adornment it has only a tuft or comb on the crown, or a cheek beard, sometimes also a slight shoulder mantle. It has a body length of 23–28 inches and a tail length of 27–34 inches, and is thus about the same size as the black-and-white colobus or guereza which has a similar distribution. In Fernando Po and in the Cameroons on the mainland opposite the black-and-white colobus has a pure black representative, the black colobus. The black-and-white colobus has elongated hair tracts which are more or less white; these hang down from the shoulder, flanks and tail tuft. This is shown best in the east African form which is a black animal with a white facial ring and a long white mantle and tail; as it leaps through the branches, it makes a beautiful picture with its white draperies flowing in the breeze.

The troops of red and of black-and-white monkeys live peacefully together. Young are born throughout the year after a gestation period of about six months. They are pale-coloured and even completely white in the black-and-white colobus. They do not become sexually mature for several years.

We now have sufficient knowledge about leaf-monkeys to keep them in captivity satisfactorily for a long time; they are adaptable, not particularly active but they are highly specialised and intelligent. More detailed information about their breeding and rearing is being acquired. In captivity they may live for 15–20 years.

The black-and-white colobus monkey was hunted for decades on account of its beautiful skin, which played a great role in ladies' fashions. At the end of the first World War however the excessive shooting (over 100,000 per year) which threatened the population ceased. Today the three east African subspecies of the red colobus and also the subspecies on Zanzibar are threatened by the deforestation of their habitat which has never been very extensive.

Common Guillemot

Uria aalge p. 50

Bird cliffs are a characteristic of northern seas. They can be found on all coasts of the northern continents. Rock stacks rising out of the sea with crevices, ledges, caves and holes, offer huge numbers of sea birds a place in which to breed. Guillemots, razor-bills, puffins, black guillemots, kittiwakes, various large gulls, storm petrels, occasionally gannets and cormorants, little auks in the north and many other auks in the coastal areas of the Pacific, all these sea birds come to land to find nesting sites during the breeding season.

Everyone who has seen such a giant colony of sea birds agrees that it is an extremely impressive sight. The cliff walls are dotted with grey, black, white and black-and-white shapes of sea birds. There is a continuous stream of birds in flight, passing to and fro near the cliffs, a kind of perpetual whirring motion. Large numbers fly in the same direction but a single individual can often be seen threading its way through the milling throng. The noise is of the same intensity as the activity. The calls are raucous and shrill, often drowning the sound of the wind and swell. Every so often the whole colony takes to the air at the same time; the rush of wings and the clamour of cries are quite deafening.

The available nesting sites are divided up according to the special requirements of the individual species. The storm petrels for preference choose niches or holes, partly or completely covered over and often in the upper part of the cliff; the kittiwakes build nests on all kinds of bastions and ledges, the razor-bills prefer sheltered places in crevices and under boulders, the guillemots take possession of narrow ledges. On these they sit densely packed with so little space that their long bills are raised almost vertically when facing the steep wall of rock; rows of them can be seen facing inwards as they incubate their single egg. The attractively marked egg of the guillemot is almost the shape of a top. The pronounced narrowing of one end has the advantage that the eggs do not roll off the ledges so easily; when knocked aside during frequent squabbles they roll in a small arc. The guillemots do not build any kind of a nest. The egg is laid directly on the bare rock.

The newly hatched chick is covered by a thick downy plumage. After about a fortnight this is replaced by feathers; shortly afterwards, when the young are feathered but still not half grown, they leave the nest site and go to sea. They jump off the cliffs and fall, beating their still unfledged wings, diagonally down into the waves far below them. But the fall does not appear to harm them. They surmount the swell and, led by their parents, strike out into the open sea, where far from any land they spend almost the whole of their lives.

In former times the large sea bird cliffs were exploited by the human populations almost everywhere. Masses of eggs were collected and the adult birds were also caught. In places where this still happens today and the colony is not fully protected, the exploitation is usually regulated in such a way that the population of the colony is not endangered. Soviet scientists, in particular, have studied the lives of the large sea bird colonies in great detail and have specified precisely to what point a colony will stand exploitation.

CONDOR see Andean Condor

CRANE see Manchurian Crane; Whooping Crane

CROCODILIANS see Alligators and Crocodiles

CROWNED PIGEON see Victoria Crowned Pigeon

DALL'S SHEEP see Wild Sheep

DUCK see Blue Duck; Eider Duck

Duck-billed Platypus

Ornithorhynchus anatinus p. 138

The duck-billed platypus and the spiny anteaters or echidnas are the most primitive of living mammals. They still show several characteristics inherited from their reptilian ancestors. Long before the Tertiary period at the end of the Jurassic and the beginning of the Cretaceous period—at least 150 million years ago—their connection with the other early mammals was severed. Since then they have followed their own evolutionary path as monotremes or mammals with a cloaca.

The name monotreme is very appropriate: the hind-gut and the genital and urinary ducts all end in a chamber, the cloaca, with a single external opening, as in the reptiles. The monotremes have only been able to survive until today because Australia, Tasmania and New Guinea became separated from the continent of Asia at such an early period, thus ensuring that none of the higher predators reached these areas. Their most striking characteristic is the laying of reptile-like eggs with parchment shells. In the platypus these are incubated completely outside the mother's body in a nest in the ground; in the echidnas they are incubated in a pocket of skin on the belly.

In the platypus the length of the body and head together is 12–17 inches, the tail adding another 4–5 inches, and the weight is 2–4 lb. The animal is so named from the duck-like flat horny bill which overlays the jaw bones. With this bill and the rather short uniformly dense fur the animal looks like a cross between a duck and a beaver. Its feet are webbed. In all monotremes the male has a horny spur on each of the hind feet which in the platypus contains the outlet of a poison gland. Wounds made by this poison spur will cause the death of members of its own species and even result in serious injury to man.

The duck-billed platypus occurs in eastern and southern Australia and in Tasmania. It is found on the edges of slow-flowing or standing waters in the plains and in the mountains to 6000 feet and upwards. It digs itself simple burrows up to 3 feet long to live in and breeding burrows up to 20 feet deep; the entrances to the burrows usually lie above the level of the water. Platypuses have small, darting eyes and are very restless and quick to take flight. They are capable of running fast on land and can also swim and dive well. Although they have no external ears and the ear holes are covered with fur, they have a good sense of hearing.

Their fur is water-repellent and the eyes and ears are firmly closed when diving. They rely on their sense of smell, which is very acutely developed, in their search for food. They prey on small aquatic animals, snails, worms, insects and their larvae and so on, which they store temporarily in the cheek pouches; they crush and swallow their food after they have swum up to the surface. They usually remain submerged for about a minute at a time but under certain circumstances they can remain below for up to five minutes. They require a lot of food, an adult male will eat almost a pound daily.

In general, platypuses are only active for about an hour every morning and evening but during the mating season, from August to November, they are active for a longer period of time. The female digs the deep nesting burrow and lines it with damp leaves which she carries pressed between the belly and tail. Two weeks after mating she lays one to three eggs $\frac{1}{2}$–$\frac{5}{8}$ inch long and about $\frac{1}{2}$ inch wide; she curls her body around them and thus incubates. The naked and blind young hatch after 7–10 days; they are then 1 inch long and they immediately begin to lick the milk which exudes on to the belly hairs from small pores in the milk gland area. The female does not have nipples. She remains in the burrow with the young until they are about 4 months old; at this stage they are about 11 inches long, their fur is fully developed and they are very active. Platypuses live for 10-15 years.

Platypuses were formerly much in demand for their pelts and persistent hunting led to their extermination in many areas. Today they are fully protected. They have scarcely any natural enemies and nowadays they mostly get killed in fish-traps, in which they are inadvertently caught.

DUGONG see Sirenians

EAGLE see Golden Eagle; Imperial Eagle

Eagle Owl

Bubo bubo p. 30

The eagle owl is often referred to as a supernatural character in folk tales, particularly in German literature. There are few people, however, apart from experienced ornithologists, who have seen this large nocturnal bird in the wild. In a zoo one usually sees it sitting motionless on a bare branch and every so often its orange-red eyes are covered by the nictitating membrane which is a kind of third eyelid in birds. Like all the owls, the eagle owl appears to be larger than it actually is on account of the loose plumage. Its weight is roughly that of a domestic fowl.

The eagle owl is very powerful and will kill even medium-sized mammals and birds with its needle-sharp talons. Sometimes it successfully attacks larger birds, including raptors, while they are asleep. It will take prey the size of a hare but usually hunts smaller mammals, its main source of food being the small rodents which are abundant in its hunting area. Mice are taken frequently, sometimes wild rabbits and occasionally squirrels.

The European eagle owl does not wander far. It usually spends a lot of time perching in prominent places, such as a rock face, where it has an uninterrupted view and an easy take-off. Nest-sites include hollow trees, rock crevices and disused nests of birds of prey. It has the typical noiseless flight of the owls as it emerges at dusk and, even in the twilight, the head looks noticeably large. Deep hooting notes are audible at some distance.

The distribution range of this large owl is from Europe to Asia and related species are found in America and Africa. It has now become extinct, however, in areas which are densely populated by man. In Germany, for instance, it is still found in Pomerania and westwards to parts of central Germany. It is still present in the Ardennes in Belgium and in a few mountain districts of France and Spain. Even in these areas, however, it is nowhere abundant. It is protected all the year round but in spite of this, the few remaining survivors are increasingly threatened as each year goes by.

Pigeon fanciers destroy every nest they can find and in addition the small population is subjected to depredation in the interests of sport. Although eagle owls may not be hunted or shot, the conservation laws in western Germany permit the taking of live birds for use as decoys. The eagle owl is frequently mobbed by other birds in daylight and it can be used as a decoy in crow-shoots and to attract birds of prey. The owl is placed on a post in front of a hut where the hunter is hidden. Eagle owls are much in demand for this sport and fetch a high price.

German conservationists decided to keep special watch over the nests of eagle owls in Franconia. In 1964 twelve nests were reported occupied but in 1965 only two nests were occupied in the same area. This catastrophic decline may have been the result of unfavourable weather conditions during the breeding season. The usual clutch consists of three eggs which are incubated for about 35 days, the young leaving the nest after 5–6 weeks. In captivity an eagle owl has been known to live for 68 years.

Eared Seals

Otariidae p. 113

In contrast to the walruses and true seals (Phocidae) which have no visible external ears, the eared seals (a group which contains the sea-lions and fur seals) have small external ears. Within the eared seal family there are two groups differing in the character of the fur: the fur-seals which have a dense undercoat making their skins a valuable fur, and the sea-lions which have short hair, with no undercoat.

Like the elephant seals, the eared seals are also gregarious and in high latitudes they congregate during the breeding season. In warmer waters some may congregate throughout the year in large or small groups on beaches and cliffs. The cows are divided up into harems in which they remain, after giving birth, with their young. The harems, consisting of half a dozen up to several dozen cows, are ruled by a mature, powerful bull who is continuously on the lookout for rivals during the period of births and the next mating which follows on immediately. At these times he scarcely feeds at all but lives on his extensive reserves of fat.

As the eared seals have rather long and mobile front limbs and are also able to use their slender hind limbs for locomotion, they can move fairly fast and nimbly on land. The bull sits on watch with his head up and the front part of the body held erect. This allows him to look around so that he can rush at any adult male that approaches his harem. The older bulls have many gashes and wounds which they have received in such fights.

At one time the eared seals were hunted excessively and were exterminated in many areas. The fur-seals were particularly endangered on account of their valuable fur. Each year numbers of these animals assemble at their breeding grounds, almost exclusively on the Pribiloff Islands. In 1911 it was estimated that only 200,000 remained, out of a former population of four million; as a result, the Americans, Russians and Japanese agreed to control the catching of fur-seals. The present population is estimated at about three million.

Echidnas or Spiny Anteaters

Echidnidae p. 139

The echidnas or spiny anteaters are monotremes like the duck-billed platypus. There are two living species of echidna in Tasmania, Australia and New Guinea. They are divided into two groups, the long-snouted and the short-snouted, according to the length of the conical snout which is roundish in cross-section.

Echidnas are thick-set, short-legged animals of plump appearance, 15–30 inches long and 7–12 inches tall. They have a short, conical tail. The body is covered with short hairs which are dense only in the genus *Zaglossus*, but on the upper side there are strong medium-sized spines. The eyes of the echidnas, like those of the duck-billed platypus, are very small. The ears are also small or invisible externally, so that the small flat head lacks distinctive features. The brain is poorly developed except for the part concerned with smell. The bony snout has only a narrow mouth opening, but the tongue is long and snake-like. The echidnas live mainly on termites. The palate and the back of the tongue are provided with horny serrations or ridges against which the prey is squashed. Teeth are completely absent in the echidnas, whereas the platypus has some at birth which are soon replaced by horny plates.

Echidnas live in forested or savannah country, showing a preference for rocky terrain. They can be found up to heights of 10,500 feet in the mountains. They are mainly active at night and in twilight; they rest during the day in holes among tree roots, crevices, holes in the ground and similar places. When searching for food they move about slowly and in general are much less active than the platypus. When threatened they can dig themselves in quickly using the claws on the feet. Their muscles are unusually powerful and are a great help to them in rolling over rocks and stumps, under which their prey is found. When suddenly confronted with an enemy they roll themselves up like a hedgehog with the help of the powerful skin muscles. Whereas the platypus makes a kind of growling sound, the echidnas can only spit and snuffle.

Echidnas are solitary animals which are only found together during the mating season in June–July. About one month later the female lays a single egg (about ¾ inch long and ⅝ inch broad) which she puts into the abdominal brood pouch formed by an infolding of skin. Seven to ten days later the naked, blind and larva-like young hatches. It licks the mother's milk which runs on to hairs around the two areas of milk glands. At 6–8 weeks the young leaves the brood pouch but still remains in the shelter of the mother, until its eyes open at about 10 weeks. It becomes sexually mature when one year old and may live for up to 30 years.

The retiring and nocturnal habits of the echidnas must have helped them to survive for some 150 million years. From the evolutionary standpoint they have a very primitive mammalian structure. Comparison of an echidna with a monkey shows very clearly the wide range of structure to be found within the mammals.

EGRET see Cattle Egret; Great White Egret

Eider Duck

Somateria mollissima p. 35

In the northern countries of Europe the eider duck is as well known as the mallard is farther south. People living in central Europe usually only see them if they make a special journey north. On a boat trip through the myriads of islands in the Finnish skerry region, in spring or early summer, one cannot fail to see them. Depending on the month, there will be mixed parties of males and females or groups consisting of males only; later there are crèches of ducklings in the charge of one or two females, swimming in calm water. The drakes have a handsome black and white pattern with some moss-green at the back of the head; the ducks are much more drab with a brown plumage that is barred with black.

The eider is essentially a marine bird. It lives in summer along the north coasts of America and Europe and on some of the Arctic island groups but is absent from most of the coastline of northern Asia. One can regard the German and Dutch North Sea coasts as the southern limit of their breeding distribution in Europe.

Fortunately the eider is neither rare nor in immediate danger as a species. But on our densely populated planet the eider, like so many other animals, can only thrive well where its nesting sites are protected. It is not so long ago that eiders were subjected to severe persecution at many places, particularly during the breeding season. The down was collected from the nests and usually the eggs were taken as well. Eider down is the finest of all the downs. It was sold for a high price and in some manufacturing areas it became an important article of commerce. The nest is made of grass and seaweed and lined with feathers and down which, as in all ducks, the female plucks from her breast. When she leaves the nest at intervals during the incubation period, she covers the eggs with the down; this helps to camouflage the eggs from predators and to keep them warm. Collecting for commercial purposes was particularly productive in areas where several thousand pairs nested close together. However there are many places where eiders nest singly. Favoured nesting sites are on flat rocky coasts, particularly on small islands; the Finnish skerries provide several ideal sites. Today many of the large breeding sites lie in extensive reserves and here the birds are no longer farmed commercially.

The striking display of the handsome drake is occasionally seen in winter as well as in the spring. This consists of a series of stereotyped movements in which the boldly patterned plumage is shown off to best advantage, accompanied by deep crooning calls. Towards the end of April the pair comes ashore and inspects suitable nest sites; later the female alone incubates the eggs. As soon as the young have hatched and are dry they are taken to the sea by the female. The ducklings are independent but they join up in groups or crèches which are looked after by several females.

Outside the breeding season eiders scarcely ever go on land. Occasionally they seek out the inland waters of Europe for a short time during their wanderings. Their food consists of bivalve molluscs and other small marine animals which they always catch by diving, usually in depths of 10–20 feet.

Eland

Taurotragus oryx p. 234

Among the 26 species of true antelope which inhabit Africa some of the best known are those with horns forming close spirals on their own axes; these species are medium-sized to very large and are also remarkably elegant. They are similar to each other in skull structure, body form, coloration, patterning and habits; it is thus possible to establish a complete series from harnessed antelope and sitatunga through plains and mountain nyala to the lesser and greater kudu, bongo and eland. The largest representative of the genus is the eland. With a shoulder height of up to 6 feet and a weight of up to one ton the adult bull is the size of a big ox.

The eland has a wide distribution in Africa and about 50 years ago it occurred throughout the continent south of the Sahara and Ethiopia. In this vast area it developed a number of subspecies or forms varying somewhat from one another.

Lord Derby's or Giant Eland was distributed from Senegal and Gambia to south-west Sudan and in northern Uganda west of the Nile. Today this subspecies, which is one of the rarer large antelopes, still survives in Upper Gambia, upper Senegal and north Ivory Coast. The range of its equally large relative, the eland, has unfortunately diminished considerably; it is now found in east and southern Africa.

Eland make a colourful picture with their clear and striking white body stripes, which become paler towards the south of the species range, and the brownish-black tail which has a white underside. In the eland both sexes have horns (up to 37 inches long in the bull, 39 inches in the cow). In the Union of South Africa they are virtually restricted to individual reserve areas and it is only in Bechuanaland and the north-eastern parts of South Africa that they are still common in the wild.

Open plains, sandy semi-desert and bush or wooded country form the habitat of the eland. They avoid dense forest but keep to the forest edges. Although eland look heavy they can climb well; they have been encountered on mountain slopes at heights of over 12,000 feet. They also jump well and think nothing of leaping over a 6-foot fence. They are chiefly browsers but also eat grass and herbs whereas the giant eland, which lives in open country with plenty of scrub, prefers a diet of leaves and shoots.

As a rule a single bull lives with several cows and their young. But larger groups may be formed and sometimes there are even one to two hundred animals in a herd. Outside the mating season old bulls prefer to remain on their own but the young bulls which do not yet possess a harem associate together. Generally speaking they lead a peaceful existence but sometimes rival bulls may come to blows, indulging in fierce fights over the cows.

The breeding season is not limited to any particular time of the year. The cow gives birth after a gestation period of 8½–9 months to a single calf which becomes sexually mature in 1½–2½ years. In zoos, eland live for up to 25 years but in the wild they attain an age of 20 years at the most.

On account of their peaceful nature elands are suitable for domestication. Calves caught when young quickly become tame. The cows even allow themselves to be milked. On poor, dry pasture, where cattle starve, the eland will still find sufficient food. In addition they appear to be immune to many endemic diseases and are able to endure conditions of drought. In view of these obvious advantages, it is remarkable that it is only in the last few years that people in Africa have seriously gone into the question of domesticating the eland.

Elephants

Elephantidae pp. 180, 181, 246–248

The two species of elephant living today are the last modern examples of a group which was once rich in species. Since the Eocene period the order Proboscidea has evolved six families. Of these the elephants form a single family, which over a period of 7 million years developed along its own line into some 27 species. In all, more than 50 proboscideans have inhabited the earth at one time or another. Of this wealth of species only the African and Indian elephants survive.

Both species have lost a lot of ground in the course of time and large areas of their former range are no longer occupied by them. The Indian elephant is now restricted to the tropical rain-forest region of southern Asia (India, Ceylon, Burma, Siam, Malaya, Sumatra and North Borneo); at one time it was also present in Asia Minor, Syria, Mesopotamia, Persia and south China. The African elephant was formerly distributed over the whole of North Africa and most parts of South Africa. Habitats were lost owing to drainage and deforestation measures and populations also declined as the elephants were hunted, shot or captured—all this was done in the interests of man and his insatiable desire to conquer nature for his own ends which persists to this day. Unfortunately the population of wild Indian elephants is still on the decline today, particularly in India and Ceylon, and in South Africa the African elephant is being driven into ever decreasing areas by the pressure of human settlements and the need to cultivate the land.

Both the Indian and the African elephant live in groups or herds which are continually on the move. Such a large animal, standing on average between 8 foot 6 inches and 11 foot 6 inches at the shoulders and weighing up to about 5 tons, requires a lot of food and water. Even in a zoo where an elephant does not move about much it receives a daily ration of 100 lb. of hay and

20 to 40 lb. of grain, bread and root vegetables. In the wild it would need still larger quantities. As it feeds to a large extent on leaves and branches, the elephant spends most of the day searching for food. In places where a herd of elephants has passed through, hundreds of shoots and branches will have been torn off, dozens of young trees heeled over and defoliated, tasty roots of trees and shrubs uprooted and so on. Water must also be available for them for on a hot day an adult elephant drinks a good 45 gallons. In addition they like to bathe and wallow. It is scarcely surprising that left to themselves elephants will wander about over a wide area covering hundreds of miles; in this way the vegetation of each place in turn has a chance to recover.

If too many elephants are restricted to a small area, the habitat becomes worked out and the elephants destroy it, as has now happened in the Tsavo National Park in Kenya. Although this park covers about 7500 square miles there is not sufficient food for the many thousand elephants that are now concentrated there. The result is a serious destruction of trees and bushes, the land becoming like a desert. Five thousand elephants must be shot immediately if the park is to recover again and support the remaining population of elephants and other wild species. However it is impossible to deal with so many fresh carcasses; the technical equipment for processing them as food for immediate human consumption or for commercial dehydration is totally lacking. Man, by his own actions, has got himself into a situation from which it is almost impossible to extricate himself. The mills of God grind slowly and delicately but man does not usually stop to think when he interferes so drastically with the finely balanced pattern of nature.

The African elephant has never become so closely linked with man as the Indian elephant, which for thousands of years has been caught and trained for work. In classical times when elephants were still living in North Africa, they were used for war, as for example by Hannibal; since then man has regarded them as game and has hunted them for ivory and meat. Today the African elephant is still regarded as game but in a double sense: on the one hand excess populations are shot, the carcasses being used usually for food and for the ivory trade, and on the other hand, elephants are regarded as part of the tourist trade. Tourists hunt them in the wild with their cameras and there are still hunters who are happy to pay a good price for a permit to shoot. How delightful it would be if the elephant could only be shot with a camera in the future. No animal lover can face the thought of having to shoot an animal which leads such a model family and social life, even by human standards, and which apparently displays such intelligence in coming to the assistance of its own kind.

A baby elephant which is born after a gestation period of some 22 months, with a weight of about 240 lb. and a shoulder height of 3 feet, takes at least 10–12 years to reach sexual maturity. It is not fully grown until at least 20 years old and if fate favours it may reach an age of about 70 years. Man, however, is capable of destroying this 5-ton work of nature in a fraction of a second with only a few ounces of lead. When it becomes necessary to shoot such a magnificent animal, it should be done more in sorrow than with pride.

Elephant Seal

Mirounga p. 112

The elephant seals are the largest of all the living seals. Within the seal group as a whole (Pinnipedia) they belong to the true seal family (Phocidae) which can be divided into a northern and a southern group. In addition to the southern elephant seal the southern group also contains the Ross and Weddell seals, crabeater and leopard seals. The elephant seals are represented in the north by the northern elephant seal, which probably at one time moved far northwards in the cold Humboldt Current along the coast of South America, where the southern elephant seal still lives today, till it reached the waters off Mexico and California. Since then the two species of elephant seal have been separated from each other by a good 2500 miles.

Their popular name refers to their size and also to the trunk-like inflatable nasal sac which hangs down over the mouth. Northern and southern elephants are much the same size. The bulls are up to about 18 feet in girth, and 18–20 feet in length and weigh upwards of 5000 lb. whereas the cows only attain a length of 10 feet and a weight of about 1800 lb. The head and trunk of the northern elephant seal are narrow and the trunk is more pointed.

The northern elephant seal once lived along the coasts of Mexico and California and on the off-lying islands including Guadalupe. Lone wanderers were seen up to the south coast of Alaska. Excessive hunting has brought the population almost to the verge of extinction. The protection of the last decades has, however, allowed it to increase to a population of about 10,000.

The southern elephant seal lives in the waters around the Antarctic from the edge of the pack-ice to the antarctic islands and the coasts of South America. Its main breeding places however lie on the islands north to the South Shetlands, with particularly large populations on the Falkland Islands and South Georgia. It too has suffered from seal-hunting, but has now increased again to a population of 500,000–600,000.

Both species are social, particularly at their breeding grounds where the cows are grouped in harems under the leadership of a powerful bull. The young are born only a short time after the cows arrive on land; at birth they weigh about a hundredweight and are about 4½ feet long. The milk of the cows has a 50% fat content; the young are only suckled for three weeks. During these few weeks they put on a lot of weight, about 350 lb., but only grow about 12 inches in length. At this stage they are mainly laying down a thick layer of blubber as a protection against the cold of their surroundings. The mother remains on the land from the time that she hauls out to give birth; she does not go out to sea to fish, but fasts. Soon after giving birth she mates again. The mating bulls do not pay much heed to the pups and some are trampled to death. Others also suffer from a disturbance to the process which regulates their body temperature; their skin becomes too hot and the snow on which they are lying melts, causing them to sink into a deep hole. They cannot get out and starvation follows.

Nowadays the hunting of elephant seals is regulated so that it is mainly only the excess young bulls which cannot yet fight for a harem that are killed; their blubber is converted into first quality oil.

Elk (This animal is called the Moose in the United States—where "Elk" is another name for the Wapiti)

Alces alces p. 90

Geologically speaking the elk is a fairly modern deer. It did not acquire the elk-like appearance until the beginning of the Ice Age. In this context one can regard it as still a young animal and its appearance has all the vigour of youth. The big east Siberian and Alaskan elks of today can still give us an idea of the giants of the Ice Age. The distribution of the elk extended over the whole north temperate zone of the Old and New Worlds. After the Ice Age up to the beginning of the Middle Ages it occurred in northern Europe southwards to the Alps, westwards to Brandenburg, and up to 150 years ago it was still present in the Caucasus. In Asia and North America the southern limit of its distribution now lies generally at about 50°N, but in parts of eastern Asia and in the region of the Rocky Mountains and the Great Lakes of North America, it extends a further 5° southwards.

During the last century the elk population suffered extensive losses through uncontrolled hunting but it is now protected by close season regulations and hunting is controlled and restricted in all areas where the elk occurs. This has had a beneficial effect on numbers and in Sweden, for example, the annual shooting of about 70,000 head is not hindering their steady increase; elks are more numerous than ever before and they are extending their range southwards. In the USSR, control has also brought results: the elk has already reached the suburbs of Moscow, it approaches the Black Sea by way of the forests planted as windbreaks on the south Russian steppes, and recently it has again got as far as the northern edge of the Caucasus.

This heavy-looking deer is well able to hold its own at the present time. It has the advantage of having a comparatively fast rate of reproduction. The females often become sexually mature at 1½ years and then produce their first young during their third year: twins are more frequent than single births. The Russians have set up a special elk research station to breed and domesticate the elk. They have already demonstrated that elks can be trained for pulling sledges and haulage work, and also as riding and pack animals.

Elks live solitarily, coming together only in the mating season in September or combining into small herds in winter. They mainly live in swamps, marshes, moorland, bogs, marshy woodland or in softwood forests with scattered lakes. In spite of their size and weight they move easily over soft ground, due to their spreading cloven hooves; and they can cover long distances at a steady pace. They browse mainly on willows, aspen, poplar, birch and similar trees and on shrubs, berries, marsh plants and aquatic vegetation. They are very much at home in the water and will stand submerged, placing their head right under the surface to get at aquatic plants; they are also good swimmers and will keep it up for long periods. A bull in search of a female makes a comparatively quiet bellow. When he finds a responsive female they remain together for a few days and he then goes off in search of another cow. The calves are born in May. They grow up quickly and at one year are almost the size of the mother but they remain with her for almost two years.

Emperor Penguin

Aptenodytes forsteri pp. 118–120

Man has always been fascinated by penguins whenever and wherever he has encountered them: this applies equally to the antarctic explorers who have seen them in their remote surroundings in the wild and to the public who watch penguins in zoos, as well as to many others who only know them from film and photographs.

No one can fail to enjoy the sight of a procession of plump penguins prostrate on their bellies, propelling themselves along the ground with their flippers as they gather speed down a gentle slope. They look as though they are tobogganing and in this mode of progression they can easily travel as fast as a man on skis. There is something about their characteristic upright stance which particularly appeals to us: with their black and white plumage and erect gait, they look like neatly attired but portly gentlemen. Apart from their bills, they look more like a human waddling along than a bird.

In addition to their superficial appeal, intensive studies have revealed penguins to be highly specialised birds, offering a wealth of remarkable facts. In the last few decades antarctic research has received considerable impetus from various points of view and our knowledge of the lives of penguins has also been greatly increased.

The development of the penguin's anatomy and physiology is such that it serves one purpose: it is specially adapted to life on the open sea, only coming to land during the breeding season and the moult. Warmth is conserved by a thick layer of fat and by a uniformly dense covering of tiny feathers; the wings are modified and reduced to narrow flippers.

Penguins swim by propelling themselves through the water with fast strokes of the flippers. The larger species can reach a speed of over 18 m.p.h. under the water. They can jump six feet out of the water to land on an ice-floe. In the sea they hunt fish, squid and various crustaceans; they themselves are hunted by leopard seals and predatory whales.

The largest species is the emperor penguin which attains a height of 46 inches and weighs up to 100 lb. The conditions under which it lives are unimaginably harsh. The breeding season is in the middle of the antarctic winter which lasts for 8–9 months; the young develop slowly and just become independent at a time when they can profit by the better conditions of the short summer in these latitudes.

The nesting sites lie on the ice of the antarctic continent. To reach them the birds have to travel up to 100 miles on foot across the ice. The male alone incubates, standing erect, with the single egg lying in a fold of belly skin on the thick feet. The young hatches after about 64 days. During this period the male cannot feed, because adult penguins can only feed in the water. It uses up its stored fat and becomes emaciated. The newly hatched young are fed at first by a crop secretion from the male. Then the female, who in the meantime has been fattening up at sea, returns with plenty of food and takes over the care of the young; the male is then free to go to sea which by this time is not so far away owing to the melting of the ice.

After 5–6 weeks both parents bring food to the young which then grow more quickly and when they are about 5 months old they are able to fend for themselves. The juvenile penguins then go to sea which is the natural element of all the penguins.

(See Adélie penguin.)

Flamingoes

Phoenicopteridae p. 242

Some animals are solitary all their lives—except for the period when they mate; when they meet one of their own kind they either avoid one another or they fight. Others, however, are so dependent upon the company of members of their own species, that they are scarcely capable of existing as individuals on their own, even though fully developed and capable of free movement. To these belong the colonial insects—ants, termites, bees—and also some birds, for example the flamingoes. Nobody has ever seen a pair of flamingoes nesting on their own. They always nest in the company of several pairs, preferably in enormous colonies up to a size of hundreds of thousands of pairs. On some lakes of the Great Rift in east Africa one can see flocks of almost a million.

Everybody is familiar with flamingoes. They can be seen in every zoo, as elegant as mannequins but with even longer necks, like enchantingly decorative china figures. But the impression they create in the wild is even more memorable, particularly when one sees huge numbers in flight in the sparkling light above blue-green lakes, forming a phalanx of pink in the sky; this beautiful spectacle, accompanied by hundreds of trumpeting calls heard in the distance, is an experience that is indeed unforgettable.

In spite of its size—it is almost 3 feet tall when standing erect—the flamingo feeds on the tiniest particles imaginable: on microscopically small diatoms and blue-green algae. Some species also feed on very small aquatic animals. All the food is drawn into the bill together with water and mud, sucked and gobbled up as the bill is drawn through the water upside down. The water is expelled while the food is held by fine horny lamellae which act as a sieve. On account of this diet flamingoes only live on shallow, alkaline salt-lakes, which are avoided by most other water birds. Places where they are found include the Rift Valley of Africa, the Bahamas and the high Andes of Bolivia; they are also scattered in localised spots in Asia and in the Rhone delta in Europe.

The five different forms are classified by ornithologists into three or four species, the others being regarded as races. In some areas the flamingoes do not breed regularly year after year in the same place, they sometimes break the regular sequence, no one knows exactly why. In general, flamingoes will only breed where they have a large completely undisturbed area at their disposal. In the wild they are extremely sensitive to disturbance during the first phase of breeding, while the eggs are being incubated. They react then to the slightest disturbance by deserting the nest-site and thus a whole population may not produce offspring that year.

Even when the young have hatched, incautious visits to the nesting places may cause great damage. Europe's only flamingo breeding colony only survives today because it is under strict watch by the organisation entrusted with its protection. Unauthorised intruders are ruthlessly driven away; this is essential if the birds are to survive. Bird-lovers who have a permit for a visit to the reserve can only observe the birds from a great distance. In the midst of a civilised world, one can see how difficult it is to preserve animal species which demand large, undisturbed areas in reasonably untouched countryside for their very existence.

The habits of the giant flamingo flocks still living on the

salt lakes of east Africa have been described by Leslie Brown in his book *The Mystery of the Flamingoes* (London, 1959, Country Life). In his investigation into the life of the flamingo in the treacherous swamps, Leslie Brown risked—and almost lost—his own life.

Gannet

Sula bassana pp. 52, 53

The Bass Rock in the Firth of Forth was first mentioned as a breeding place of the gannet in 1447. The name of this sea bird, *Sula bassana*, is derived from this bare rock stack.

The gannet has white plumage like a gull, the adults having a pale ochre tint on the head, and black wing-tips. This peculiar sea bird is almost as large as a goose and it is obviously not a gull with its powerful, tapering bill which curves slightly downwards at the tip. The rather long tail which also tapers and the very long pointed wings give the bird a characteristic cigar-shaped silhouette in flight. The gannet is, in fact, related to the cormorants, pelicans, and certain other sea birds of quite different appearance, including the elegant tropical frigate-birds.

A gannet in flight has indescribable grace and elegance. It glides and soars in wide circles above its exposed breeding-site, and flies in with measured wing-beats. When fishing the gannet watches the water with its pale, almost white eyes, and then tilts to one side and plunges down, diving into the sea. Other gannets arrive and one after the other they dive into the sea with half-closed wings and disappear below the surface. The force of the dive may take them down to about 60 feet. They seize the prey with accurate aim, possibly not taking it until they are on their way to the surface again.

In the crowded breeding colonies the nests are often closely packed, the distance between them being just sufficient to enable a bird to land without hitting neighbours with its long wings. Every time a bird arrives at the nest a greeting ceremony takes place, accompanied by low grunting calls. The wings are spread, waving slowly backwards and forwards; the partners also bow to each other and the movements of neck and tail make the ceremony an impressive sight.

This species of gannet is a purely Atlantic bird. Most of the large breeding colonies lie around the coasts of Great Britain, a few off Iceland and the south coast of Norway, with a small group on the east coast of North America around the latitude of Newfoundland. It is easy to see that the breeding colonies of this striking bird can only be preserved in the modern world if they are left undisturbed and given strict protection.

GEMSBOK see Oryx

Gerenuk

Lithocranius walleri p. 240

Among the fourteen species of gazelle found in Africa the gerenuk and dibatag are particularly striking on account of their slender build. Long legs and an unusually long neck are special characteristics.

The dibatag which stands 30–35 inches high at the shoulders is the smaller of these remarkable animals; the gerenuk is somewhat larger, with a shoulder height of 35–40 inches and a longer neck. Both species are essentially animals of arid areas which can go for weeks without water. Both are restricted to the north-east part of Africa. The dibatag is found only in Somaliland. Unfortunately they are much hunted by the natives for their skins which give a soft leather and they have already been exterminated in several places.

In prehistoric times the gerenuk colonised the western coastal area of the Red Sea between the Nile and the sea from the Gulf of Suez southwards to Eritrea. The post-glacial desiccation of this area to true desert resulted in their total disappearance from this region. Today their range extends from northernmost Somaliland southwards through Ogaden, Somalia and Kenya to northern Tanzania in approximately latitude 5°N. Within this area there is a paler and larger northern subspecies and a darker and smaller southern subspecies; these two subspecies are separated from each other by a gap in colonisation in central and north Kenya. It is difficult to explain the reason for this gap unless it was due to a former extension of the rain-forest belt across Kenya.

The gerenuk lives in bush country whether it be dry, stony and sandy or with plenty of water and grass; its habitat extends from the plains up to about 5,000 feet in hilly country. They are dainty feeders and never eat large quantities at a time. They feed more on the leaves of bushes and trees than on grasses and herbs, taking the former as high up as they can reach when standing with hind legs fully extended. This vertical position can be held for a long time without difficulty because the hip-joint is constructed in such a way that the head of the femur fits perfectly into the pelvis.

Gerenuks are territorial animals, living mostly in small family groups consisting of a male and several females with their young. Only the males carry horns. They are somewhat larger and heavier than the females and when sexually mature they can also be identified by a conspicuously thickened neck. Gerenuks browse in the morning and late afternoon. During the heat of midday they stand motionless in the shade of a tree, chewing the cud. Young may be encountered in almost any month of the year. The gestation period is seven months and the female usually gives birth to one young at a time, rarely two. Sexual maturity takes place at 1–1½ years. We still do not have any precise information on the longevity of gerenuks.

Within their range gerenuks are only hunted to a limited extent. At the present time there is no danger of the population being threatened.

Giant Tortoises

Testudo elephantopus and others p. 106

Sixty million years ago giant tortoises lived in America, India and Europe. As shown from the fossil bones in the collection of the American Museum of Natural History in New York, each animal must have weighed about 2,000 lb. But with the spread of more adaptable mammals, the helpless giant tortoises had to give way. Remnants of this ancient group managed to survive on only a few remote islands where there were no predatory mammals, as for example on the Mascarene Islands east of Madagascar and on the Galapagos Islands in the Pacific. The latter were in fact named after this striking reptile. Galapago is the Spanish word for tortoise.

With the arrival of man on these hitherto undisturbed islands the giant tortoise populations of the Mascarenes and the Galapagos quickly disappeared. They were killed for their meat and fat; others were destroyed by the introduced domestic animals, particularly by dogs and pigs. The Mascarene giant tortoises now only survive on Aldabra Island, which lies north-west of Madagascar.

The position is somewhat better on the Galapagos Islands. Here giant tortoises have managed to survive on several islands, if only as somewhat sparse remnants. During recent years a careful search on Hood Island yielded only four tortoises. It is very doubtful whether this population can be maintained or increased. Feral goats are very numerous and they eat most of the food of the tortoises. On Duncan Island, Miguel Castro, Conservation officer of the Charles Darwin Station, marked over 60 adult tortoises but found no young, as they had been eaten by rats immediately after hatching. They are now planning to rear the young animals at the Station and release them later. A promising start has already been made with the hatching of 32 eggs of the Duncan Island tortoises. On other islands feral pigs and dogs have reached pest proportions. They eat the eggs as well as the young tortoises. Finally, man also hunts the tortoises. The only satisfactory stocks are those on Indefatigable (Santa Cruz) and Albemarle (Isabela).

It would be a great pity if it transpired that these tortoises could only be preserved on one or two islands, because the main interest of the Galapagos tortoises lies in their differentiation into various island races. A different race, each with a special carapace form, is found on every island that is inhabited by tortoises. Basically there are two types of carapace: those which are arched all the way round and those which are laterally compressed at the front with a high arch behind the head. Tortoises with the latter type of carapace mainly inhabit the dry islands on which they feed on shrubs and cacti. The arched frontal part of the carapace allows them a greater freedom of movement in the vertical plane. Darwin was the first to notice these differences.

The tortoises live in the low-lying, dry coastal belt around the islands and also in the somewhat more humid areas of the higher ground. But they avoid the forests and the highlands of the large islands with their rich vegetation of ferns. They are mostly found in the transition zone between the dry and the damp regions, where there are green meadows, clumps of bushes and ponds in which the tortoises like to bathe for hours at a time. The daily routine of these reptiles is always leisurely: the adults wake up in the morning, feed, bathe and when the sun is high they creep into the shade of the bushes. Where ponds are rare the animals lap the dew or the sparse rain-water which collects temporarily in shallow depressions in the rocks. These rocks have been polished smooth by generations of tortoises.

Mating takes place in March and April. The female lays the eggs in November in the coastal region on the larger islands. She digs several pits up to 15 inches deep with her hind limbs. In each hole she lays 10 to 15 eggs which have the appearance and size of billiard balls. It is interesting that the young are nocturnal at first; this is probably an adaptation to the hot, dry climate. The young tortoises grow very quickly; for instance, a weight increase from about 9 oz. to 13 lb. in two years was recorded for one animal. The final weight reached by the old animals is 400 to 600 lb. and they may live to the remarkable age of 200 years.

Gibbons

Hylobatidae p. 197

The gibbons were at one time included among the anthropoid apes on account of their intelligence and the fact that they are capable of running in an erect position like humans. Nowadays only the chimpanzee, gorilla and orang are regarded as anthropoid apes. The gibbons are classified in their own family of monkeys. As early as the Oligocene period the gibbons started to diverge from the true anthropoid apes and to evolve gradually into highly specialised brachiators.

They are restricted to south-east Asia where they live in the forests of Burma, Thailand, Malaysia, Sumatra, Java and Borneo. There are about six species in this part of the world.

The largest is the siamang, black in colour, which stands about 35 inches high and weighs 20–30 lb. The smallest is the dwarf form of the siamang from the Mentawi Archipelago off the south-west coast of Sumatra which is about 16 inches high and 10 lb. in weight; it is also black but has no throat sac and the fingers are only partially fused.

The siamang occurs in Sumatra and in the mountain forests of Selangor on the Malayan Peninsula opposite Sumatra. It is distinguished from the other gibbons by having a web uniting the second and third toes, also by the naked throat sac (present in both sexes) which inflates to the size of the head when they call, and by its choleric temperament.

The other species are about 18–27 inches high and 10–12 lb. in weight. Of these, the black gibbon occurs in Hainan, Indo-China and from Tonkin to Laos, Annam and Thailand. In this gibbon the hair on the crown of the head is erect and the male has an inflatable throat sac which is not so large, however, as in the siamang. The colour of the fur varies from black to buff according to the locality. The hoolock from Assam, Upper Burma, Tenasserim, northern Thailand and northern Laos, is black in the male, pale brown in the female. It can be recognised by the pale band on the forehead above the eyes. In contrast the grey gibbon or wauwau of Java always has grey fur without a pale bar over the brow or a ring round the face. The agile gibbon, of which there is one subspecies in Malaya and one in Sumatra and parts of the mainland varies in colour from yellowish-brown to brownish-black but always has a more or less well defined pale brown to whitish ring of fur round the face. The white-handed or lar gibbon from Lower Burma, Thailand and Malaysia also has a pale, usually whitish, ring of fur round the black face; in addition, it has white hands and feet which contrast sharply with the rest of the blackish or brownish fur.

The gibbons can run efficiently and fast on the ground, but their full acrobatic prowess is displayed in the tree canopy. By day they move through their forest home—an area which may vary from one to several acres according to the amount of food available—feeding on fruits, buds, young shoots and tender leaves, and on insects, snails, tree-frogs, lizards, birds' eggs and young birds. Sometimes they move so fast that they catch birds in flight while swinging from branch to branch.

Gibbons are sociable animals. They always move about in troops which are led by an experienced male or female. In addition to a fully mature pair, each troop contains young animals and also old animals that can no longer be regarded as rivals. Individual troops have their own territory and invisible boundaries with neighbouring territories are recognised. When the members of separate troops meet in the boundary area, they scream in full voice until the troop which produces the lesser volume of sound gives way. The day begins and ends with communal singing by the troop. Their loud song can then be heard from a great distance, particularly that of the siamang which possesses considerable amplification in its vocal sac.

The birth of the young is not tied to any particular season. Born after a gestation period of seven months, the young are usually differently coloured from the parents. They take their first solid food at an age of four months. At this stage they also make their first attempts at climbing. Two months later they can climb without help and also begin to walk upright. They do not attain sexual maturity until they are about 6 years old. The prolonged care of the young only allows the female to reproduce every second or third year. Gibbons may reach an age of 30 years but this has only been achieved once in captivity.

Fortunately none of the gibbon species appears to be threatened. They have no natural enemies which might constitute a serious danger.

Giraffe

Giraffa camelopardalis pp. 238, 239

This animal not only looks distinctly odd but it also has a peculiar sounding name. When the Arabs in Ethiopia got to know the giraffe, they called it 'surafa' which was a foreign word to them. This name which came from Africa has been taken over by Europeans.

The first giraffe to arrive in Europe was brought from Alexandria by Cæsar. It was not until the Renaissance that the next one came; it arrived in 1486 as a gift from the Bey of Tunis to Lorenzo of Medici, at Fano in the dukedom of Urbino. After this, giraffes did not reach Europe until the beginning of the 19th century. In 1827 the Viceroy of Egypt, Mohammed Ali, presented one giraffe each to London and Paris and one to Vienna in 1828. One of the first giraffe births in Europe took place in the Schönbrunn Zoo in Vienna in 1858 where on the 20th July a healthy Kordofan giraffe calf was born and later reared successfully.

The two living representatives of the giraffe family, the okapi and the giraffe, stem from a group which lived in Asia in the Miocene period; they comprised 16 genera which spread to Europe, Africa and eastern Asia. At the end of the Ice Age they were reduced to the two species which survive today.

With an average height of 18 feet to the top of the head the giraffe is the tallest living mammal. It reaches a shoulder height of 10 feet, the head and neck adding another 8 feet. The body is short, the ratio of neck length to body being 4:3; with the elongated legs, the ratio of height at the withers to body length is about 2.15:1. With a weight of 1000–1500 lb. and the extraordinary proportions of the body, the animal tends to be ungainly in its movements and has difficulty in adopting certain positions. All its movements therefore are deliberate. The long legs carry the animal forward with an uninterrupted, ambling gait and when necessary it can even accelerate into a gallop. Its lung capacity is only about 21 pints of air as against 52 pints in the horse; it is not surprising, therefore, that it has not got much staying power and can easily be overtaken by a horse.

The main habitat of the giraffe is the acacia savannah. It is well adapted to this kind of terrain. It has no food competitor. Its main diet consists of the leaves of acacia which it browses from the tree-tops. When it wants to eat grasses and low herbs from the ground, or drink water from the watering-places, it has to straddle with its forelegs spread out in order to get at the herbs with its powerful tongue or to reach the surface of the water with its mobile lips.

Giraffes are by no means mute as is generally thought: the calf gives a variety of low bleats, particularly when abandoned, and a cattle-like lowing when thoroughly alarmed. The adults may also bleat and grunt but only do so rarely.

Giraffes are sociable. Usually they form loose groups consisting of a male and several females with their young. Large aggregations also occur sometimes. Giraffes have scarcely any enemies. Calves are killed by lions from time to time but the lions have to be on their guard against the lethal hooves of the adult giraffes. Rival bulls do not use their hooves when fighting each other but strike with the short hairy horns or bony knobs on the head, making a violent impact on the neck or body of their rival. One of them eventually withdraws when it has had enough. The females also bear knobs on the forehead; there are usually two but there may be up to five. The calf (twins are rare) is born after a gestation period of 14–15½ months, is suckled for 10 months and reaches sexual maturity at three years.

At the end of the Ice Age the giraffe was still present in Mesopotamia and Palestine. At the beginning of historical times it also occurred in North Africa, so that at that time it had a wide distribution over all the open plain and savannah land of the Near East and the whole of Africa (with the exception of eastern Somaliland, north Mozambique and the Cape). Today it only survives south of the Sahara and north of the Orange River. Man has driven it from all the other areas. There are some eight subspecies of giraffe of which the reticulated form is one of the better known in zoos. As the hunting of giraffes is forbidden the greatest danger to them at the present time is the cultivation of their habitat.

Golden Eagle

Aquila chrysaetos p. 29

The golden eagle is the traditional eagle of heraldry. Its image is depicted on coats of arms and was blazoned on the standards carried at the head of Roman legions and by the regiments of the Emperor Napoleon. Throughout history this bird has been regarded by the noble and great as a symbol of leadership.

To lesser men and to those in humbler walks of life, the eagle did not arouse admiration; on the contrary, it was an object of hate and was hunted because it stole their lambs. It was even claimed that the eagle carried off children. Seen against this background of public opinion, the notorious eagle-hunter, Leo Dorn, even acquired a certain degree of fame, however dubious. In the last decade of the nineteenth century Dorn shot over one hundred golden eagles in the Allgäu in Bavaria and temporarily exterminated the golden eagle as a breeding species in this region.

The golden eagle has now become one of the rarest birds in Germany. As a breeding species it is restricted to a narrow strip of the German Alps where only a few pairs still manage to survive. It has also become rare in other countries but bearing in mind its total range, it cannot be regarded as a rare species. Its range is extensive: from Alaska to Mexico in the New World and from the mountains of north Africa to almost the whole of Asia in the Old World. By nature, the golden eagle is by no means a bird of the high mountains; it is only that at higher altitudes it frequently finds its last refuge.

The golden eagle relies as a predator on medium-sized birds and mammals. A large bird—with a wing-span of over six feet—cannot live successfully in such large numbers as a smaller animal. For survival each pair requires an extensive territory, in which another pair is not tolerated. Daily flights are made over the territory as the eagles hunt for food. The lower the density of prey animals within the territory, the larger the area held by one pair. Within this area each pair has two or even more nests; the eyries are occupied alternately as they become fouled during the process of rearing young. The female usually lays only two eggs. The relatively large number of nests present is gladly used by people who want to shoot eagles; by presenting a false picture of an intolerably high density of eagles, they hope to create a climate of opinion favourable to shooting.

The food of this eagle consists chiefly of species that are common in the area, such as small mammals and larger birds, with a preference for game birds. In the Alps the occurrence of the golden eagle is largely tied to the distribution of the marmots.

The eagle is often wrongly accused of exterminating its prey, particularly when the latter happens to be of value to man as a game species. It must be remembered, however, that the eagle has existed for millions of years, far longer in fact than man, and it would have died out long ago had it been in a position to exterminate its prey. A satisfactory population of eagles can only be maintained where the prey animals are able to compensate for the loss of individuals by a high rate of reproduction. The preservation of the predator species is thus dependent on the continued survival of the prey species. This process of nature is very effective in practical terms, even though it makes no allowance for sentiment as expressed in terms of the human approach to survival.

Great Bustard

Otis tarda pp. 36, 37

The great bustard is a long-legged bird about the size of a swan, which runs like an ostrich but can also fly well and whose head resembles that of an outsize domestic fowl. However, it is neither an ostrich nor a fowl, but is classified in a group related to the cranes and rails.

There are some 22 species of bustard in the world, the majority of which live on the plains, savannahs and semi-deserts of Africa, a few on the same kind of open country in Europe and Asia, and there is one species in Australia. In Western Europe the great bustard has a scattered distribution. For example in Germany there is a small, gradually decreasing population in Saxony and a large one of a few thousand in the Mark of Brandenburg. The western outlier of the bustard population of Hungary and south-east Europe extends into the Burgenland of Austria.

The great bustard was at one time valued as a game bird. Nowadays, however, it is protected throughout the year in most countries. Experience with other large birds might lead one to suppose that the great bustard would only be found in remote areas and that any encroachment of civilisation would quickly result in its being driven away completely. This is only partially true. Although the bustard is shy and wary, the opening up of the original forest country of central Europe has, in fact, favoured its spread. The bustard is primarily adapted to living in arable country but the area must be spacious and as free as possible from disturbance. Great bustards like to be able to wander daily over several miles of their territory and they do not like fences.

The courtship display of the great bustard is well known. This remarkable spectacle puts in the shade anything else of its kind that the European bird world can produce. Looking out at dawn over bustard country at the time of year when the display reaches its height, it is difficult to believe that the patches of white—which agitate slightly, move about, disappear and reappear again suddenly—are in fact birds at all. The shape of the bird is transformed to such an extent during the display that it no longer looks like a bird but a billowing mass of white. A written description of this transformation is as mystifying as actually observing the display. It is scarcely 40 years since careful observations have clarified the type of display and the sequence of events.

First of all the cock bird turns up the non-fanned tail in a sharp bend over the back, so that the loose feathers on the pure white underside are revealed. Then it fills the throat sac in its thick neck with air so that it is distended to the size of a child's balloon; this misshapen, swollen structure shows bluish stripes on the skin. Its head is sunk into the neck and the erect bristly feathers round the chin look like white whiskers. The really startling effect, however, is produced by the wings. These are normally folded but during the display they droop. With a jerk the elbow is extended so that the upper and lower arm point backwards; the wrist remains flexed. The large primary feathers which are folded now lie on the back; the wing-coverts are raised and brought forwards and the inner secondary feathers are also erected so that they almost meet behind the head. Broadly speaking, these are the most important details of the display which has been likened to the unfurling of the petals of giant white flowers, simulated by the movement of the white feathers. The display arouses the interest of the female bustard and undeniably causes astonishment in the human observer.

Great Indian Rhinoceros

Rhinoceros unicornis pp. 182, 183

Like the elephants, the five species of rhinoceros still living on the earth (great Indian, Sumatran, Javan, white and black) are the last survivors of a group of ungulates which was once rich in species; it was represented by about 30 genera and many more species in Europe, Asia, Africa and North America.

In the Early Tertiary period, over 60 million years ago, this group evolved into small forms which were only the size of a pig, including horned and hornless forms, short-legged forms and barrel-shaped forms like hippos; there were also representatives which were the size of elephants. Among them was the world's largest ever land mammal: the hornless *Baluchitherium osborni*, which was 15 feet tall and which lived in Mongolia during the Oligocene period. Out of all the wealth of species only the five rhinos mentioned survived the Ice Age.

Together with the African white rhinoceros, the great Indian rhinoceros is the most powerful and most impressive of the rhino group. About 200 years ago it was still common from West Punjab along the great river valleys south of the Himalayas to Burma and Siam. Today there are only about 500 animals left; these live in eight Indian reserve areas and in the Rapti Valley in Nepal. It is not absolutely certain that they can be preserved for the future. It is well-nigh impossible to teach the great mass of uneducated natives about the irreplaceable value of such primitive large animals and to get over to them that their belief in the magical properties of rhino horn is only a myth. The equivalent of about £35 is paid for a pound of the alleged magical horn and to people who earn only a few pence per day, the incentive to poach is very great indeed. Even armed guards and the threat of severe penalties are insufficient deterrents. In addition there is the difficulty of effective supervision of animals in jungle swamps that can only be penetrated with riding elephants.

The outlook for the great Indian rhino is indeed a gloomy one but there is one ray of hope in that these animals can now be kept in paddocks without too much difficulty. In captivity they live to a good age, up to 20 years. Moreover, since 1956, young have been born in captivity on four occasions. All those born in the zoos at Basle and Whipsnade were reared successfully and from these a breeding pair was established at Milwaukee Zoo in the United States. It is therefore to be hoped that the species will at least be preserved in zoos, even if it becomes extinct in the wild.

Great White Egret

Egretta alba p. 38

The elegant great white egret is slightly smaller than the grey or common heron (*Ardea cinerea*) but it has a more slender neck and longer legs. It is a bird of the open countryside.

Looking at a map of the geographical distribution of the great white egret one might come to the conclusion that this species is common: it has the widest distribution of all the species of heron—of which there are about 60 in the world. The great white egret is represented by various races, which differ only slightly, on all the continents and broadly speaking is only absent from the northern half of the northern continents. It is primarily at home in the warmer countries. In Europe its north-western nesting place is on the Neusiedler Lake in Austria.

The map however is deceptive. In reality the great white egret is nowhere common, on the contrary in most places it is rather a rarity. There are several reasons for this. First, it only breeds in very extensive areas where water is present and today these areas are becoming increasingly scarce. Secondly, the great white egret has suffered a lot of persecution; it has been ruthlessly hunted for a long time for its feathers.

During the breeding season most species of heron carry ornamental plumes on the head, neck and shoulders. These are very finely constructed, the feathers are narrow and the barbs are long and free, giving a filigree effect. The ornamental plumes of the great white egret are more handsome than those of other species and they attain a length of 18 inches. For hundreds of years these plumes were highly valued among eastern European and Asiatic peoples as adornments for civil and military head-gear. Only noblemen and persons of rank were permitted to wear them.

Just as the hunter in Upper Bavaria wears a chamois-beard in his hat, so in former times the Hungarian grandee used to wear a spray of egret plumes. Plumes of egrets were expensive: even before the First World War. Plumes from several birds were needed to make up a really handsome spray and, decorated with diamonds, the spray cost as much as a mink coat today. They were valued accordingly and were among the gifts by which princes expressed the bestowal of favours. Thus after the Battle of Aboukir Bay, Admiral Nelson received handsome egret plumes as acknowledgment from the Sultan of Egypt. At one time European ladies' fashions also demanded egret feathers. The result was that the great white egret was ruthlessly hunted throughout the world.

The fully developed ornamental plumes are at their best at the beginning of the breeding season and later they become abraded and bedraggled; the adult egrets were therefore killed at their nesting sites. As a result whole colonies were destroyed. Today we are faced with the problem of how to preserve the few remaining great white egrets. Those on Neusiedler Lake, numbering about 260 pairs, have been put under strict protection.

GRÉVY'S ZEBRA see Zebras

GRIZZLY BEAR see Brown Bear

GUANACO see South American Camels

GUILLEMOT see Common Guillemot

Hawaiian Goose

Branta sandvicensis pp. 104, 105

The Hawaiian goose or ne-ne, as it is called in the islands where it occurs, is a peculiar offshoot of the Canada and Brent goose. Its distribution has always been restricted to some of the Hawaiian Islands, where it occurred mainly on Hawaii and Maui.

The ne-ne has given up a life associated with water and swamp such as is led by most other geese. Their habitat is the crevassed surface of old lava fields of the big island volcanoes. The lava region where these geese live provides an almost completely dry habitat, although there are some small ponds where they occasionally swim. They are good swimmers but are seldom seen on the ponds. They also fly well but do not undertake large-scale migrations like so many of their relatives. They usually live at high altitudes where the forest on the volcanic slopes is not too dense. In some places, however, they come down to sea level. It has been observed that they undertake seasonal movements between the highlands and lowlands, which appear to coincide with the periodic drought that allows the vegetation in the low-lying areas to dry up. The ne-ne is so well adapted to life in a dry habitat that the web between the toes of the long, powerful legs is much reduced, leaving a good proportion of the toes free. The sharp claws are used to grip the rough surface of the rocks when running and climbing.

In the 18th century the population of the ne-ne was estimated to be about 25,000. Then the white man arrived bringing with him dogs, cats, mongoose and pigs, some of which became feral and threatened the island fauna which was not adapted for dealing with these new enemies. Naturally, man also did his share with guns and by making extensive changes in the habitat. The goose population decreased rapidly up to 1900 and, after these early catastrophic losses, it dropped slowly until the 'thirties of this century. We do not know the precise reason for this serious decline but it was definitely not due to lack of food or to the loss of any particular food plant. In about 1950 there were still 33 ne-nes in the wild and 35 in captivity—the fate of this species seemed to be a foregone conclusion.

Then a couple of energetic men decided to try to save this vanishing bird for posterity. They wanted to prevent yet another animal species from being driven from the face of the earth by the indifference of man. It now looks as though their efforts have been successful.

As early as 1823 Hawaiian geese had been brought to European zoos where they were also bred successfully. However none of these captive specimens survived the air raids of the Second World War. After the war, there were only a few ne-nes living in the wild in Hawaii and a small group were also living there in an enclosure. A pair of these was given to the big collection of waterfowl of the Severn Wildfowl Trust at Slimbridge in England which is directed by Peter Scott. By careful breeding he succeeded in increasing the stock so that in 1962 the total world population of Hawaiian geese, including those in the wild, had risen to 432. Of these about 150 were living wild in Hawaii, due to the success of protective measures which were energetically enforced, in spite of many difficulties, by the local authorities. The birds bred in captivity at Slimbridge were distributed according to a carefully worked out plan to suitable breeding stations throughout the world, in order to nullify the effects of a possible catastrophe at any one place. A number of these captive birds have been given their freedom on the Hawaiian island of Maui and have now returned to the wild state.

The example of the ne-ne shows that in some cases threatened animals can be saved by measures which are additional to protecting their last refuges in the wild. For species which breed well in captivity, a plan can be worked out, by the co-operation of zoos and wildlife reserves, which under some circumstances is more likely to lead to success. The breeding of Hawaiian geese, however, is not a simple matter. First, this tropical bird is sensitive to winter cold, and secondly the ganders sometimes show themselves to be extremely aggressive, even towards their own families. They have been known to kill their own mate; in captivity the female is unable to escape in the confined space of a paddock whereas in the wild she could elude the attacks of her mate.

Hippopotamuses

Hippopotamidae p. 243

The hippopotamuses are classified in their own family within the order Artiodactyla, their closest relatives being the pigs. Before the Ice Age hippopotamuses lived in south and south-western Asia and Europe as well as in Africa. After the Ice Age they only survived in Mesopotamia and Africa. However they disappeared from Mesopotamia and from north Africa with the increasing drainage of the land and through being hunted by man. Today their distribution is restricted to Africa south of the Sahara but they have already been lost from the greater part of southern Africa.

The pygmy hippopotamus, a separate species in its own genus, lives in the rain-forests of Guinea, Sierra Leone, Liberia, western Ghana and Nigeria. It is only about 5 feet long and 30 inches tall with a weight of about 550 lb. During the day it rests singly or in pairs in holes in the banks of streams or in the cover of bushy thickets; it wanders about at night in search of food, such as marsh and water plants, roots, tubers and fallen forest fruits. Swamps and the adjacent undergrowth in dense forest form its habitat. It can run well and when alarmed it leaves the water and takes to the land. It only leaves its territory, an area of forest, when pressed. After a gestation period of about seven months the pygmy hippopotamus female gives birth on land to a calf which weighs 10–14 lb. The young become sexually mature in the third year; they then lead an independent existence and may live up to 25 years.

The weight at birth of the large or common hippopotamus is about 60 lb. It already starts to feed at an age of one month but it is suckled for about sixteen months. After the period of suckling it is independent but does not become sexually mature until 4–5 years old. When fully grown it attains a length of about 12 feet, a shoulder height of 56 inches and a weight of 2–3 tons or even more. The short tail is about 15 inches long. Hippos can go on breeding until they are about 30 years old and the greatest age attained is probably 50 years.

Hippopotamuses live socially in numbers varying from groups to herds along the edges of lakes and on the banks of rivers; they spend the day lying lazily in the water or out on land and at night they wander away from the bank to feed on land. Such a fleshy and heavy animal requires all kinds of food to fill its gut which is 50–60 yards long. The diet includes grasses, herbs, fruits and water plants.

Since hippopotamuses have scarcely any enemies except man, in national parks and wildlife reserves they multiply to such an extent that they graze their shore territories bare; they also trample about, leaving the soil exposed to erosion by rain. This is what is happening in the Kivu National Park on the west bank and in the Queen Elizabeth National Park on the east side of Lake Edward, where there are about 35,000 hippos. In order to check this destruction of the habitat at least 5,000 hippos need to be killed initially and then an annual cull will have to be made.

In the wild, hippopotamuses divide up the shallows and the adjacent banks into territories. There are bull, cow and neutral territories which are used for specific purposes; above all the bulls defend their territories and this often leads to serious fights, in which the animals inflict deep and sometimes fatal wounds with their sharp, tusk-like canines. Threat display consists of opening the mouth wide in order to show the powerful canine tusks.

IBEX see Alpine Ibex

IBIS see Bald Ibis

Impala
Aepyceros melampus p. 245

The impala is one of the most elegant and agile of the antelopes. It has characteristic black tufts on the cannon bones of the hind legs. It also has various other black markings, including patches on the rump which serve as recognition marks.

The impala is a medium-sized antelope, standing about 30–38 inches at the shoulders. It still occurs everywhere in the open country of Africa. It is distributed from central Kenya southwards to Transvaal and south Bechuanaland and extends westwards to the edge of the Congo rain-forest and southwards from the Congo through south-west Angola and south-west Africa.

One meets herds of impala in open scrub to dense bush and savannah, along the edges of forests and in open forests, in plains and in hilly country. Water must be readily available as they drink every day. They avoid areas without trees or bushes and waterless regions. They feed in the morning and in the late afternoon. They pluck leaves, buds and shoots from trees and bushes and also grasses and herbs from the ground. In the heat of midday they rest in shady places.

As social animals impala usually form into small to medium-sized groups of one to several dozen animals. The herds are led by a powerful buck. Seasonally, particularly towards the end of the dry season, they gather into herds of 50–100 animals. At this time there may be several older bucks in a herd. A mature female often leads the herd down to water, while the dominant buck brings up the rear.

The impala is particularly elegant when it starts to move in a hurry. Its grace and agility are seen to best advantage as it gathers speed. In full flight the impala frequently makes orientation jumps, leaping 9 feet into the air; the animal is perfectly balanced with head held high and the powerful hindlegs ready to give it immediate impetus as it lands. They can leap effortlessly over obstacles, such as bushes and rocks, landing again at a distance of 30 feet from the take-off. When fleeing in front of a car, the impala's speed can be clocked on the vehicle's speedometer; under these conditions a speed of 30–34 miles per hour has been registered.

The period of mating is not tied precisely to any particular season; in east Africa it takes place mainly in February to May, in south-west and southern Africa more often in October–November. The dominant males are challenged by the younger males reaching maturity and vigorous fights take place. The gestation period is about 200 days. The female usually gives birth to one young which weighs about 12 lb. at birth. Sexual maturity is reached at 1½ years of age. A fully grown buck weighs from 120–180 lb., a female 80–140 lb. They live for about twelve years.

Imperial Eagle
Aquila heliaca p. 41

There are several species of eagle which prey almost exclusively on small plains-dwelling mammals that can be caught easily. These eagles are not such powerful or versatile hunters as for instance the golden eagle. Their hunting methods are more akin to those of the buzzards which are less active. One of these species is the imperial eagle which has striking white shoulders when adult and claws which are not nearly as powerful as those of the golden eagle. The imperial eagle is not of course purely a plains dweller like the true 'plains eagles' which even nest on the ground. It prefers to breed in open, park-like country where there are a number of trees but it hunts in open country.

The range of the imperial eagle is discontinuous in Europe. It breeds in the Iberian peninsula and in the south-east of the continent but is absent in the intervening areas of Central Europe which were originally pure forest country. The much more extensive eastern group has its western limit in eastern Austria and in the Balkans—on the edges of the old steppes.

From there it extends over the whole of the wooded steppe country of south Russia and central Asia, where even today the imperial eagle is not considered to be rare in many places. However the Balkan population has already dwindled considerably due to the increasing development and opening up of these countries. The imperial eagle of eastern Europe feeds almost exclusively on susliks and is largely dependent upon the distribution of this small steppe rodent. The Spanish imperial eagle on the other hand usually has a more varied diet at its disposal which includes rabbits, rodents, birds and reptiles.

The Spanish area which is isolated from the rest of the European breeding range is inhabited by a special geographical race. These eagles have never been very common here and today they are regarded as considerable rarities in most places. The relatively few eyries are found in the pine and cork forests of the Coto Donana, the coastal stretch bordering the estuary of the Guadalquivir. Most of the trees grow to only a low height and the nests are readily accessible, with the result that the population of eagles is seriously threatened. The future preservation of this handsome eagle can only be ensured if the breeding areas in the present nature reserve are given effective protection and if steps are taken to prevent the eagles being shot outside the reserve.

Indian Wild Ass

Equus hemionus khur p. 187

The ghorkar of the Indians is known to us as the Indian wild ass. Together with the onager, kulan and kiang it forms a large species which stands intermediate between the horses and the African wild asses. After the Ice Age the wild horse occurred from the Iberian Peninsula, France and Britain eastwards to Mongolia; the wild asses of Africa lived in the north and north-east of that continent. Between these two groups lay the range of the Asiatic wild asses, which extended from north-west India through Mesopotamia, Anatolia, Afghanistan, Persia and Turkmenistan to Tibet and Mongolia.

Excluding specimens in captivity, the wild horses are now represented by a few dozen Przewalski's horses living free in Mongolia. The African wild asses have disappeared from the whole of north Africa and only scanty remnants occur in Somaliland and possibly also in Nubia. The position of the wild asses of Asia is not much better. Of the kulan or Mongolian wild ass which once occurred in large herds from Mongolia to the Kirgiz Steppes, there are only about 750 animals surviving. The onager or Persian wild ass, which roamed the desert plains of Persia and north-west Afghanistan in herds of several hundred head some centuries ago, has now been reduced to 200–300 animals. The Syrian wild ass of Mesopotamia has been completely exterminated. The Anatolian wild ass had been already exterminated during the early ages of history. It is only the kiang or Tibetan wild ass of north Ladakh, Nepal, Sikkim and Tibet to the Kukunor area of Chinese Turkestan which is fairly secure in some parts of its range, although it has disappeared in others.

At one time the ghorkar lived throughout the desert and dry plains of north-west India. Nowadays there are less than a thousand in the saltmarsh desert of the Little Rann of Kutch.

The blame for the almost complete disappearance of the wild Equidae rests entirely on man, who has hunted them indiscriminately from the Middle Ages up to the present time. Their flesh was always regarded as a delicacy. So long as man only had horses available for hunting and pursuing them, there was always the possibility that these animals could escape into the desert where they were excellently adapted to the harsh conditions. Man found it very difficult to follow them into the desert wastes. But when long-range breech-loading weapons were introduced into the home ranges of the wild Equidae, their chances of survival became less and less. And after the replacement of the horse by the cross-country jeep they had no chance at all. Finally, the people who live in the range of the wild Equidae do not know the meaning of the term animal conservation and it will not be many years before the last onager of Persia and the last ghorkar of India has gone the way of all flesh —in spite of all the efforts of the international nature conservation organisations to save wildlife.

Javan Rhinoceros

Rhinoceros sondaicus p. 193

The Javan rhinoceros has folds of skin between the head and neck and where the limbs are joined to the body, similar to those in the great Indian rhino. The folds give the impression that the surface of the body is covered with armour plating. In addition the skin has a granular or scaly appearance with small bumps on it which are arranged as in a mosaic.

Whereas the Indian rhino reaches a shoulder height of about 65–68 inches the Javan species is somewhat smaller in stature with a height of 62–65 inches. Its head, however, is considerably smaller than that of its Indian relative. Both these rhinos carry only one horn in contrast to the other three species which are two-horned (Sumatran, white and black).

The Javan rhinoceros likes a terrain with dense vegetation and with plenty of places with water for wallowing. It does not matter whether the water is clear or muddy, nor whether the watering places are in the lowlands or at altitudes over 6000 feet. In spite of their heavy build these animals can climb well. A daily bath is an absolute necessity for them. In places where muddy wallows are used, the trees and bushes are spattered with mud as the rhinos like to chafe themselves after a wallow.

The Javan rhinoceros normally lives solitarily; they are only found in pairs when the bulls are mating with the cows or when the mother is looking after her calf. The calf is suckled for at least two years and becomes sexually mature at the earliest at four years of age. Since a female is pregnant for about 16 months and suckles for two years, she can produce a calf at the most every third year; usually it is only every four years. In view of this slow rate of reproduction, it is not surprising that man can bring about the extermination of this species with comparative ease and, as the numbers decline, the process of extermination is accelerated. This armoured animal has scarcely any natural enemies, except perhaps the tiger which may occasionally kill a calf when the mother is not on the alert.

The Javan rhinoceros was formerly distributed from Upper Burma over the whole of south-east Asia including the Malayan Peninsula to Sumatra and Java, and it occurred in all suitable habitats. The high price paid for the horn, particularly by Chinese apothecaries, is due to the damnable legend that in pulverised form it works wonders as an aphrodisiac. This belief led automatically to intensive hunting first of the Asiatic species of rhinoceros (Indian, Javan and Sumatran) and when these were almost exterminated, to the hunting of the African species (white and black rhinoceros).

Thus the Javan rhinoceros has been reduced to two dozen head at the most, which live in the reserve area of Udjong Kulon in the extreme west of Java. It is possible that there are still half a dozen individual animals scattered on the mainland, presumably looking for mates. The reproduction rate is also thought to be very low in Udjong Kulon. Unfortunately there is not a single individual of this animal species in any zoo—hitherto only seven Javan rhinos have been kept in zoos for any length of time—so the last instalment of the story of Javan rhinos on this planet will soon be finished.

Kakapo or Owl Parrot

Strigops habroptilus p. 148

There are more than 300 species of parrot, among which the kakapo is the most peculiar and one of the most interesting. It lives in New Zealand, a country which has many remarkable and ancient bird forms.

The kakapo's short, rounded wings look like two fans when spread out. They are not used for proper flight but assist the bird's progress as it climbs about in trees or glides down to the ground; the wings are also slightly extended and used as balancing organs, as they run fast along the ground. The long feathers which radiate like the facial disk of a barn owl have earned them the popular name of owl parrots, although these birds have no other similarity to an owl and are of course quite unrelated to the owls.

In the moss-festooned southern beechwoods of the mountain gorges in which the kakapo occurs, one does not normally see it during the day, although one may come across characteristic signs of its presence, as for example well-trodden paths in dense undergrowth which are reminiscent of mammal runs. During the day the kakapos remain hidden in holes among the stilt-like roots of the forest trees; they are principally active at night.

Their food consists almost entirely of the shoots and leaves of plants, particularly ferns and grasses, but also berries. The bird does not swallow the green parts whole but chews them in the bill breaking them up so that one never finds fibres in the stomach or intestine. The masticated fibres become lumped together and are left lying around. This bird is not easy to track down but the lumps of chewed fibres and the trampled paths provide signs of its presence.

The two to three white eggs, which are small for the imposing size of the bird are laid in a hole beneath a tree root. Apparently never more than two young are reared, often only one.

The kakapo was not discovered until the middle of the last century. At that time it still occurred in North and South Islands of New Zealand and in places it was even comparatively common. But within a few decades it had disappeared from North Island and had become very rare on South Island. Today there are possibly not more than 20 individuals living in a secluded valley on the south-west coast of South Island.

The kakapo must now be regarded as one of the rarest birds in the world. How has this situation arisen? For a long time it was considered that the white colonisers of New Zealand should bear the sole responsibility for the disappearance of the kakapo from the greater part of its former range. Today, however, scientists who have been engaged on intensive studies concerning the decline of so many species in the Old New Zealand fauna, believe that the matter is not so simple and the reasons for the decline of the kakapo may date back still farther. There is no conclusive evidence as yet and probably many factors are involved in the decline. Nevertheless, there are impressive eyewitness accounts from older naturalists who saw dogs pulling the kakapos out of holes and killing them and doubtless, if one is to believe these stories, the white man's dogs may well have been responsible for the extermination of kakapos in many valleys. This cannot be the sole reason for their disappearance, however, as there are many secluded valleys in the thinly populated South Island which are practically never disturbed and these areas could provide the kakapo with a suitable habitat.

Kangaroos

Macropodidae p. 140

The most familiar of the marsupials are the kangaroos. It is not so well known that there are kangaroos varying in size from that of a rat to a man and that marsupials not only live in Australia, but also in Tasmania, the islands in the Bass Strait, New Guinea, the Aru and Kei islands and in parts of the Bismarck Archipelago, as well as in the Solomon Islands.

The main characteristic of the kangaroos is the unequal length of the fore and hind limbs, which is most marked in the large species. Associated with the lengthening of the hind legs is the lengthening and strengthening of the tail, which thereby becomes a powerful and significant support for the body. The largest representatives measure up to 6 or even 7 feet in height and weigh up to 200 lb. There are two species of really large kangaroos: the great grey and the red. Both are restricted to Australia and are much the same in size and build. The great grey kangaroo at one time occurred from north-east Queensland to southern and south-western Australia, on Kangaroo Island and in Tasmania, but it has now been exterminated in many parts of its former range.

Before the white man arrived in Australia with his domestic animals—sheep and cattle—the large kangaroos were the grazers of the open plains which they inhabited in their millions. As large herbivores they occupied the equivalent niches in the natural economy as the ungulates (artiodactyls and perissodactyls) of Eurasia, Africa and America. The plains lying to the west of the east Australian mountain ranges are typically dry; they have many of the characteristics of semi-deserts and may even go over into complete desert. Enormous areas are therefore needed by the Australian farmers to support their flocks of sheep.

From this viewpoint the large kangaroos are direct food competitors of the sheep and are accordingly hunted relentlessly. On the other hand, the farmers have contributed to the spread of the kangaroos by making many areas more habitable for these animals: by installing wells and dams they have produced water not only for their stock but also for the kangaroos and other wild animals. In addition, there is the fact that the kangaroos, by rearing their young in a pouch, have an advantage over the sheep. The young are born after a gestation period of only about 33 days; they only weigh about one ounce at birth and are 4–6 lb. after about 7–8 months. For a long time they require only very little milk; this greatly assists the females to withstand drought.

The female mates again immediately after the birth but after two days preliminary development, the egg remains quiescent in the uterus until the young in the pouch stops suckling. If this young one should die early, the stimulus of suckling ceases and the egg lying in the uterus resumes development; within about a month, the young kangaroo is born. The embryonic newly born kangaroo makes its own way into the pouch.

The female sheep only has one or two lambs a year, which also require comparatively large amounts of milk; the female kangaroo on the other hand is always rearing a young 'joey'. In times of serious drought the whole lambing fails. The kangaroos also have the advantage of making good use of the available food.

Although the kangaroos are only primitive mammals they have not yet lost the battle waged against them by the white man with his guns, cars and poison. The conservation approach is gaining ground in Australia and the larger kangaroos now have a chance of survival. It is to be hoped that future generations will still be able to watch kangaroos travelling over the plains at 30 m.p.h. and covering the ground with leaps of up to 30 feet.

Kea

Nestor notabilis p. 149

There were originally four species in the *Nestor* genus of parrots of which today only two exist: the kaka, an arboreal bird living in forests and the kea, which lives in the highland regions, including areas above the tree limit. The gregarious kea lives in the inhospitable climate of the high mountains between 4500 and 6000 feet and particularly in the region of the tree limit. It moves with agility and runs fast along the ground where it spends a lot of time searching for food. It feeds on roots, buds, berries, larvae, beetles and flower nectar.

If the kea had not suddenly fallen foul of the New Zealand sheep-farmers it would hardly have been disturbed at all in its mountain fastnesses. As it was, the Government arranged to pay a premium for every kea that was killed. At present the premium amounts to £1 per head and it is operative outside the reserve areas. The decision to pay a reward for every kea killed came about in the following way: one day towards the end of the 'sixties of the last century, shepherds discovered that some of their sheep were suffering from peculiar wounds. The sheep had holes up to the size of a hand in their skin and their wool was encrusted with blood. It was claimed that these wounds had been inflicted by keas, which had allegedly attacked the sheep in order to eat the flesh from the living animal. The origin of this story is shrouded in obscurity but it resulted in a ruthless campaign of extermination. The story was accepted at its face value and at that time it was not considered important to check its accuracy. This was only done later. In recent years people who, did not believe the old stories gathered all the available evidence studied it critically and assessed it accordingly. The result was that when followed up nearly all the alleged eye-witness reports vanished into thin air. For example when Mr J. O'Neill, an experienced sheep valuer who had inspected between 20,000 and 40,000 mountain sheep over a period of ten years, was asked how often he had seen animals with wounds caused by the attacks of keas, he replied that he had never done so. Nevertheless an occasional attack by keas on sheep could not be entirely excluded and over the years some truth in the stories led to the popular belief in New Zealand that keas would attack live sheep. Occasionally keas eat the carcass of a sheep that has died from an accident, or the offal from slaughter yards. But this is not a regular part of their diet as they are largely vegetarian and the eating of sheep carrion is probably confined to individuals.

New Zealand ornithologists have come to the conclusion that these incidents are not of any general significance but are an exceptional phenomenon. The kea suffers from a lot of persecution and in some places it has already become rare. An attempt is now being made to get it protected so that the species may be preserved for posterity. The story of the sheep-killing kea should also be preserved but as a myth for posterity.

Kiwi

Apteryx australis p. 146

The kiwi scarcely looks like a bird at all. Its name comes from the Maori language and refers to the rather thin piping call of the male. These strange-looking birds were unknown to science 150 years ago but due to the interest shown in them by zoologists all over the world, they have achieved popular fame. The kiwi is restricted to New Zealand and has become the national emblem of that country and New Zealand soldiers serving abroad even call themselves 'kiwis'.

Roughly the size of a domestic fowl, the kiwi is unusual in general form as it has no externally visible wings or tail. The skeleton and the small vestigial wings provide evidence that in the far distant past ancestors of the kiwi were once able to fly. The wing stumps are completely hidden in the thick feathers which are ruffled, giving the impression of a shaggy pelt rather than a bird's plumage. There are three different species which are similar in structure and habits.

The kiwi searches for its food like a hedgehog, using its bill to snuffle along the ground. No other bird possesses such a well-developed sense of smell. The nostrils are situated near the tip of the long bill and the bird extracts earthworms out of holes and crevices, drawing the food out delicately so that it is not torn.

Kiwis live in the dense vegetation of damp forests which originally covered areas of New Zealand but which are much reduced today. Here they sleep by day in a hiding-place between tree roots, from which they emerge at twilight. They are quiet and agile in their movements, hurrying along on short, powerful legs, looking rather like rats. The males are smaller than the females and undertake the duties of incubation. One or two comparatively large white eggs are laid in a hole which may be enlarged by digging. The weight of an egg is roughly a quarter the weight of a female. Incubation lasts for just over 10 weeks. The female plays no part in the incubation or in caring for the young. We do not know much more than this about the kiwi and a modern scientific investigation on the life history and behaviour of a population of these unique birds in their natural surroundings is still not available.

Although the range of the kiwi has been considerably reduced owing to deforestation the bird has however been able to hold its own quite well up to the present time. In this respect the strict protection afforded it by the New Zealand Government is of importance. Even the capture of a single kiwi for a zoo requires the special approval of Parliament. In the past thousands of kiwis were destroyed by dogs and feral cats or even shot; their feathers were made into flies for the use of anglers. Today the general public is in sympathy with the aims of conservation and this is the only way in which protective measures can be made really effective.

Koala

Phascolarctos cinereus p. 141

The koala looks like a teddy bear, although it is not more closely related to a young brown bear than a cow to a kangaroo. The koala is in fact a true marsupial and is classified among the climbing marsupials. It owes its resemblance to a young bear to its squat shape, its uniformly dense woolly pelt and its large bear-like head.

The koala, which is also known as Australian teddy bear, attains a total head and body length of 22–30 inches, and it weighs between 10 and 30 lb. The tail is much reduced which further enhances its rounded outline. The animal appears to have an expression of friendly astonishment with its black beady eyes and shiny black nose which stand out well against the grey fur on the head; the large roundish ears are fringed with long woolly hairs, enhancing its cuddly appeal. Even people who are only mildly interested in animals find themselves nursing one in their arms and stroking the fur.

Although not very lively, it has a cheerful and even affectionate manner which endears it to people; these apparently human qualities, together with its inquisitiveness and lack of fear have finally won the hearts of the Australians.

This, however, is only a recent development and koalas were

hunted indiscriminately from the time of the early colonists up to the present day. The dense woolly fur yielded attractive pelts and, with its lack of fear and slow movements, the koala presented an easy target. Before this animal was put under protection, hundreds of thousands of koala pelts reached the market every year. Thus the koala, which was once distributed in the forests of eastern Australia from central Queensland in the north to Victoria in the south, was largely exterminated. Such a slow breeding animal as the koala cannot compensate for heavy losses due to man's hunting as well as for losses due to bush fires and disease.

The koala only becomes sexually mature in its third or fourth year and the female normally produces only one young—twins are rare. The young spends six months in the pouch which has two nipples and opens towards the rear. By eating certain contents of the mother's rectum it then loses a taste for milk and transfers to a diet of eucalyptus leaves which are difficult to digest. After this the young is still carried about pick-a-back by the mother for a further six months. Thus the female, which may live for 15 years or more, produces only one young every second year. The mating season is in September–October and, as in other marsupials, the young are born after a very short gestation period (25–30 days in the koala). When the young koala is born it is still very undeveloped—the weight at birth is only 5 grams—and it therefore needs a long period in the pouch in order to mature.

As a result of their restricted diet of eucalyptus leaves koalas are equipped with a caecum which is three to four times the length of the body. There are 600 species of eucalyptus growing in Australia but the koalas know exactly which of these species are digestible according to the season and the nature of the countryside. However the leaves of some species of eucalyptus are capable of generating prussic acid at certain times of the year. In addition they have varying amounts of phellandrene, which is said to raise the body temperature, and cineol which lowers the temperature and the blood pressure. A wrong choice of food would be fatal. This is why it is so difficult, generally speaking, to keep koalas in zoos outside Australia.

The koala has now been re-introduced into Victoria where it had been completely exterminated and into New South Wales where it had almost vanished. Australia has already lost a number of species of marsupials and there are still a number which are in serious danger of being exterminated. In the meantime the attitude of the Australians has changed and is now directed at conserving their unique native flora and fauna. Their success with the koala is a happy omen for the future.

Komodo Dragon

Varanus komodoensis pp. 190, 191

There are a great many lizards living today but scarcely any of them comes so close to the proverbial picture of a dragon as the members of the monitor family, to which the Komodo dragon belongs. With its long head, from which a narrow deeply cleft tongue emerges, its stout and flattened body, powerful tail and strong legs with large claws, the Komodo dragon has a marked resemblance to the terrifying beast of the legends. It only differs in that it does not spit fire.

The largest of the monitors, the Komodo dragon, was discovered rather late. The first descriptions exaggerated its size. Nevertheless it measures about 9 feet in length and has thus the right to be known as the largest lizard in the world. The monitors are not all noted for their large size. The streak-tailed goanna which comes from western Australia only reaches a length of 8 inches. Of the other monitors, seven scarcely exceed the 30-inch mark, a further ten grow to 3–4½ feet long and four reach a length of 6 feet.

The monitor family contains only the single genus *Varanus* and in spite of the different sizes of members of the family, they are all very similar. In general the monitors lack the variety of form which occurs in some of the other lizard groups.

Monitors live in trees or on the ground, in rivers and lakes, or even underground. Some are excellent swimmers, driving themselves through the water like crocodiles by snake-like movements of the laterally compressed tail, keeping the legs close to the flanks. Others are skilful at climbing trees.

They feed on fish, frogs, crabs, birds, rats and rotting flesh. The Komodo dragon prefers carcasses, from which it tears the flesh with teeth and claws. The pieces torn off are not chewed but swallowed whole. To watch several of these monsters feeding on a dead animal at the same time is certainly reminiscent of the popular conception of a scene from pre-history.

Monitors have a preference for fowls and eggs which brings them into disfavour with farmers and results in their persecution. When caught in the act they usually make off. Some take to the water, others climb trees, each takes flight according to its own habits. If, however, they are cornered, they display by inflating themselves, opening their mouth wide, spitting wildly and lashing about with the tail.

All monitors lay parchment-shelled eggs. In the Komodo dragon these are about 3–4 inches in size. Clutches, which may contain 7–35 eggs, are laid in holes in the ground or in tree holes; some species lay their eggs in termite colonies. The eggs take several months to develop. Some monitors have a wide distribution, as for instance the two-banded monitor. By contrast the Komodo dragon is known to occur at the present time only on the small island whose name it bears, on two neighbouring islands that are even smaller and in a limited area on the Indonesian island of Flores. Even in these comparatively remote areas it is under pressure from the presence of man; the rapid progress which is being made with land cultivation means that it must be put under strict protection.

Leadbeater's Opossum

Gymnobelideus p. 142

In the early history of the mammals there was a considerable number of marsupial species. Those living today in America—mainly in South America—and in Australia represent only the remnants of this former wealth. Nevertheless there are more marsupials surviving today than is generally thought: there are still 241 species classified in 71 genera and 9 families.

Most of the families are Australasian. In the seclusion of Australia and neighbouring islands the marsupials have had sufficient time, from the evolutionary viewpoint, to adapt themselves to every kind of habitat. They have invaded plains with grasses, bushes and trees, mountain slopes, semi-deserts, deserts, water-meadows, mountain forest and rain-forest; they have evolved as leapers and hoppers, lurkers, burrowers, diggers, climbers and gliders.

The Australasian opossums form a family of arboreal marsupials, containing 41 species, which show the most varied body form, types of movement and habits. Among them are pigmy opossums the size of a dormouse and large brush-tail opossums, and dashing gliding opossums as well as the more cautious climbing cuscus. Leadbeater's opossum, named in honour of its discoverer, also belongs to this family; it occupies an intermediate position in the family as regards bodily structure and method of locomotion. It is a skilful climber but is not capable of gliding like some of its relatives. With its mouse-grey fur, large dark eyes and slender nose, medium-sized rounded ears and long bushy tail, it is reminiscent of the European dormice. In addition it has a black stripe extending from the head to the base of the tail, which is longer than the body; the underparts are creamy yellow. The length of the head and body is about 6 inches and the tail is about 6½ inches long. Like the European dormice this animal is a nocturnal climber. It hunts for insects and other small animals and also takes flower nectar, but scarcely eats any fruits or seeds.

The female has a well-developed pouch with four nipples, an indication that the number of young is small. Mating probably takes place in September. After a gestation period of about 3 weeks the young are born in a very undeveloped stage. There are still many details of the life history of this small nocturnal marsupial which we do not know; for instance we have no information about the length of time taken by the young to become fully grown. Leadbeater's opossum sleeps by day in holes in trees and in this way it remains almost completely hidden from man.

The secretiveness of its habits is also the reason for its renown among zoologists and nature conservationists. It was first discovered in 1867 and up to 1909 only five specimens were known. Then for about 50 years it was thought to be extinct. However it was found again in 1961 and 1962, in dense eucalyptus mountain forest in the vicinity of Melbourne.

At the time of the colonisation of Australia by Europeans, Leadbeater's opossum was no longer abundant; it was already on the decline owing to changes in the environment. This is confirmed by the investigations undertaken in the caves of southern Victoria. With the aid of a pair taken into captivity and another male, it is hoped to be able to report on their behaviour, reproduction and longevity and to establish a breeding strain. The information gained in this research should be of use in protecting the few specimens which have been re-discovered in the wild.

Leathery Turtle

Dermochelys coriacea pp. 198, 199

The leathery turtle occupies a special place among the marine turtles. It is not only larger and heavier than every other land or aquatic chelonian—it sometimes reaches a length of more than 6 feet and a weight of over 1000 lb. It is also clearly distinguished from the other tortoises and turtles by a number of anatomical characters and is classified in its own family.

It derives its name from the smooth, leathery skin which covers the body and replaces the horny plates of other marine turtles. There are seven raised ridges running longitudinally over the back and five along the belly. The bony part of the armour consists, not of individual symmetrically arranged plates as in all the other chelonians, but of small bony plates of irregular shape, which lie embedded in the thick skin as in a mosaic. The backbone and ribs are not fused with the armour, but lie free. In the young animal the front limbs are as long as the carapace (or dorsal armour); in the adults somewhat shorter. The adults are dark brown or blackish above with pale yellow or whitish spots and flecks; they are paler below.

The leathery turtle is distributed over all tropical seas. It occasionally appears in temperate latitudes as for instance on the Atlantic coasts of Europe, along the coasts of the United States or Chile; although extremely rare it even penetrates into the Mediterranean. Leathery turtles feed on crustaceans, molluscs, small fish and marine plants.

Even though these turtles are widely distributed, little is known yet about their habits. We know that they spend almost their entire life at sea, probably in fairly deep water, but they are not often seen. They only approach land during the breeding season.

The female crawls laboriously up the beach, leaving a track almost 7 feet wide. At a distance of about 40 to 60 feet from the high-water mark, she then digs a hole which is deeper than that made by any of the other turtles. During the excavation of the nest and the laying of the eggs she allows nothing to disturb her, neither the approach of passers-by nor noise. Once the eggs have been laid, she covers the pit over again with sand and smooths the surface so that the position of the nest is no different from the surrounding area. May and June are the main periods for the egg-laying. Each nest contains approximately 80 to 120 eggs. Eggs are laid several times a year. The size of the eggs generally varies around 2 inches in diameter. The eggs take about 65 to 70 days to hatch and the young can walk immediately; they also swim and dive efficiently.

The flesh of the leathery turtle is dark and tough and is not eaten much, indeed some natives consider it to be poisonous. The eggs, by contrast, are highly coveted. They are collected so persistently that the population is decimated year by year. Unfortunately this reptile already qualifies for a place on the list of seriously threatened or vanishing species.

Leiopelma

Leiopelma archeyi p. 153

Formerly the classification of frogs and toads was based on the presence or absence of a tongue and on the structure of the pectoral girdle. Nowadays the forms of the vertebrae are used as distinguishing characters. These flat bony discs may in fact be slightly concave at the front and the back, or only at the front or only at the back, or the individual vertebrae may vary.

Among the frogs living today in the world there are two genera in which the vertebrae are amphicoelous, that is, they are slightly concave at the front and back. It is remarkable that these two genera, which are grouped together as primitive frogs, live in two areas widely separated from each other. One genus, *Ascaphus*, lives in fast, cold rivers and streams in western North America, the other to which the name *Leiopelma* has been given occurs only in New Zealand. The union in one family of the two genera appears to be confirmed by a further peculiarity: although, like all frogs and toads they no longer have a true tail when adult, they still retain the remains of the muscles which at one time served to move the tail.

The genus *Leiopelma* contains three species which live mainly on the higher ground of the islands of New Zealand. They are quite small animals which do not exceed $1\frac{7}{8}$ inches in length.

Leiopelma archeyi lays its eggs under stones or bits of wood and the young hatch in a completely developed condition. Like the young of other amphibians living in mountains they have become independent of the water and make do with the moisture yielded by the soil, plants and dew.

The eggs of another species, *Leiopelma hochstetteri*, can be found in the vicinity of springs, in small pits and holes in which the adults also live. The egg clutch normally consists of two to eight eggs and is thus very small. The young frogs hatch about 41 days after egg-laying. They still have sufficient yolk to provide nourishment for almost a month. The long tail which they still have at hatching serves to break the egg covering. As the ovaries of the female contain a large number of ova which are released independently of one another, it is probable that eggs are laid at intervals.

These rare small frogs belong among those animals which were formerly widely distributed but today they only occupy small areas; they still show characters which can be regarded as primitive and ancestral. Owing to these peculiarities and in view of their rarity they deserve strict protection.

Leopard

Panthera pardus p. 200

The leopard is the most adaptable of the big cats which include the lion, tiger, jaguar, leopard, snow leopard, clouded leopard, puma and cheetah. It can exist everywhere that cover is available from hot humid rain-forest to dry rocky mountain sides, and under snow conditions in the forests at high altitudes down to the reedy banks of lakes. The leopard, together with the puma, has the widest distribution of all the big cats. The puma is to be found in all climatic zones and types of country in the New World, from Canada to Patagonia; the leopard is likewise found in a similarly wide range of climatic zones, including the wintry mountain forests of Korea and the hot deserts of Morocco and South Africa.

The leopard is of medium size and not very heavily built, with a shoulder height of 27–29 inches and a weight of 100–180 lb. Its speed, boldness and ability to jump and climb, coupled with its alert wariness and keen senses, make it the terror of all medium-sized game. It can also be dangerous to man.

Primarily a solitary animal, it usually lies up during the midday heat in a shady place, preferably on the broad branch of a tree; it normally does not start hunting for prey before late afternoon, evening or after dark. Its favourite prey are monkeys, dogs and goats. The leopard plays an important role in controlling the population of monkeys and, in east Africa, where too many leopards were being shot or poached on account of their valuable skins, it has been put under protection. Baboons are omnivorous and are capable of causing considerable damage to crops; they have a fast rate of reproduction and in the absence of leopards it would be very difficult to control their numbers.

Dogs are sometimes taken by leopards in broad daylight right in the centre of the villages. The leopard is also not afraid of breaking into pens for goats and chickens. Under certain circumstances, usually when a leopard has suffered injuries which prevent it from overpowering healthy animals, it will turn to man-eating. It then shows considerable cunning and is very difficult to track down. A man-eating leopard becomes the terror of whole areas of the countryside. The most dangerous man-eater of this species in recent times was the leopard of Rudrapayag in the Ganges valley: between 9 June 1918 and 14 April 1926 it was proved to have killed at least 126 humans, before it was finally killed by Colonel Jim Corbett.

Within its large range the leopard has evolved a number of subspecies (30 are recognised at present), which differ to a certain extent from each other in ground colour, size and colour of spots. In hot, dry areas that are poor in cover it is sandy in colour with brownish spots, in hot humid rain-forests it is darker with black spots or completely black, particularly in south-east Asia. These black forms, known as black panthers, are only colour variants which may occur together with normally coloured cubs in the same litter. The leopard of Korea has particularly long fur and large spots arranged in rosettes. The attractiveness of its skin has brought it almost to the brink of extinction.

Man has hunted and killed this beautiful and powerful animal for thousands of years but he has not taken the trouble to investigate the conditions which are essential to its existence. Legends and myths have not yet been separated from facts. Little detailed information is available regarding its life history and habits. Leopards can exist side by side with man in areas which are not densely populated and we also know that they perform a useful service in controlling the populations of monkeys. Nevertheless the leopard still continues to have a bad name and is virtually regarded as an outlaw.

Lesser Bird of Paradise

Paradisea minor p. 159

Birds of paradise are the most handsome birds in the world and to tell even part of their story would require a chapter to itself. Even if one omits the biology of the numerous species and restricts oneself to the history of their discovery, a period of almost half a millenium has to be covered.

The first species to be known was the lesser bird of paradise. Knowledge of all 43 species was not assembled until over 400 years later.

The first five skins of birds of paradise were brought to Europe in 1522 by Portuguese sailors, who were companions of the circumnavigator Magellan. One of the skins was deemed worthy as a gift to the Emperor Charles V.

At the same period of history, the Papuans in New Guinea wore ornamental plumes of birds of paradise as ostentatious decoration of their otherwise sparse clothing for festivals. They cut the feet and wings off the dead birds. The dried skins with the handsome ornamental plumes and the thread-like tail feathers were brought to Europe wrapped around a stick and thus arrived in a mutilated condition. Even learned men accepted the idea that such imperfect creatures really existed. In the mystical world of their contemporaries, the 'limbless ones' were exalted in imagination to the status of ethereal creatures which fed on the dew from heaven and floated in the air like plankton or were carried along by beating the ornamental plumes against the sides of their bodies. Such stories, varied and embellished in many ways, were firmly believed for over 100 years after the appearance of skins with wings and legs.

Slowly the view on the habitat and habits of birds of paradise changed. It was 300 years after the first dead skins arrived in Europe that the European naturalist, René Lesson, was permitted, on landing in New Guinea, to see the first living bird of paradise which was a *Paradisea minor*. Knowledge of other species was slowly gathered. It was not until after 1824 when European naturalists increasingly penetrated into the habitat of the birds of paradise and collected proper observations that the tangle of legends began to be sorted out and was replaced by definite information. The Berlin ornithologist Prof. Erwin Stresemann has written a brilliant summary of the exciting story of the discovery of the birds of paradise. Up to now however, an equally full account of the biology of these birds is still lacking although much is known of certain aspects. The distribution range of the birds of paradise is New Guinea together with a few neighbouring islands; only a few species live in the tropical rain forests of north-east Australia. The lesser bird of paradise is found in the lowlands forests of New Guinea and on the islands of Misol and Japen. It does not, however, go very far up the mountain slopes. The highlands of this island are covered with forests that are difficult to penetrate. But the higher the scientist goes, the most astonishing are the species of birds of paradise and he also meets the closely related bower birds.

(See also little king bird of paradise)

Lion

Panthera leo pp. 184, 185, 217–219

Lions are exhibited in all large zoos and we have become thoroughly familiar with them. Added to this, thousands of visitors go on safari every year through the savannahs of east Africa; the most important item in their programme is the sighting and photographing of lions lazing peacefully in the grass. Under these conditions lions appear to be peacefully surveying the scene in a contemplative mood. Inevitably they seem much less harmful to us than to our grandfathers, who returned from strenuous hunting trips with columns of porters and retailed impressive stories of laying low the savage beasts.

Naturally the lion is not entirely harmless, even if it gives this impression to the animal lover as it lazes in the shade of an acacia tree. Lions regard motor cars as neutral beings and a man in a car is virtually part of the same object. Thus it is only by means of a vehicle that man can approach a lion sufficiently close to take a good photograph of it.

Lions which rest in the shade of a tree by day, sometimes lying up in the branches, go out in the evening to hunt. At this time they are by no means harmless. This is why it is always a strict rule that visitors to national parks and nature reserves must leave at dusk. Nevertheless accidents occur repeatedly, due to the inability of the townsman to behave in a way which is consistent with the laws of the jungle.

The lion plays an extremely important role in the economy of nature, acting as a check on the numbers of large ungulates. Zebra and large to medium-sized antelopes form its main prey. It only hunts when it is hungry. A gnu or a zebra is sufficient food for an adult lion for several days. The annual toll of medium-sized to large prey animals is between fifty and eighty.

The lion is the only species of cat which lives in groups or prides; they tolerate each other and the families live together. This gregariousness is also the basis for the ease with which lions are kept in captivity. A powerful male lion lives together with several lionesses. The male is polygamous and the females often produce their litters at different times. The gestation period is about 110 days and the young are nursed by the mothers for two years. Thus an attractive family group of mixed ages can often be seen in the company of a male.

The family goes out together to hunt. The adults drive and kill the prey, the females adopting the more active role. Ambushes are also laid. When the cubs are old enough, they trot along with the family and are thus introduced to the business of killing prey. Although an inborn trait, the technique of killing can only be perfected through training.

The lioness looks after her cubs lovingly and protects them fearlessly. She also brings them up carefully, as the Adamsons in north Kenya found some years ago. They described in detail the behaviour of the lioness Elsa, who was originally tamed from the wild although not kept in captivity. After Elsa had given birth to a litter in the wild, she brought the cubs, when they were six weeks old, to the Adamsons. Although they remained there for some time, the cubs were always much shyer than Elsa. They showed significant differences in temperament. All large mammals, generally speaking, show individual temperaments, which could be described as amounting to definite personalities. The observations obtained from years of living together with Elsa provided evidence of many behaviour traits, showing a high degree of well-defined reaction to various events in their lives.

Unfortunately the lion is now restricted to less than half its former range. At the beginning of the last century it was still found throughout the whole of north-west Africa and was seen in circuses and zoos as the big-maned Berber lion. In Egypt, where a subspecies formerly occurred, it had already disappeared earlier. In South Africa, too, where there was a large-maned subspecies, it was exterminated about the middle of the last century. Today the southern limit of lion distribution lies in northern South-west Africa and in northern Swaziland. In the Sudan area of west Africa it has also become largely extinct.

It is less well known that the lion once occurred in south-east Europe and was distributed from Macedonia through Thrace, Asia Minor, Persia, Mesopotamia and the coastal areas of the eastern Mediterranean to Baluchistan, south-west Afghanistan and north-west India. It was exterminated from many of these areas by man in prehistoric and early historic times. It was persistently hunted as it caused damage to cattle herds and it was also a favourite form of game. Its decline was also due to the desolation by man of large areas, which were denuded of the large antelopes and other ungulates; the lions thus lost their means of subsistence and also disappeared.

To hunt lions with spears and bows and arrows was a demonstration of courage and valour; sagas of the hunts of the early kings are full of the glorification of such deeds. With the First World War the countries of western Asia were supplied with large numbers of modern weapons and with these the lions of Persia and Mesopotamia were soon exterminated. Numbers in India were also severely reduced.

During the British occupation of India certain dry areas of open forest were given protection. Although accurate figures have never been available, it is thought that there were 200–250 lions still living in the Gir Forest reserve in 1959. The Indian Government, in particular the authorities in the State of Bombay, have taken positive steps for the preservation of these last Indian lions.

The Gir Forest Reserve is about 470 square miles in area and some 50,000 domestic water buffaloes and zebus are kept there, together with innumerable thousands of goats. Game is also present in the reserve but the land is being laid waste by overgrazing and there is insufficient wild prey to support the lions which naturally turn to domestic stock. It is not possible to guard these animals adequately and the villagers, angry at losing their stock, put out poisoned bait for the lions.

Today there are probably no more than 200 lions surviving in the reserve. It cannot be long before they are completely exterminated. People now want to move them elsewhere. A start was made in 1957 with the introduction of a few lions into the protected area of Chandraprabha in the Vindhya Mountains not far from Varanasi. It is now hoped to re-introduce still more lions. With the population at such a low level it is regrettably a matter of some doubt as to whether the Indian lion can be saved. At least it is fortunate that the lion breeds readily in captivity and it should be able to survive, even as a 'domesticated lion', for a much longer period of time.

Little King Bird of Paradise

Cicinnurus regius p. 158

Iridescent colours and bizarre ornamental plumes are characteristic only of the males of birds of paradise. No other group of birds shows such a striking difference in form and coloration amongst many of the males. The females are inconspicuous and lacking in ornamentation. There is such a startling difference between males and females that this appears to be an extravagance of nature. But when one appreciates that the striking difference between the sexes serves a useful purpose, it no longer seems excessive. Coloration and ornamental plumes are not an arbitrary quirk of nature; they are necessary in that they serve as visual signals between the sexes at the stage of pair-formation; signal characters are promoted by natural selection, thus maintaining the differences between species which have already been established. Many birds of paradise do not live, like most song birds, in a marriage-like union in which both sexes share in the rearing of their young. The sexes only come together to mate. The female then builds a nest and undertakes all the care of the offspring. For several months in the year the males only visit their display arenas, which in many species are at the top of a tall tree; there they carry out their courtship display which is just as singular as their appearance. The female recognises instinctively a partner of the same species even though the male is very different in appearance. The characteristics of related species must be as strikingly different as possible in order that mistakes in recognition are not made; otherwise a female might visit the display area of another species in error. Although this sexual dimorphism exists in all the birds of paradise which do not form monogamous pairs, more interspecific hybrids occur amongst birds of paradise than in almost any other family of birds. Before this was realised many of the hybrids were described as separate species.

In the display of the little king bird of paradise the green-edged breast feathers are curved around the raised head to form a fan-like cape. The wings are raised and the tail with the two ornamental feathers is held stiffly erect, so that the thread-like feathers with green eyespots resemble a lyre raised above the head. The snowy feathers on the belly are puffed out into a silken ball.

Other species position the ornamental plumes at the side of the breast so that in the right light they appear as ruffs, capes or crests; ornamental plumes are also agitated so that the plumage appears to be constantly shivering. During these displays the males adopt most extraordinary positions and will even hang head downwards from a branch and accomplish a complete somersault, like a gymnast on the horizontal bar. Their display is accompanied by a song or at least by a loud vocalisation.

The display performances of the male in breeding plumage not only attract the attention of females but also that of enemies. As so often the most cunning of these is man. The Papuans have hunted birds of paradise since time immemorial; the pursuit of the adult males, however, was never a threat to the population. When the first Europeans landed in New Guinea almost all the species were still common. It was not until the white traders asked the Papuans to obtain quantities of these beautiful feathers for marketing commercially that the hunting took on threatening proportions. Some species quickly became rare. About the end of the First World War feathers gradually dropped out of fashion and the situation was further improved when governments imposed strict protective measures and forbade the export of skins. In recent times an illegal trade in feathers has started again in the Indonesian area, formerly the Dutch part of New Guinea; this cannot be controlled and the consequences are incalculable.

Protective measures, however, can only be successful while the immense rain-forests of this enormous island remain undisturbed. At present they still cover the mountains and valleys in an endless series. If these forests should ever give way to the 'cultivation' of the island, this would be the end of the unique birds of paradise which are so diverse in form (see lesser bird of paradise).

LIZARDS see Komodo Dragon; Marine Iguana

Lyrebird

Menura superba p. 143

An inexperienced observer who saw this dark brown bird, which is about the size of a domestic fowl, strutting about on its long strong legs with enormous toes and trailing its tail, would be likely to mistake it for a pheasant. This is exactly what happened when the lyrebird was first discovered by a former convict named Wilson. On a day in January in the year 1798 Wilson discovered a strange bird approximately 60 miles south-west of Sydney, and after a few days he brought it into a settlement where people looked at it with astonishment. It was the first lyrebird to be seen by a white man.

At first some ornithologists in Europe thought that the lyrebird was a pheasant on account of its general appearance and its fowl-like behaviour on the ground. This erroneous view was also supported by fabricated descriptions of its alleged nesting habits. It was not until later that detailed studies were made into its breeding behaviour, its voice and the organs producing the sounds. As a result of this work it became clear that the lyrebird properly belonged among the song birds.

The two species of lyrebird, together with the scrub-birds which are also Australian species, are classified in their own suborder; a number of peculiarities separates them from the other song birds.

The lyrebird lives in the dense forests of south-east Australia. Secretive and wary in its behaviour, it would probably not have been able to survive until now if it had not lived in such an inaccessible habitat. It has been hunted for about 190 years; people made shoddy home ornaments out of its ornamental tail feathers and these were even exported from Australia. Today the lyrebirds have become more accustomed to human beings in certain areas. For instance, not far from the big cities of Sydney and Melbourne, people often go to see the lyrebirds, not for the purpose of killing them but to enjoy watching the spectacle of their fairy-like courtship.

The courtship display of the lyrebird is a truly remarkable sight. The decorative tail of the male consists of many peculiarly shaped feathers which are swung forwards over his back like a very delicate fan of silver filigree; these feathers completely cover the nondescript shape of the rather plump bird. The male builds a slightly raised platform in the forest and uses this as a stage on which to give his display. He twists and turns in the darkness of the forest, the beauty of his tail veiling his otherwise undistinguished appearance, and in this way he attempts to attract the attention of the earth-brown females who sneak off into the undergrowth like bashful maidens. The male does not confine his self-advertisement to visual signals but has a wide variety of notes and calls. He alternates his own powerful notes with imitations of sounds made by other birds. The male lyrebird is the most remarkable songster among Australian birds and indeed would bear comparison with the best singers of the bird world.

Anyone who has witnessed the remarkable performance of the male lyrebird during the breeding season will readily understand the Australians' pride in this unusual showman of the bird world.

Malayan Tapir

Tapirus indicus p. 195

In some respects the tapirs embody the most ancient of the ungulates living today. This is shown in the skull, the low-crowned cheek teeth and also in the limbs which have four toes on the forefeet and three on the hindfeet.

The tapirs have a long evolutionary history that goes back to the Eocene period of the Tertiary. They were once widely distributed over Europe and Asia; they reached North America at the change from the Oligocene to Miocene and South America at the change from the Tertiary to the Ice Age. They have never occurred, however, in Africa.

Today tapirs are found only in central and south America and in southern Asia. These widely separated areas are the sole remnants of a former extensive distribution range. There are still three species of tapir in America but only one in Asia: the Malayan tapir.

The Malayan tapir lives in Sumatra and on the mainland opposite, extending through the Malayan Peninsula northwards to the Siamese–Burmese frontier region. In contrast to its plain and uniformly dark to red-brown American relatives, it has one of the most contrasting colorations of all the mammals: it is black on the foreparts and hindparts and greyish-white in the middle. This pattern looks very conspicuous in a captive tapir but it helps to conceal the animal in the play of light and shade in the jungle. Perhaps this is one of the main reasons why the Malayan tapir so seldom falls prey to predators. Its chief enemies are the tiger, the leopard and the Indian wild dog. In addition, of course, its acute hearing and excellent sense of smell help to ensure that it reaches safety in good time. It lacks tusks or any form of weapon on the head.

The Malayan tapir measures 40–42 inches at the shoulders and attains a weight of 400–500 lb. It is solitary and shy, moving about through forest, bamboo and grass jungle, except during the breeding season (there is no fixed season for mating) or when the female has a young one at heel. Its habitat is in fact jungle which is interspersed with clearings, swamps, ponds, rivers and similar waters. Here it rests in the heat of midday in a shady place where it is well camouflaged by its coloration. In the morning and afternoon it goes in search of fresh grasses, herbs, buds and leaves and also for salt-licks and places to bathe for it is very fond of the water.

The female produces one or sometimes even two young after a gestation period of 390 to 400 days. The young tapir is born with a very striking pattern of elongated white spots on a dark brown background, which gives it good camouflage in the wealth of shadows in the jungle; it loses this pattern after about six months.

The jungle life of the Malayan tapir and of its American relatives accounts for the small amount we know of the habits of these secretive animals which seldom make any sound. This seclusion has fortunately protected them so far from extensive persecution by man. The population of tapir, including that of the Malayan tapir, has so far not been threatened directly.

MANATEE see Sirenians

Manchurian Crane

Grus japonensis pp. 178, 179

The crane family is relatively small—there are only some 14 species—and several members of the family belong amongst the rarest birds in the world today. Cranes are such large and striking birds that they have always aroused the interest of man. For the most part they have stimulated man's hunting instincts but not in every part of the world.

At one time the Manchurian crane was widely distributed on the two main islands of Japan; indeed, it was almost a common breeding species. In the medieval Tokugawa Period when the Japanese islands were already densely populated with humans, many animals enjoyed an almost idyllic existence. The imperial house and the nobles held a protecting hand over the largest and most beautiful animal species in their country. This was particularly true of the crane, the *tancho*, which from time immemorial had been treated as the symbol of eternal life in the legends, stories and superstitions of the Japanese people. The prohibition on eating meat and killing animals, which is a basic tenet of Buddhism, supported the effectiveness of this protection. No one dared to harm a crane. Every nest that happened to be found had to be reported and it was incumbent on the finder to care for its safety. Only the Emperor could kill such a noble animal as the *tancho* which he hunted with trained goshawks. Not every goshawk was capable of taking a crane, but if it was successful the hawk was honoured with a purple hood.

With the restoration of the Meiji dynasty the old feudal system was changed and at the same time Buddhism was replaced by Shintoism. Restraints were removed and a wild lust to hunt spread throughout the people. In a short time the crane, previously under a taboo, was exterminated, except for a single population in one breeding area which was in a secluded swamp on the northern island of Hokkaido. This place is only accessible during severe frost and here a small breeding population survived, which did not leave the breeding area during the winter and thus avoided the risk of being hunted on migration.

Protective measures were introduced towards the end of the 19th century and have subsequently been improved. Fortunately these measures were introduced in time to save the cranes. The population has survived the troubles of war and there are about fifty pairs now breeding here. Over the years the initial shyness of the cranes has been overcome. They are now comparatively tame and allow the farmers to feed them in winter when the severity of the weather deprives them of their normal source of food in the swamps.

The rate of reproduction is low: the clutch consists of only 1–2 eggs and it is unusual for more than one young bird to be reared by each pair. In spite of this the number of cranes in the Kushiro Swamp has happily risen since the war. Such small relict populations of a species are extremely vulnerable. Their future existence depends above all on the attitude of man towards conservation. Elsewhere small breeding populations of the Manchurian crane exist only in a few places in the Ussuri region of eastern Siberia. The fate of these is less well known than that of the population in the Kushiro Swamp in Hokkaido.

Marine Iguana

Amblyrhynchus cristatus p. 107

The marine iguana is one of the most striking looking and peculiar animals of the Galapagos Islands. It lives on the coast and at a number of places in the archipelago several hundred of these dark lizards, each about three feet long, form a crowd on the lava cliffs. It is the only iguanid which enters the sea. It feeds on various seaweeds which it usually browses when the weeds are exposed at low tide. It also swims out to sea and dives to the bottom to browse there. A lizard walking about among the fish makes a strange sight.

These reptiles are adapted to amphibious life with a laterally compressed rudder-like tail; the powerful legs are armed with claws with which they can hang on during periods of swell. They have special salt glands lying in front of the eyes which excrete the excess salt taken in with the food and sea water. Due to these glands these lizards are even able to drink sea water.

In general, marine iguanas are very peaceable. During the breeding season, however, the males take up small territories in which they live with several females. They repel rivals by threat gestures. If an intruder fails to yield then a fight ensues but no blood is shed. The animals do not bite but try to force their opponent to give ground, by pressing the roof of their skulls against each other and pushing with all their strength. Finally the weaker gives in and lies down flat in a submissive posture in front of the victor.

The latter accepts the submission and adopts a threat posture, waiting for the defeated opponent to leave the field. The females, on the other hand, appear to be less chivalrous. Fights take place in areas where the eggs are laid and the females bite each other in earnest. The eggs are laid in a hole which is dug out and then filled in. Each female lays two eggs which are about 3½ inches long and $1\frac{1}{2}$ inches in diameter. On Hood Island they guard their egg-laying places for several days against other females.

There are several races of the marine iguana on the Galapagos Islands. The most beautiful are those on Hood Island which are a handsome red and green colour. Their main enemies on land are the Galapagos buzzard and, in the sea, the numerous sharks. They have an exceedingly friendly relationship with the small ground finches which climb about on them and pick off the troublesome ticks, acting as 'lizard cleaners'.

MARSUPIALS see Kangaroos; Koala; Leadbeater's Opossum; Tree Kangaroos

MONITORS see Komodo Dragon

MONKEYS see Barbary Ape; Colobus Monkey; Gibbon

MOUNTAIN ZEBRA see Zebras

Musk-ox

Ovibos moschatus p. 54

In its general shape the musk-ox is intermediate between sheep and cattle. This is why its scientific name is *Ovibos*—sheep-ox—even though it is not closely related to either sheep or cattle. It is classified among the horned ungulates in its own subfamily.

Today the musk-ox is essentially an inhabitant of the arctic tundras. Its ancestors were Tertiary steppe animals which accustomed themselves to cold climates at the onset of the Ice Age. They lived in the company of mammoth, woolly rhinoceros and reindeer during the Ice Age, grazing the tundras of the New and Old Worlds. Mammoth and woolly rhinoceros died out towards the end of the Ice Age; only reindeer and musk-ox survived to the present time.

As the cold climate and the ice edge of the tundra made progress to the far south, the musk-ox and reindeer moved with it, reaching the Pyrenees, the Danube valley, Lake Baikal and the Gulf of Mexico. Remains have been found in all these areas. With the retreat of the ice and the warming up of the climate all these regions had to be vacated again; in the process the musk-ox retreated still farther into the arctic tundra than the reindeer. It disappeared completely from Europe, it held on longer in northern Siberia, but soon also died out there. It now occurs wild only in North America (from Alaska to Hudson Bay), on the Canadian Arctic islands and in Greenland.

There was still some doubt, however, regarding the ability of these remnants to survive. In 1917 they were placed under protection in many areas but in general the populations did not increase. Experiments in introducing them elsewhere have met with mixed success. The first attempt of taking Greenland musk-ox to Scandinavia was a failure; however, the animals transported from Greenland to Spitsbergen in 1929 have since increased to about 150. The experiment of introducing them to the Dovrefjell in Norway after the last war has also been successful; at the moment there are about 20 adults and calves there.

Not long ago a farm was started at Edmonton in Canada with half a dozen musk-ox. An investigation will be carried out there to find out if the musk-ox can be domesticated. If the experiment s successful the musk-ox could become as important in the arctic as the domesticated yaks are in Tibet.

The musk-ox is about 5 feet high at the shoulders and attains a weight of 400 to 700 lb. On the average the cows are about three-quarters the size of the bulls.

The popular name of the musk-ox refers to the musky smell which emanates from its coat. In winter this is very thick and fine, the wool growing to a considerable length; it then hangs down below the wrist and ankle joints. The short summer coat is only carried in June–July. The winter coat protects the animal well from the rigours of the arctic climate, from heavy snowstorms and very low temperatures, but it provides poor protection against rain. For this reason the musk-ox requires a dry and cold climate if it is to thrive.

They feed on grasses, herbs, the leaves and buds of dwarf shrubs, lichens, moss and fungi; even in winter they manage to find sufficient food in places where the ground has been cleared of snow by the wind.

A bull lives together with a few cows and their calves. In the winter darkness the family groups join together into larger herds. The mating season is from the end of July to the beginning of September, and the cows give birth from the end of April to the beginning of June, the gestation period being $8\frac{1}{2}$–9 months. A cow usually has only one calf, rarely two. The calf is suckled for about six months but it already begins to feed itself at one month. It is tended by the mother for two years; thus the cow can only give birth once every two years. Sexual maturity is reached in the third or fourth year in the cows, in the fifth or sixth in the bulls. They can attain an age of over 20 years.

Musk-ox have only two enemies: wolf and man. When threatened by an enemy, the adults form a phalanx with the calves in the centre, the adults flanking the younger animals and facing outwards, ready to use their horns.

NE-NE see Hawaiian Goose

Nilgai

Boselaphus tragocamelus p. 186

The nilgai is the only representative of the large antelopes which occurs in south Asia. The other members of this group live in Africa; some of them also occurred in Arabia and Mesopotamia until fairly recently when they were exterminated.

The nilgai is one of the largest members of the antelope group and its closest relatives are the bongo, eland, kudu, nyala, sitatunga and harnessed antelope of Africa. Members of this group are all marked with white in much the same way, on the head, neck and shoulders; the nilgai also has these characteristic markings. Whereas the African forms carry medium-long to long twisted horns, the nilgai only has short horns; these are at the most 12 inches long and they curve forwards. The females of the nilgai are hornless, like other members of the group, with the exception of the bongo and the eland.

The nilgai is also known as the blue bull and this refers to the iron- to blue-grey colour of the pelt of the mature males; the pale brown of the immature pelt starts to change colour at an age of two years. The females retain the brown colour throughout their life. Further characteristics of the species are the gentle slope of the back towards the tail, the mane on the neck and the long hair on the underside of the throat. Finally there is also a tuft of hair on the dewlap in the bulls. The male is heavier and also somewhat larger than the female. The neck is not very long but it is strong and broad; this together with the heavily built forequarters gives it a powerful appearance. It attains a height of 56 inches at the withers and a weight of up to 600 lb. The long tail, which is tufted at the end, is usually carried tucked between the legs.

The nilgai is found in India south of the Himalaya. It is absent from the pure deserts, the Malabar coast, east Bengal and also from Ceylon. Its habitat consists of open bush country with scattered individual large trees, or grassy plains with isolated patches of bush or forest plantations; it occurs both in the plains and in hilly country. Dense, closed forests are usually avoided but arable land is acceptable.

The animals are active throughout the day, grazing in the morning and evening, resting in the shade at midday and chewing the cud. They usually form small groups consisting of a few females with their young. An adult bull is often seen in their company but old males prefer a solitary life or go about with other aged bulls. Sometimes a few family groups join up to form herds of one to two dozen head. They remain in one locality for a long time if plenty of suitable food is available. Within this area they have habitual places for resting, excreting and drinking, and they keep returning to the same sites. Water need not necessarily be in the immediate vicinity because the equivalent of one bucket every second or third day is sufficient during the cooler part of the year.

Nilgai browse on the leaves and buds of bushes and trees, and also graze on grasses and herbs. They also like fruit. When grazing they often go down on to their wrists so that they do not have to stretch their necks too much.

In south India the nilgai has no fixed mating season; in the north they mate mainly in March and April and the young are born in November and December after a gestation period of about eight months. Two rival bulls will engage in fierce fights: they lower themselves on to their knees and strike each other with forehead and horns, or press each others' necks down, until one of the two submits. The female produces one or two young; the calves lie down for the first few days before following the mother. They become sexually mature at 1½ years and may attain an age of 20 years. Their enemies include tigers, leopards, wolves, Indian wild dogs and they also fall victim to human hunters.

NOTORNIS see Takahe

Nyala

Tragelaphus angasi p. 241

The nyala is one of the large antelopes belonging to the same group as the harnessed antelope, sitatunga, eland, bongo, kudu and nilgai. These species are all characterised by having white markings on the head, neck, body and legs or pale transverse stripes on the body; the males also have horns which are twisted in a loose spiral.

The beauty of these animals is further enhanced by the rich red, red-brown, grey-brown, brown, greyish-black or bluish-black background colour of the hair. In addition, the bull eland has a patch of erect hair on the forehead and a pronounced dewlap; the great kudu bull has a short mane on the back and a long fringe on the underside of the throat. This additional hair adornment is, however, most strongly developed in the lowlands nyala bull. The bull of the mountain nyala, its closest relative, does not have any attractive hair adornment except for some dorsal hairs which are not held erect; the cow is similar to the bull but has no horns, like all the females in this group except for the eland and the bongo.

Apart from the hair adornment of the males, the two species of nyala also differ in colour and size. The smaller lowlands nyala (shoulder height 40 inches in the male, 30–38 inches in the female) has developed striking sexual dimorphism. The red-brown, hornless, smooth-haired females are sharply contrasted with the horned, strongly maned blue-black males. In the larger mountain nyala (shoulder height 46–53 inches in the male, 35–40 inches in the female), on the other hand, the two sexes are almost the same. In appearance, habits and sexual dimorphism, the lowland nyala is more similar to the bushbuck or harnessed antelope and to the sitatunga or marshbuck, whereas the mountain nyala is strongly reminiscent of the greater kudu in the characteristics already mentioned.

The lowlands nyala lives in southern Africa from south Nyasaland and Mozambique to east Transvaal, Swaziland and Zululand; the mountain nyala occurs only in north-east Africa in a very restricted area of Arussi Province in south Ethiopia. The wide separation in geographical range of the two species suggests that they have been separated for a long time, and this is emphasised by morphological differences.

The lowlands nyala occurs in the plains or in hilly country, in forest along the river banks or in woodland close to water and in dense to scattered bush in the savannah areas. It likes cover and is mainly active at twilight and after dark. It is not easy to get a sight of this shy animal and this has helped to preserve its population up to now. Its diet consists of leaves and shoots as well as grasses and herbs. The female produces a single calf—rarely two—after a gestation period of about seven months. There is no sharply defined breeding season. One can only say that most of the calves are born between August and March. Owing to its secretive habits very little is known of the detailed life history of this species of nyala.

The same can be said of the mountain nyala which lives in grassy, rocky bush-covered terrain on mountain slopes above the tree line at altitudes between 7500 and 9000 feet. It is known that the calves are born at the beginning of the rainy season in June to July. The exact period of gestation is unknown, but it is probably 7½–8 months. The animals live in small groups. Hitherto only a few white men have hunted the mountain nyala and unfortunately very few of these have troubled to report their experiences with these game animals. Their distribution is restricted to an area of only a few hundred square miles in the mountains of Chilalo, Gugu and Sahatu. Owing to the fact that man has not yet made any attempt to use these wild mountain 'heaths' to any extent, it is fairly certain that this species is not yet in danger, even though its distribution is so limited.

Orang Utan

Pongo pygmaeus pp. 188, 189

Of the four species of anthropoid ape now living, the gorilla, the chimpanzee and the dwarf chimpanzee occur in West Africa. Only the orang utan lives in Asia.

At the time of the last Ice Age the orang was still distributed on the mainland of Asia from south China through south-east Asia to the Malayan Peninsula. In historical times it has only been known to occur in the large islands of Sumatra and Borneo. About a hundred years ago it was present in most of the rain-forest areas on these islands; however, it was never found in large numbers. The orang only lives in small individual family groups, unlike the chimpanzee and the gorilla in which a number of families join together, forming large troops.

Anthropoid apes grow relatively slowly and on the average do not become sexually mature until they are about eight years old. The gestation period is also lengthy, being 7–9 months in the orang utan. They have a longevity of about 30 years, although this is not often reached in the wild, and the females remain capable of reproducing until they are 23–25 years old. As a rule they only produce one young every four years and the mortality of the babies and juveniles is about 40 per cent. One can therefore reckon that during its life each female only produces two to three young that reach maturity.

On its home islands of Borneo and Sumatra the orang utan *had* scarcely any enemies. As a completely arboreal animal, it was scarcely threatened by the tiger in Sumatra and there were no tigers in Borneo. The natives did not hunt it to any significant extent. The rate of reproduction was sufficient to maintain the population.

The position changed after the departure of the Dutch from Indonesia and of the British from Singapore after the Second World War. At this time there was also an increase in the number of zoos in the world and orangs for exhibition in their collections were much in demand. The result was that the future of the orang utan became seriously endangered. First, the strict protective measures laid down by the Dutch became void. Secondly Singapore was the main transhipment port for the export of orangs from Indonesia and the trading regulations imposed by the British ceased to operate. Zoos offered high sums of money for orangs and the natives shot the mothers, capturing the young which they then sold. A very high proportion of these young died, owing to lack of suitable care, before they even reached their destination where they could be looked after by experienced zoo keepers.

The extermination of the orang in the wild proceeded at an alarming rate. Today the total population is estimated to be 4000–5000. It is clear from the information already given on their slow reproductive rate that the numbers will decline still further.

Today attempts are being made to ensure that really good protective laws are enforced. The members of the International Union of Zoo Directors have agreed not to buy any more wild orangs. The zoos are also making up breeding pairs by agreement in order to promote breeding in captivity. There are approximately 180 orang utans living in 92 zoos and these have already produced about 20 young—a most promising start. The situation would be very much better, however, if the Malays of Indonesia could be made conscious of their precious heritage of wild orangs and if the senseless poaching of orangs could be effectively prevented.

Oryx

Oryx pp. 230, 231

When the Boers arrived in South Africa they found a large antelope and in the absence of any suitable native name they called it gemsbok, meaning chamois buck. This name was in no way appropriate because apart from the fact that it has horns, it has little in common with the chamois. In fact, the Boers had not discovered a new type of animal. This animal was already known in the ancient world and was called *oryzes* by the Greeks, from which the scientific name of *Oryx* was derived.

The oryx is distributed from Cape Province through the whole of Africa, except in the dense rain-forest regions, up to the northern edge of the Sahara, Arabia, the Sinai Peninsula, Jordan, Palestine, Iraq and Syria. In ancient times it also occurred in Egypt where large numbers were kept in semi-domestication for sacrificial purposes.

It is not surprising that this handsome antelope, standing between 40 and 55 inches at the shoulders, should have evolved into several subspecies within such a vast geographical range. Thus in northern Africa from Rio de Oro and Senegal in the west, through the Sahara to Sudan and Egypt in the east, there is a desert form known as the scimitar oryx which has a very pale coloration and a pair of long horns that curve slightly backwards. Although eminently adapted to desert life there are not many of these beautiful animals left. Since man has learned to master even the permanent desert with jeeps he has seen fit to hunt the oryx with the aid of mechanical transport. Thus the scimitar oryx is still present in small numbers only in the southern parts of the Sahara including the neighbouring parts of Sudan to the east; it has been exterminated everywhere else.

The Arabian oryx is just as well-adapted to living in the desert. It once lived in the arid parts of Mesopotamia, Syria and Palestine down to the Persian Gulf, and throughout Arabia. It is likely that there are now only about 100 of these animals surviving in this whole area. The discovery of oil has been the main factor in this tragic story. Previously the Arabs only had the dromedary, the horse and the ass to assist them in their long journeys. Oil has now made them prosperous and they are able to use cars, aeroplanes, machine-guns and so on. Inveterate hunters with a lust for killing, they now race across the desert in columns of vehicles, shooting everything within sight. It is little wonder that today the whole Arabian peninsula is emptied of gazelles and antelopes. Threatened with total extinction, a few Arabian oryx have now been taken into captivity with the aid of the World Wildlife Fund and a small breeding colony of half a dozen animals has been established in Arizona, where happily three calves have already been born.

Darker coloured oryx occur in the savannahs and bush country from Eritrea and Ethiopia southwards through east, south and south-west Africa to south-west Angola. In east Africa the basic colour of the coat is brownish, in the south grey. The east African form, which is known as the beisa oryx, is still relatively common in Kenya. The greyish south African form is the gemsbok of the Boers. It also lives in the Kalahari Desert and like its relatives in the Sahara and Arabia, it can exist for months at a time without water.

Oryx live socially in small herds of a few to several dozen animals. Usually there is a mature buck with several females and their young. Larger aggregations are rare. At the time that it was still numerous the scimitar oryx sometimes gathered into large herds with several thousand animals. Both sexes of the oryx are horned. In the breeding season, which is not tied to any particular season and also varies from one region to another, the bucks take part in strenuous fights and sometimes the horns are broken. After a gestation period of 8–9 months the female gives birth usually to one young, which becomes sexually mature in 2½ years at the latest. Oryx may live for 20 years.

Otters

Lutrinae p. 100

The otters are carnivores belonging to the mustelid family which includes stoat, mink and badger. They are classified in their own subfamily and are particularly well adapted to aquatic life. There are some 15 species distributed throughout Eurasia, Africa and America. The best known and most widely distributed genus is that of the true otters, of which there are 11 species in Europe, Asia, Africa and North and South America. The European otter and the Canadian otter are members of this genus. South America has the six-foot long giant Brazilian otter of the Amazon basin which is classified in its own genus. In Africa south of the Sahara there are two species of clawless otter, so named because they lack claws on the front feet and on the first and fifth toes of the hind feet. The sea otter of the north Pacific coasts is also placed in its own genus and is chiefly known for its valuable pelt.

The Canadian and the European otters are very similar in appearance: the upper parts are brown, the underparts paler, often with a greyish-white patch at the throat. The tail accounts for about a third of the total length which is approximately 4 feet. The legs are short, the toes are connected by webs and the height is about 8 inches at the shoulders. The male or dog-otter weighs from 20 to 25 lb., being about a third heavier than the female or bitch.

The Canadian otter is distributed over the whole of North America. It lives on all kinds of natural waters: streams, rivers, ponds, lakes, swamps and lagoons. It is even found on the sea coasts. It is an uncommonly alert and energetic animal which is active by night as well as by day. It rests in holes in the banks, reed-beds, bushes with ground cover of grass and hollow trees; it also occupies burrows or holes in the banks with entrances above and below the water surface. It spends a great deal of time in the water, diving frequently and remaining submerged for up to four minutes. It feeds mainly on fish and crustaceans but also takes frogs, newts, water-tortoises, snakes, earthworms, insects, eggs and young of aquatic birds, mice and their litters, musk-rats and rabbits. In summer it also eats berries and fruits. The commoner species of fish are taken first, together with any sickly specimens which are not able to escape easily. The otter is as necessary for the maintenance of the health of fish populations as the wolf is for that of herds of reindeer and deer.

Each otter has a well defined territory through which it makes regular rounds. When doing this it may go some distance over land and in the mating season it may wander for miles. A single male will then seek out several bitches and keep each one company for a number of days. There does not appear to be any fixed mating season for the European otter and the gestation period is usually stated to be about 62 days. In the Canadian otter, however, there are records of a gestation period of 9 to 12 months and the cubs are usually born from February to April, or even earlier in the southern part of the range. There may be 1 to 4 cubs, usually 2 to 3; they only weigh about 3 oz. at birth and are born blind, opening their eyes for the first time when they are about 1 month old. They first leave the holt when they are about 2 months old and spend a lot of time playing in the vicinity. Two weeks later the mother leads them down to the water. They have to be encouraged to swim and dive; at first they appear timid and hesitant but soon behave as though they were completely in their element. The male often remains in the vicinity of the bitch during the period of gestation, but she does not allow him to enter the breeding holt; however, he joins the family in their antics in the water. The male eventually wanders off but the cubs remain with their mother until they are about 8 months old.

Young otters reared by hand become very tame. They are clean about the house and are always ready to be played with. One of the problems which faces the owner of a pet otter is that it easily gets bored, starts to pine and then goes sick. Otters are naturally alert and full of energy, consequently they need constant attention as pets.

OWL see Eagle Owl; Snowy Owl

OWL PARROT see Kakapo

PENGUIN see Adélie Penguin; Emperor Penguin

Père David's Deer

Elaphurus davidianus p. 47

Père David's deer gets its name from its discoverer, the French missionary Armand David, who undertook three journeys to China and contributed much of importance to the investigation of China's natural history. In 1865 he observed the last specimens of Père David's deer living in the Imperial Park at Peking, where they were strictly protected and shielded from the view of ordinary mortals. In 1869 Sir Rutherford Alcock, the British Ambassador in Peking, obtained a pair which he presented to the London Zoo. In the course of the following years a few specimens reached other European zoos including Paris and Berlin.

In 1898 the Duke of Bedford bought the few Père David's deer which then existed in Europe and united them into a herd which roamed free on his estate at Woburn Park. The animals did so well there that by 1950 they had already increased to over 300. It was not until then that the Duke started to distribute breeding pairs to zoos in Europe and overseas, so that daughter herds could be established and thus the future of the species be further ensured. In 1956 The Zoological Society of London sent two pairs of Père David's deer back to Peking for the zoo there.

In 1894 a flood of the Hwang Ho partly destroyed the walls of the Imperial Park at Peking. The deer escaped into the surrounding country and were killed and eaten by the starving population. Of the small remnant in the Imperial Park only a few survived the Boxer Rebellion in 1900. By 1911 there were only two of these deer in Peking and the last one died in 1921. The Duke of Bedford's actions were indeed timely. For about 3000 years none of these deer had existed in the wild. If he had not united the scattered individuals in Europe into a breeding herd, the species would have disappeared from the face of the earth.

After the Ice Age, Père David's deer was distributed as an inhabitant of swamps and marshy ground by rivers in large areas of north and central China; during the Ice Age it also occurred in Manchuria and before the Ice Age it was found in southern Japan as well. During the Chang Dynasty (1766–1122 B.C.), when the fertile lowlands were increasingly settled, it disappeared completely from the wild and was only preserved in parks. Finally, for several centuries it survived only in the Imperial Park at Peking.

Details of the habits of Père David's deer are only known to us from modern experience gained by keeping them in parks. The animals like to wade, swim and wallow; they seek the water in hot weather to cool themselves. This behaviour, together with their large spreading hooves confirms the idea that in their original range they lived in swamps and marshes.

Père David's deer mate in June or July. After a gestation period of about 260 days the female gives birth to one or two young; the young form a 'nursery' association for a while and become sexually mature after 2¼ years at the latest. The deer grow summer antlers at the end of February or beginning of March, which they clean at the end of May or beginning of June and shed in October. In November they start to grow small winter antlers which they clean in January and only carry until the end of February. This double growth of antlers occurs in no other deer. Today, however, this is only partly true as most of Père David's deer now produce only one set of antlers per year.

By Père David's secret peep over the walls of the Peking Park in 1865 the world became aware of a new species of deer whose fate was already sealed in its country of origin. Just as the alpine ibex was saved in the Gran Paradiso by the efforts of an Italian king, so Père David's deer was saved in Woburn Park by an English nobleman.

Polar Bear

Thalarctos maritimus p. 55

The polar bear evolved in the course of the Ice Age from ancestors similar to the brown bear. During the long period of cold conditions the northernmost representatives of the brown bear group became perfectly adapted to the inclemency of the Arctic. If their ancestors were omnivores, the polar bears became almost completely carnivorous. Blueberries and crowberries which they find during the short Arctic summer would only be sufficient to nourish an animal of the size of a polar bear for a few weeks.

Polar bears have a shoulder height of up to about 5 feet; the total length of the male is about 7–8 feet, that of the female about 6–7 feet. The males normally weigh 800–1000 lb. and in rare cases even up to 1600 lb.; the females weigh 600–800 lb.

Polar bears live mainly on the drifting pack-ice of the north polar regions. They are restless animals and wander across the coastal drift ice mainly in an east-west direction around the North Pole. Sometimes they move farther inland but only in passing. The direction they take is governed primarily by the drifting ice on which they live. They make use of the drift of the ice which takes them into areas rich in food, such as the Barents Sea or the Greenland Sea; if they want to get away from a coastal stretch which is poor in food, such as in north Siberia, the bears expedite their progress either by going faster than the drift of the ice or by pressing on against the general direction of the current. The polar bear is undoubtedly the land mammal which penetrates farthest north. It has been recorded up to 88°N and now and again it reaches the North Pole.

A thick layer of fat beneath the long, shaggy, yellowish-white fur protects the polar bear against the cold. The webs between the toes, which are half as long as the toes, increase its swimming ability. However its powers of swimming are not sufficiently outstanding to enable it to remain in the water for hours on end; it is also not a particularly fast swimmer. It does not dive very deep, going only a few yards down, and remains underwater at the most for one to two minutes. In all this it shows itself to be predominantly a land animal. It is in no way comparable with a seal or an otter.

It preys mainly on seals, particularly the little ringed seal. It either lies in wait at their holes in the ice until they come up to breathe or it swims silently up to a seal lying out on the edge of the ice. The bear usually submerges for the final approach and then suddenly shoots up in front of the seal and strikes it on the head. If seals are lacking, it will take anything from lemmings to arctic foxes, from the eggs and broods of ground-breeding birds to sledge dogs, anything that it can get. It will also rip open a reindeer if it can outwit it and in Iceland, for instance, it has been known to attack free-ranging sheep, cattle and horses. It takes spawning salmon from rivers and streams. It is also content with carrion and will plunder the stores of trappers and Arctic explorers, even eating fur boots and the leather harness of sledge dogs when driven by hunger.

The otherwise solitary polar bear starts to think of courtship at the end of March and it will follow the track of a female in season for days on end. The mating season lasts until the 3rd week of April. However the embryos within the female do not start their full development until October. By December, at the latest, the female withdraws into a deep hole in the snow where she becomes snowed up; in January one to three rat-sized cubs are born. The young are suckled for about 1¾ years. They first open their eyes at one month old, and leave the hole for the first time with their mother at an age of eight to ten weeks. It is only at the end of the second year of life that they start to become independent. Thus the female can only produce young every third year.

With safer methods of penetrating the Arctic regions for whaling and seal-catching, the polar bear has unfortunately come into conflict with man in many places; it has no other natural enemies except the killer whale, the walrus and occasionally the Arctic wolf. With helicopters and modern weapons it is easy to kill a polar bear either when it is approaching out of curiosity or taking flight. This is why the total population has fallen to about 10,000 and the world organisations for the conservation of wildlife are taking steps to stop the excessive killing.

Puffin

Fratercula arctica pp. 48, 49

The habits of puffins show extremely strong social bonds between members of the species, combined with a certain tendency towards solitary habits. In their breeding colonies puffins sometimes congregate in hundreds of thousands. But when the fully grown young leave the colony and move out into the open sea, they disperse and even avoid the company of their parents. In the winter one only sees small groups together at sea, and never the large aggregations as in the breeding areas in the spring.

Puffins live on the islands off the coasts of the North Atlantic. They nest in holes often a yard long which they dig themselves in the soil or peat covering the rocky substrate of the islands. In old colonies that have been in use for a long time they form systems of tunnels which finally collapse, as happened on the island of Grassholm off the south-west coast of Wales. As a result, all that remains is a ruined system of holes and pits and the puffins have to move out.

The female puffin lays a single egg which hatches into a downy chick. Both parents bring food. The chick soon puts on weight on the fish diet and remains in the safety of the burrow for a long time. Gradually the parents lose the urge to feed the chick and after about six weeks they stop feeding it. The chick remains in the burrow for a few more days, receiving no more food, and then one night it leaves the hole. It makes immediately for the edge of the cliff and with whirring wings, it launches into space and lands in the sea. It moves away from the danger of rocks, diving repeatedly, and makes for the open sea.

In their densely populated colonies the puffins and their young are often hunted by different enemies. Adults flying backwards and forwards provide easy prey for peregrine falcons and, in some northerly breeding colonies, for the gerfalcon. Lurking greater black-backed gulls kill them with their powerful bills when they leave the burrows; they also eat the young puffins, often as they are making their way to the cliff edge. Adults returning from the sea with bills full of small fish are also harassed by skuas, lesser black-backed and herring gulls, and are forced to relinquish their food. These losses, are, so to speak, allowed for in the population dynamics of the species and are compensated for by the number of offspring.

The worst and most deadly enemies of a colony are the rats. Originally there were no rats on the islands where puffins bred. In the course of time, however, they have been introduced on many small islands by ships. The rats, which breed very fast, eat the eggs and young of the sea birds and at night they kill the adults in their burrows or on their nests. Most colonies in which rats have got a foothold have declined considerably. There is no means of exterminating the rats. As long as a few remain they will form the nucleus of a new population explosion so long as sufficient food is available.

Unfortunately man also takes part in the destruction of puffins and other sea birds that breed in colonies. The eggs are collected, the young taken and the adults caught in a variety of ways. On most islands where the sea birds form an important supply of additional food for the inhabitants, the bird fowlers were able to control the catch for a long time, arranging it in such a way that the population of the colony was maintained. Exploitation of the birds for food was limited periodically and according to numbers.

Even in these days similar limitations are still observed in most places. On the other hand the waste oil released from the bilges of tankers is having a disastrous effect. Innumerable sea birds which come up against drifting oil become so covered with it that they can no longer clean themselves. They become numb with cold and starve pitifully. Man has money to build atom bombs and moon rockets but little or nothing is done about the horrible pollution of the sea, although the means of doing so were discovered long ago.

Puffins are still widely distributed on many of the North Atlantic coasts and there are even a few enormous colonies which are protected. However many former nesting sites have been deserted for a variety of reasons. If the nature conservationists were not continually watching the progress of colonies, the outlook for the puffin might well be very different.

Reindeer or Caribou

Rangifer tarandus p. 74

Reindeer or caribou occur in the northern forest and tundra regions of the whole of the Old and New Worlds. The distribution is therefore circumpolar and extends across the subarctic and arctic regions northwards to the coasts of the Arctic Ocean, and includes some islands in the Arctic Ocean. The southern limit of the range is along latitude 50°N and as far as 45°N in a few places.

In the regions inhabited by reindeer, there are extremely sharp winds which bring bitterly cold weather. It speaks well for the adaptability of terrestrial animals that one as large as the reindeer can not only maintain itself in such areas but even thrive there. The reindeer is well protected against all kinds of bad weather by its short densely haired ears, the almost completely haired muzzle, the short, densely haired tail and an uncommonly thick and firm pelt. The widely spreading, deeply cleft hooves and very strong joints and tendons are well adapted for crossing moorland, swamp, sandy and stony ground strewn with boulders—terrain that is covered with snow and ice for many months of the year.

Within the American range of the species there are two ecological forms: the Barren Ground caribou and the woodland caribou. The former spends most of the year on the treeless high mountain or plateau tundra and only enters the areas on the edges of the forests in winter. The latter lives mainly in the forest regions and only moves on to the high ground or plateau tundra in the summer to escape from the plagues of insects. Barren Ground caribou are usually smaller and paler than the woodland caribou, in which deep brown tones predominate. The latter include the most powerful representatives of the reindeer with magnificent antlers. They measure up to at least 3½ feet at the withers.

A fully grown male trotting along, carrying a full spread of antlers and with his white mane flying at the throat makes a remarkably impressive sight. A large number of tines are developed, particularly by the males—67 have been counted on one animal. The reindeer is the only species of deer in which both sexes carry antlers. The antlers of the male are always more magnificently developed than those of the female. Antler production is less in the females owing to the demands made on them in rearing young.

Reindeer feed on grasses, herbs, fungi, mosses and lichens, and also on the buds, leaves, shoots and fruits of berry-bearing bushes and as well as the buds and shoots of other trees and shrubs. The cushions of the lichen known as reindeer moss form the most important item in the winter diet. The animals scrape this out of the snow down to depths of three feet. The reindeer does not despise accessory foods such as lemmings, voles, young birds, eggs, fish, and so on. When driven by the need for protein they even hunt lemmings, killing them by treading on them and then eating them.

Reindeer live in groups or herds of up to several thousand head; the woodland form tends to live in smaller groups whereas the tundra form lives in large herds. Within the herds there are smaller groups, each one made up of a number of families. The females usually have only one calf at heel, sometimes two or in rare cases even three or four. Groups are always led by old females. The males spend the summer in parties, living apart from the females and at the beginning of the rutting season—principally in September—they join up with the females and remain with them over the winter.

The seasonal migrations of reindeer are an unforgettable sight. They use the old migration routes year after year. Thousands and thousands gather together along these ancient routes and sometimes a forest of antlers can be seen on the move, taking a whole day for the animals to pass by. In recent decades unfortunately, various areas which were once rich in wild reindeer have been laid waste through the folly of man. On the other hand, research and protective measures in a few areas have led to a welcome increase of other populations.

RHINOCEROS see Great Indian Rhinoceros; Javan Rhinoceros; White Rhinoceros

Rocky Mountain Goat

Oreamnos americanus pp. 84, 85

Within the artiodactyl group the subfamily Caprinae contains various groups of species which all have the ability to climb. These are first, the goral and serow, secondly, chamois and Rocky Mountain goat, and thirdly, wild goat, ibex, markhor, tahr, blue sheep or bharal and wild sheep.

The Rocky Mountain goat is the New World representative of the chamois, and it existed with the latter, together with the goral and serow, in Asia in the Pliocene at the end of the Tertiary period. Today the goral is still to be found from western Himalaya through eastern Tibet, Assam, Burma and China to Korea, Manchuria and the Amur; the serow occurs from western Himalaya eastwards to Assam, Burma, east China, Formosa and Japan and through south-east Asia to Malaya and Sumatra. The chamois, on the other hand, is more European (Pyrenees, Alps, Abruzzi, High Tatras, Carpathians, Caucasus and the mountains in the Balkans) and only enters Asia through its occurrence in Turkey. In North America the Rocky Mountain goat is found on the western mountain ranges from south Alaska to the north of the United States. There are four subspecies within this area.

Both sexes carry black, sharply pointed, sabre-like horns; these are 9–11 inches long, circular in cross section and curve slightly to the rear. Similar to the scent glands of the chamois, the Rocky Mountain goat also has a sunken marking gland behind the horns which is more developed in the male than in the female. The habitat of the Rocky Mountain goat lies in the rugged terrain of high mountains, mainly above the tree-limit, where there are steep rocky cliffs and ravines. In winter, however, it also occurs in lower lying areas, and in the coastal mountains or on islands it comes right down to sea level in certain places. It is obvious that only an animal with exceptional climbing ability could survive in such terrain. Every day the Rocky Mountain goat performs remarkable feats of rock climbing. This has always made it a difficult animal to hunt and has helped to preserve its population up to the present time. Nowadays its hunting is strictly controlled and it can only be killed in limited numbers.

The Rocky Mountain goat is gregarious and grazes in small parties to larger family groups, the older males keeping apart. The mating season is in November and the males remain with the females for some time afterwards. There is undoubtedly a seasonal partnership and it is possible that there is a more lasting union, but this has not yet been investigated in detail. One to two kids are born in April to June (according to the latitude) after a gestation period of about six months. The female looks after them for a long time and often only becomes pregnant again in alternate years. The young are sexually mature at 2½ years old and only then become completely independent.

Royal Albatross

Diomedea epomophora p. 150

The name albatross is a corruption—by English sailors—of the Portuguese 'alcatraz'. Seamen were indeed the first to meet these birds and they were naturally of interest to men who were bored by the endless sight of nothing else but the sea. Nevertheless the sailors were not impressed by the mental equipment of a bird which could apparently spend the whole day happily wandering about the ocean and doing little else.

Albatrosses cover thousands of miles in a year, travelling in all weathers and only coming to land to breed. They are not related to the gulls or gannets, as one might think, but to the shearwaters and petrels.

Albatrosses lay a single egg which is incubated for a period of 2–3 months, both parents sharing in the duties of incubation. Remote islands provide breeding sites and they are often covered with damp cloud or lashed by storms. Endurance and stamina are essential together with an unerring sense of direction. Navigation over the seven seas seems no easy matter by human standards of intelligence and yet albatrosses appear never to lose the sense of where they are.

The 13 species are difficult to distinguish. For sailors the division into 'black' and 'white' is sufficient. The largest species, the wandering albatross, has a wing span of 11½ feet or more. The royal albatross is one of the particularly large species. It breeds on islands off New Zealand and from there wanders over the oceans. The individual nests are often spread over a wide area. Each nest is constructed out of vegetable matter; it is built up into a mound and then hollowed out from inside for as far as the bird can reach. As soon as spring comes in the south, the 'oceanauts' appear at the nesting places. They breed only at two-yearly intervals and arrive at the breeding grounds at approximately the right time, spending weeks on courtship and nest-building. Courtship display includes the partners standing facing each other, raising their bills ecstatically to the heavens, spreading the wings to their full extent and sometimes uttering guttural sounds.

The fledgling is supplied with food for 9 to 10 months on a diet similar to that of the parents, namely fish and squid. It then sets off on its own adventurous journey across the oceans.

Albatrosses which nest in dense colonies have sometimes suffered heavily from the depredations of man. Thus the north Pacific short-tailed albatross was reduced to a few individuals by collectors, the feathers being used commercially. It appears that, thanks to rigorous protection by the Japanese Government, this remnant population may develop to a viable level on an island in the Sea of Japan. Other colonies have been decimated by removal of the eggs for making dried eggs or by the slaughter of adults and young.

In the post-war period war broke out on Midway Island between the American Air Force and the Laysan albatrosses nesting there. For a long time frequent collisions of the giant birds with aeroplanes—whose base lay in the region of the colony—were accepted as inevitable. With the arrival of jet planes, however, the collisions endangered the safety of the machines and consequently war was waged on the birds. Thirty thousand were killed in the region of the airfield but even with the slaughter of this number the problem was not solved. One third of the world population of the Laysan albatross breeds on the island. Are we faced with slaughtering the entire population on Midway Island? Or will other methods to reduce the incidence of collisions be found?

Sable Antelope

Hippotragus niger p. 235

Among the more imposing antelopes of Africa are two species which are the size of a horse: the sable antelope and the roan antelope. These species are distributed south of the Sahara in the upland regions, except in dense rain-forest and in the areas of true desert.

The sable antelope is so named from the black colour of the upperparts of the adult males; these form a striking contrast to the white underparts and facial markings. The bright reddish-brown outer sides of the ears form a special adornment and there is also an erect mane of medium length at the nape and withers. The tail is long with a tuft at the tip. The stout, closely ringed horns, which are curved backwards, may reach a length of 52 inches; they are dark and powerful looking, adding to the impression of strength given by a sable antelope bull which is at least 4½ feet tall at the shoulders.

The female is approximately 4 feet at the shoulders and weighs about 400 lb. as against 500 lb. in the male. The females are reddish-brown in colour and their horns are paler than those of the male and about half as long.

The largest of the sable antelopes are those of central Angola, which are known as giant sable antelopes. In addition to this isolated western subspecies, an eastern and a south African form are also recognised. The most southerly subspecies was the blue antelope which is now extinct.

In contrast to the sable antelope the roan is coloured the same in both sexes, the tone varying in the seven subspecies from ochre-red through red-brown and yellow-brown to pale brown and grey-blue. The upperparts and underparts are not sharply contrasted, the colour of the flanks shading gradually into the greyish-white of the underparts. The roan antelope also has an erect mane and a tufted tail but its horns only reach a length of about 38 inches and are not so markedly curved as those of the sable antelope. In addition it is slightly larger and heavier than the sable antelope: it reaches 4¾ feet at the shoulders and weighs 500–600 lb.

The sable and roan antelopes live in small herds of 3 to 15 animals. Sometimes there may be two dozen or more, and at the end of the dry season and at the beginning of the rainy season they form into larger herds of up to fifty animals. Usually an old male goes about with several females and their young; young males may be seen in groups and there are also pairs of solitary animals.

Not infrequently sable and roan antelopes associate with oryx, gnus and other antelopes, zebras and ostriches. The sable antelope keeps its head higher and more erect than the roan antelope when it is on the move. The herds usually keep to one area and only wander farther afield during the dry season. At such times and also during flight, the lead is usually taken by an old female; during flight the tail is flicked violently from side to side.

They feed on grasses and herbs as well as on the leaves of trees and shrubs. One meets these animals in open country as well as in scattered scrub to dense bush savannah; they are also found in open forests and in woodland clearings but not in dense forests. They live principally in flat or hilly country and scarcely ever occur in really mountainous country.

Reproduction is not tied to any particular season. After a gestation period of nine months the female gives birth to a single calf. Unless it falls prey to a lion or a pack of Cape hunting dogs, it may well live to an age of 15 years.

The roan and sable antelopes, both of them impressive animals, are unfortunately being displaced from many areas owing to widespread cultivation of the land although, taken as a whole, the population is still in no way threatened. The giant sable antelope, on the other hand, is strictly protected. It is confined to an area between the rivers Luando, Cuanza, Dunda and Luasso. Its numbers have never been large and the present population of 500–700 is not considered to be in danger. Unfortunately there are no specimens in zoos from which one could establish a breeding stock should this become necessary in the interests of conservation.

Sandwich Tern

Sterna sandvicensis p. 33

If gulls are regarded as the white crows of the sea—the companions of ships and the scavengers on the shore which sit on the harbour moles waiting for the refuse—then terns are the gracious swallows of the sea. As soon as a tern takes to the air, one cannot fail to be impressed by the elegance of the long slender wings. On the ground, however, they look clumsy and awkward as they stump around on their short legs.

The comparison with swallows is, of course, scientifically incorrect. In bird classification the terns are placed alongside the gulls. They have nothing to do with swallows. When seen in the distance the lightness of the tern's flight and the forked tail reminds one of swallows. Their method of flight, however, differs from that of swallows in that their wing-beats are deeper and somewhat slower. All the terns have a rather long, pointed bill which is red, yellow or black.

The Sandwich tern is one of 39 species of tern. It breeds on the shores of the North Sea, on both coasts of the Atlantic and in the Black and Caspian Seas, but the colonies are always widely spaced and localised. Flat coasts with clear water are a favoured habitat. Often a whole flock of terns are seen fishing together, plunging down and disappearing under the water; when they re-emerge they usually have a small fish in the bill. This method of catching prey is used symbolically as part of the courtship behaviour of most terns: it is known as the 'fish flight'. During courtship the male flies up with a fish in its bill, then flies after a female and finally presents it to her; sometimes, however, the male flies on with it himself.

Like other terns the Sandwich tern breeds in colonies. The colonies are sometimes as crowded as a small human town. There are breeding colonies in which up to 30,000 pairs nest but the majority of them are much smaller.

In a large breeding colony the individual birds live in very close proximity to each other, crowding together in huge numbers. The spacing between nests is determined by the pecking distance of the long bills. Even in a colony with thousands of nests, each pair knows the precise location of its own site and finds it unerringly. It has been found that the most coveted nest-sites in a ternery are those in the central part of the breeding ground. These nests belong to the oldest inhabitants, to those terns which have reached the imposing age of ten or even twenty years. The younger birds, particularly those breeding for the first time, have to be content with the more dangerous zones on the periphery. As each year goes by they move gradually towards the centre of the breeding ground. Birds which have once bred in a colony usually remain faithful to it and return each year to breed there throughout their lives.

Colonial nesters are stimulated by the close proximity of so many individuals and a rhythm is established in the colony during the breeding season by which individuals reach the same stage of development at approximately the same time. In spring the colony settles in quite quickly; this is followed by courtship, copulation, egg-laying and the rearing of the young. The chicks leave the nest after a few days and begin to move cautiously through the narrow alleys in the colony. At 15–20 days, they move slowly out into the shallows where the parents are fishing in calm waters. At the height of summer, as soon as the young are capable of flight, the colony of terns disperses; they wander along the coasts and gradually set out for their winter quarters. These are often a long way from the breeding areas. The winter quarters of the Sandwich tern lie in the tropical waters of the Atlantic.

SEA LIONS see Eared Seals

SEALS see Eared Seals; Elephant Seal; Walrus; Weddell Seal

Shag

Phalacrocorax aristotelis p. 51

The common cormorant is much better known than the shag or green cormorant as it is sometimes called. Both species are predominantly dark, fish-eating aquatic birds which fly and dive remarkably well and have large webbed feet. All four toes are connected by webs as in the pelicans and gannets. In general the layman does not know much about this group of birds, of which a South American species, the guanay cormorant, has even achieved considerable economic importance as one of the principal sources of the valuable fertiliser guano.

In Europe all cormorants are disliked by fishermen, who object to every kind of fish-eating animal. The cormorants are in fact remarkably adept at fishing. They hunt their food by diving, pursuing it underwater by backward strokes of the legs instead of using the wings for propulsion. In China and Japan the cormorant's fishing ability has been utilised for centuries and fish are caught with the assistance of tame cormorants. The birds are fitted with a leather collar to prevent them swallowing the fish they catch.

The shag is slightly smaller than the common cormorant and has a crest during the breeding season. It breeds along most of the coasts of north-west Europe, north to Iceland and Norway, and south to France and Spain. In the north it is frequently to be found among the large colonies of sea birds which nest on coastal cliffs. Outside the breeding season, the majority of shags do not move very far away from the breeding grounds but remain on the outskirts of their home range. They much prefer water with swell and spray to quiet bays.

The common cormorant has much the same geographical distribution in Europe as the shag, but the former selects flat or comparatively gentle slopes of rock as breeding sites by the sea, and inland it nearly always breeds in trees like the heron. By contrast the shag favours steep coastal cliffs and like all the cormorants it is normally a colonial nester. The nests are placed in sheltered places on steep cliffs, under overhangs or in open caves by the sea. They are often in places that are almost inaccessible to humans.

In contrast to the ducks which rest on the water after feeding the cormorants always leave the water to rest; they stand on rocks or posts in the water, adopting the characteristic pose of armorial birds with wings spread. Their large wings easily become wet if they remain in the water and they dry themselves in this way, holding their wings out in the same way as one stands an umbrella open to dry.

SHEEP see Wild Sheep

Shoebill

Balaeniceps rex p. 225

The most striking feature of this bird is its monstrous bill and a correspondingly large head. The wide bill is adapted to its feeding habits. It fishes food out of the water, notably plump lungfish, with its bill and thus exploits a food source which is abundant in places where the shoebill lives.

Looking rather like a crane, the 'whale-headed stork', as it is sometimes called, stands motionless in the remote swamp, often on floating vegetation, and waits until a fat catfish or lungfish swims near its feet. If nothing comes within reach after a period of waiting, it merely wanders along to the next 'island' and occasionally snaps up a fish in passing.

The shoebill is probably rather a boring bird, but it has a certain cachet for ornithologists: it has an aura of rarity which surrounds any bird that is inaccessible and about which little is known. Anyone who attempts to see it in the wild feels rather like an explorer setting out for unknown regions. Time apparently means nothing to the shoebill and this bird would make an appropriate emblem for the angler to whom time is also of no consequence.

Bengt Berg has written a book about *abu markub* as this bird is called in Arabic. Well known as a pioneer in modern animal photography, his book *Abu Markub* has 200 pages, but only fifty of them actually deal with the title figure; most of the text is taken up with describing the difficulties of obtaining a good photograph. This is no reflection on Bengt Berg and anyone trying to write a book about this species today would suffer from similar disadvantages.

Very little is known about the shoebill apart from its external appearance and certain details regarding its anatomy, distribution, diet, and its usual method of moving about. Only a few people have seen a shoebill's nest. We are not sure if it normally nests in trees, like most other storks, or on the ground in swamps.

Nowadays it is possible to see the shoebill as a rarity in some of the world's large zoos. What one sees of its behaviour in a zoo is not so very different from the details noticed about it by the few people who have succeeded in observing it in its natural environment. It appears to be lethargic by nature and just stands there, sometimes moving around a little with measured steps. In a zoo, of course, it cannot fly. In its natural habitat in the swamps the shoebill only flies once in a while when it moves to a locality some distance away; otherwise, it prefers to hop, beating its wings briefly, from one small islet to another, often only travelling a distance of yards.

The shoebill lives in the papyrus swamps of the Province of Bahr el Ghazal and along the White Nile, where floating islands drift on the shores and along the numerous canals and tributaries. So long as the 'sudd' region of the Sudan is left untouched by the advance of civilisation, the shoebill is safe and will be able to continue surviving in an undisturbed habitat of extensive swamps. Large animals require plenty of space. In cultivated country, even if a fine nature reserve were set aside for the shoebill, it is doubtful whether it would survive.

Sirenians

Sirenia p. 101

The Sirenians form their own order within the mammals. They are spindle-shaped, completely aquatic animals about 9–15 feet long and 600–800 lb. in weight, which many zoologists think evolved from a common ancestry with the elephants.

The skin of the sirenians is almost completely naked and it has a thick layer of fat. The fore limbs are developed into rounded flippers, which are quite long and movable at the elbow joint, enabling them to support their body off the ground. The hind limbs are absent and the pelvis is reduced to a few bones hidden in the musculature. They have a well-developed horizontal tail fluke. The eyes and ears are small. There are bristles round the mouth and horny papillae on the tongue. The front part of the muzzle curves downwards and has rough, horny plates, while farther back there are a number of cheek teeth in each half of the jaw. In manatees these teeth are replaced from behind as the front ones are worn down. The dugong has a pair of short, powerful, tusk-like incisors in the upper jaw which are only seen in the males.

Sailors of earlier times, who saw these animals with their rounded heads and arm-like flippers, returned with strange stories of encounters with mermaids. Standing with their bodies raised in a vertical position, revealing two nipples in the region of the breast, it is not altogether surprising that the sailors thought they had seen the legendary sea-nymphs or sirens. The scientific name for the order—Sirenia—is also based on this implausible story.

The sirenians are harmless underwater browsers which feed on seaweeds and aquatic plants in rivers, lakes, estuaries and on sea coasts. Their body is too plump and heavy for them to be able to leave the water completely and come out on land. Nevertheless they can get as far as shallow water where their head, neck and the front region of their back can be seen sticking up out of the water.

The present-day species occur only in warm waters and live in small to large groups. There is no fixed breeding season. Young can be found throughout the whole year. In spite of their inertia, the bulls show a certain amount of tenderness towards the cows during courtship and the mothers take great care of their young. They give birth to only one young after a gestation period of about 12 months; the youngster grows fast and is sexually mature at three years.

The sirenians are recognisable as a group in the Tertiary period and they evolved into five families and sixteen genera. Today they are still represented by two families with two genera and three species. In one family the tail is rounded, in the other forked. Those with rounded tails have 7–8 neck vertebrae, a strongly down-curved forehead and a rounded spatulate tail; those with forked tails have six neck vertebrae, a moderately defined bridge between the nose and the forehead, and a concave tail split into two lobes.

The latter are represented by a single species, the dugong, which occurs in the Red Sea, Indian Ocean and west Pacific from Mozambique and Madagascar to Formosa and the Philippines; it also occurs in New Caledonia and from there southwards to New Guinea and eastern and western Australia. The sirenians with rounded tails are the manatees, of which there is an American and an African species. The American species has two subspecies, of which one type lives in the Caribbean Sea, on the north-east coast of South America down to northern Brazil, in the Orinoco and neighbouring rivers flowing into the Caribbean; it is also found in the gulf of Mexico, around Florida and along the east coast of North America to North Carolina. The other subspecies lives in the Amazon region and was formerly also found on the Brazilian coast southwards to 20°S. The African manatee occurs in the rivers and along the coasts of west Africa between 16°N and 10°S.

The flesh of the sirenians is eaten by the natives and the blubber is made into oil. These harmless animals have been severely hunted and with their low rate of reproduction, they have not been able to maintain their numbers. They have already been exterminated in many places. Unless they can be given effective protection, they will suffer the same fate as Steller's sea-cow. This was a coarse-skinned sirenian, 24 feet long, which occurred in the Bering Sea and on the coast of Kamchatka. It was discovered by the German naturalist Georg Steller in 1741 but by 1854 it had been completely exterminated.

Snowy Owl

Nyctea scandiaca p. 56

The Arctic has its own fauna just as it has its own meteorological rhythm, changing from a period of perpetual light to one of continuous darkness. The snowy owl is a typical member of the arctic fauna, in its appearance as well as in the adaptations of its body and its habits. The snowy owl is comparable in size to the eagle owls and replaces them in the arctic regions.

In the continuous light of the northern summer, the snowy owl abandons the customary habits of those owls which are most active at twilight; it still reaches a peak of activity when the sun is at its lowest but it is not entirely inactive around the middle of the day. Periods of rest and activity are not so sharply demarcated in arctic animals as in those of more southerly latitudes, at least during the breeding season.

The snowy owl's life is dominated by lemmings, the mice of the arctic. The owls are only able to breed in 'good' lemming years, in places where these rodents have just bred in huge numbers. When the density of lemmings is low or even when it is of medium strength, the population is not sufficient to feed a family of owls; the parent birds hunt over a territory where competition for food may be considerable, particularly from skuas, falcons, rough-legged hawks, arctic foxes and mink.

When one considers the food requirements of these owls, the situation becomes clear. Russian observers undertook detailed studies and as a result they estimated that a family of snowy owls in eastern Siberia needed some 1500 large lemmings (each about 5 oz. in weight) during the nesting season. According to comparable investigations, American snowy owls even have a somewhat higher standard of living. They take 1900–2000 lemmings per family per season. In times of an upsurge in the numbers of lemmings the local snowy owl population may reach a density of one pair per one-third square mile, which is very high for a bird of this size. The reproductive rate is then similarly high and a clutch may contain up to 9 eggs.

We are still not very well informed about the movements of snowy owls in the Arctic outside the breeding season. We know that the owls are completely dependent upon the presence of their main prey, also that in some years when there is a food shortage, incubation appears to stop completely. We do not know to what extent a pair of breeding birds can extend their hunting territory or even change the site of the nest. In the winter when food is scarce the snowy owls wander far to the south into areas where they never breed. In spite of this they are not true migratory birds which regularly visit definite winter quarters. Their wanderings are linked directly to food.

In some regions the snowy owls appear to adjust their population rhythm to that of the lemmings, which reach their lowest point about every fourth year. The result is a marked mass emigration of snowy owls from the Arctic. In central Europe they occur fairly regularly along the southern coastal strip of the Baltic Sea during their winter wanderings. They also turn up irregularly in Scotland and vagrants occur from time to time farther south in Europe.

South American Camels

Lama vicugna, Lama guanicoe pp. 108, 109

Among the ungulates there is a group known to zoologists as the tylopods, which includes the camels. The tylopods arose a good sixty million years ago in North America from small animals about the size of a hare. This region remained their headquarters and no fewer than 25 of the total of 30 tylopod genera evolved there. In the early days of the tylopods, three genera once reached Europe but by the Oligocene period these had died out. It was not until towards the end of the Tertiary that the camels left their North American seclusion and wandered not only to Asia but also into South America. As it transpired this proved to be providential for the tylopods because these were the only areas in which they survived—as the Bactrian camel and the dromedary in the Old World and as the guanaco and vicuna in South America. They died out in their original home in North America at the end of the Ice Age.

The Old World camels are large animals, over six feet tall with one or two humps, whereas their South American relatives have a straight back and reach a shoulder height of 50 inches at the most. Of the South American species the guanaco is the larger, with a shoulder height of 35–50 inches and a weight of 120–150 lb.; the vicuna is more delicately built, with a shoulder height of 27–36 inches and a weight of only about 100 lb. Its head is more refined in appearance with a shorter nose, but in proportion to the head the eyes are larger and the ears longer. In addition the vicuna has a special adornment in the form of a white mane; the hairs at the base of the neck and upper part of the breast are 8–10 inches long. Both species have light or dark reddish-brown upperparts. In the guanaco the whitish underparts contrast sharply with the upperparts whereas in the vicuna the transition is gradual.

These animals live on grassy plains, rocky hillsides and comparatively barren land in the mountains. The guanaco occurs from the lowlands to the uplands at altitudes of up to 12,000 feet; the vicuna can be found between 10,000 and 18,000 feet. Both species feed on grasses, herbs and mosses. They will lick calcareous and salty rocks and drink salt and brackish water in addition to fresh water. These animals are mainly active by day, moving about gregariously in small family groups which contain up to two dozen individuals; in good grazing areas the guanaco may also collect into large herds. The groups of females and young are led by a male and are largely faithful to one area. They also habitually use the same place for excretion and large mounds of dung are formed in the course of time.

The guanaco mates in the southern summer, has a gestation period of 10–11 months and the young are born about November. In the vicuna mating takes place from April to June, the gestation period is 10 months and the young are born between January and March. As a rule there is only one young, but the guanaco occasionally produces two. After the birth, which takes place lying down, the calf is not licked dry; it is suckled for almost four months but also starts to feed itself at one week. Vicunas are sexually mature at one year, guanacos not before the second or third year. They live for 15–30 years.

The guanaco was formerly distributed from northern Peru to Tierra del Fuego and La Plata. On the coasts it is not averse to swimming across sea inlets; like the Old World camels, they can swim exceedingly well when the need arises. They are also amblers like the large camels. Unfortunately the guanaco has been exterminated from the eastern foothills of the Andes to the Parana and the Atlantic coast between La Plata and Bahia Blanca. The vicuna which once lived in the Andes from south Ecuador to central Chile and into the neighbouring parts of western Bolivia has already been exterminated locally, especially in the southern part of its range in Chile. There now appears to be a change of heart and extensive hunting is being replaced by strict measures for their protection.

Spectacled Bear

Tremarctos ornatus p. 110

The bears are a family of carnivores with relatively few living species. In addition to the brown and black bears there are also the Himalayan black bear, the Japanese bear, the Malay and the Spectacled. The brown bear has the widest distribution; it extends throughout the temperate zone of the northern hemisphere. The brown bear is also the only species which occurs in both the Old and the New Worlds. The Himalayan black, the Japanese and the Malay bears on the other hand are purely Asiatic and the black and spectacled bears purely American.

Nowadays the distribution of the spectacled bear is restricted to the slopes of the Andes in South America from Venezuela and northern Colombia to south Peru and north Bolivia. It is more numerous on the gentle slopes on the eastern side of the mountain range than on the steeper western slopes, where it is only known for certain to occur from northern Ecuador to central Peru. Individual animals have also been seen in the northern part of the Merida Cordilleras of Venezuela and the frontier area between Colombia and Panama. It has never been recorded as numerous in any part of its range and usually occurs solitarily. It is therefore very rare to meet a spectacled bear in the wild. The photograph in this book is most probably the first ever to be taken and published of a wild spectacled bear.

The habitat of the spectacled bear is the slopes of the Andes which are densely covered with forest or bushes between about 4500 and 6000 feet. Sometimes the bear also goes down to the lowlands at the foot of the mountains. It rarely goes higher than 9000 feet or crosses the ridge, thus the bears on the west slopes lead a virtually separate existence from those on the east slopes. The spectacled bear is the most vegetarian member of the bear family and even in captivity it scarcely takes any meat. The densely covered mountain slopes of its home range offer it a sufficient supply of tasty leaves, buds, shoots, fruits, roots, bulbs, herbs and so on.

In the southern summer, mainly in December, the sexes come together to mate. After at least eight months' gestation the female produces one to three cubs, usually two, which at birth only weigh about half a pound. Their eyes are open at five weeks and at nine months they are almost as large as their mothers. At the latest they become sexually mature in the third year of life, the young females usually in the second year. The males are about a third heavier than the females and reach a shoulder height of about 30 inches and a body length of 52 inches. The weights of adult specimens are not yet known because spectacled bears are rarely obtained by zoos and very little detail has been recorded of their life in the wild. We only know that they climb a lot and are skilful at reaching the fruits of trees, also that they build sleeping nests in the trees.

This bear is usually uniformly black except for a yellow or whitish facial pattern which runs from the snout and around the eyes to give it the appearance of wearing spectacles.

Spoonbill

Platalea leucorodia p. 34

The distinctive feature of this pure white bird is its long pincer-like bill which is broadened at the tip, although strictly speaking the bill is not the shape of a spoon, nor does the bird use it as such.

The spoonbill is distinctly photogenic with its peculiar bill, long legs and snow-white plumage, which has a pendant crest at the back of the crown in summer. Every photographer falls for its charming appearance but the ciné-photographer has the additional challenge of trying to capture its movements, which are extremely attractive on film. Courtship displays in a breeding colony of spoonbills make delightful studies for the photographer: the birds expand their crests and indulge in mutual preening, caressing the neck-feathers of their partners with the long spatulate bills. The slow, heron-like flight, in which the neck is extended but held in a slight curve, is also an impressive sight.

The spoonbill's method of feeding is unique in the world of birds. They wade in shallow water, often a number of them side by side, and walk slowly but steadily forwards, holding the bill almost vertical in the water but sweeping it from side to side and describing a quarter circle. The action is reminiscent of mowing with a scythe. Small animals such as crustaceans, worms, water insects and others, are trapped in this manner and probably swept into the throat by the powerful lateral swinging motion of the bill.

In prehistoric times, when large untouched areas of water occurred in many parts of Europe, the spoonbill probably bred in many places on the continent. Today it is only to be found regularly at very few places, and then only because the breeding colonies are carefully protected. It still occurs in two or three localities in the Netherlands, on Neusiedler Lake in Austria, in Hungary and in south Spain. The spoonbill requires extensive areas of swamp with open, shallow water rich in food, in which it can wade; the breeding grounds are in less open terrain with dense masses of vegetation which provide the necessary shelter for the colonies, in which many nests are sited close together. In some places the nests are built in bushes or in low trees, in others on the ground among reeds. Ornithologists classify the spoonbill in the same order as the storks and herons, from which it only differs significantly in the peculiarly shaped bill and the habits for which this is adapted.

Few people can fail to be deeply impressed by this striking bird when they see it in the wild. As each year goes by the shape of our world becomes increasingly moulded by the requirements of civilisation and we can only conserve such birds as the spoonbill by setting aside individual places which satisfy their requirements. The problem with the spoonbill is that it needs an extensive habitat and it is no longer easy to establish large-scale reserves.

STORKS see Black Stork; Wood Ibis

SWAN see Trumpeter Swan

Takahe

Notornis mantelli p. 145

Among the close relatives of the powerful, heavily built takahe is the purple gallinule. The latter is widely distributed in the warmer zones of the world and is a very successful species. It still occurs in Europe and although rare as a breeding species, it breeds in southern Spain.

The takahe, on the other hand, shows signs that it is a declining species and may well be on the brink of natural extinction. Its rate of reproduction is extremely low. A female lays a maximum of four eggs per year, of which a high percentage is infertile. It has lost the ability to fly and is thus vulnerable to enemies on the ground. Finally, for reasons that are not fully understood, its range has been considerably reduced in recent times. It is now confined to a small area of inaccessible valleys in the Murchison Mountains on South Island of New Zealand.

The story of man's contact with this animal is a remarkable one and has its dramatic moments. The first specimen recorded in the annals of natural history was caught alive by a seal-hunter's dog on Resolution Island in 1849. It came into the hands of Dr Gideon Mantell who first reported on it. The skin landed up in the British Museum in London. Up to 1898 a further three specimens were caught in the same way. This was all that was known of the bird. Since then, the takahe was assumed to be extinct right up until 1948.

In April 1948 Dr G. B. Orbell of Invercargill observed footprints in a valley in the lake district of what is now the Fjordland National Park, which he ascribed to the takahe. However, he was not absolutely certain of their identity and the bird was not seen on this expedition. After the end of the southern winter in November 1948, Orbell re-visited the area and this time a few birds were seen; he caught two in a net and released them again after thorough investigation. The report in 1949 from this New Zealand naturalist that the takahe had been re-discovered after 50 years, caused a sensation among ornithologists all over the world. The fact that the re-discovery of this bird was the result, not of a chance encounter but the outcome of a planned search, made it all the more remarkable.

Fortunately access to the area in which the takahe lives is very difficult. The enemies of the takahe appear to be two mammals only, both of which were formerly introduced to the islands; the weasel and the red deer. In many of the remote forest areas of New Zealand the red deer has become a pest which is almost impossible to control. The deer trample the grazing areas and destroy clumps of snowgrass, which is the main food plant of the takahe.

In spite of its low rate of reproduction, the population of takahes appear to be increasing or at least maintaining itself.

The latest estimate in 1963 suggested a maximum of 300 specimens.

The breeding sites of the takahe lie in a flat valley bottom, with vegetation of lush grass and low shrubs, in the vicinity of water. From here the takahes move out through open forests into the higher zones. They feed almost exclusively on the soft bases of the leaves of snowgrass which covers the whole area, forming tall, dense clumps.

TAPIR see Malayan Tapir

Tarpan and other wild horses

Equus przewalskii gmelini and others p. 46

After the Ice Age, wild horses occurred throughout almost the whole of Eurasia. They were distributed from the Iberian Peninsula to Mongolia and from the Balkans to Scotland and Scandinavia; they also lived on the wide grassy plains of northern Africa which had not yet become desert.

The ancestors of these wild horses had survived the Ice Age in various pockets which the ice failed to reach in parts of south Europe and northern Africa, and in Britain, Scandinavia and Siberia. Nowadays, zoologists regard Przewalski's horse of Mongolia as the most primitive form of horse still surviving. The terrain in these different parts of the world naturally varied and the form, habits and behaviour of the various breeds evolved in different ways in the different habitats. At least four different types of wild horse are found in postglacial remains. These forms are distinguishable on the basis of the structure of the skull, skeleton and teeth.

A hardy type of pony, standing about 49 inches at the withers, surviving on rough moorland grass, still occurs on Exmoor. Although the original stock has been crossbred from time to time, there is still a recognised breed of Exmoor pony. Another breed in Britain is the Dartmoor pony which stands about 42 inches at the withers; this breed is also thought to be descended from ancient stock. There are several other breeds in Britain which may originally have been indigenous and which still live wild; these have also been crossed with various other strains, including Norwegian and Arab stocks. A long-legged ram-headed type of about 57 inches or more at the withers survived as good as pure in the Iberian peninsula. A small, clean-limbed horse of about 43 inches at the withers with a small head persisted in north Africa until this area became desert and is still represented fairly purely in uncontaminated Arab horses. It is not possible here to go into the question of how these types became the ancestors of our domestic horses nor to give the history of the many experiments in hybridisation which have taken place over the years.

Another group of horses, mouse-grey in colour and standing about 53 inches at the withers, survived in eastern Europe and in south Russia. These were known in Russia as tarpans. The last wild tarpan died in 1876, but many of its characteristics have been preserved in certain of the races of horses in eastern Europe. The last of the tarpan stock was certainly no longer completely pure-blooded. As the mares became scarce, the stallions took free-grazing domestic mares, just as happened with the Przewalski stallions in Mongolia. Of the original tarpan there only remains a skull, a picture and a good description.

In order to re-constitute the appearance of the tarpan for exhibition purposes and to be able to show it alongside the Przewalski's horse, the Director of the Munich Zoo, Dr Heinz Heck, crossed the mares of Iceland and Gotland ponies with a Przewalski stallion and then crossed the resulting hybrids. After only a few generations mouse-grey tarpan-like horses appeared, in spite of the fact that none of the parent animals had been mouse-grey. Similar experiments were carried out in Poland. Only there they crossed local stock but got the same result. Thus in zoos and in large reserves, such as Bialowieza National Park, once again we are able to enjoy the sight of 'tarpans' in action. Where the countryside is sufficiently wild, these 'tarpans' behave again like the shy wild animals of the past.

TERNS see Sandwich Tern

TORTOISE see Giant Tortoise

Tree Kangaroos

Dendrolagus ursinus etc. p. 157

There are about 50 species of leaping marsupials, varying in size from a rat to a man. The majority live in comparatively open country, relying on their speed and agility as leapers for moving about the plains or rocky terrain. A few species, however, feed and sleep in trees, and provide the paradox of a climbing kangaroo.

In limited areas of North Queensland and in vast areas of New Guinea which are covered with tropical rain-forest, there is extensive habitat suitable for tree kangaroos which are skilled climbers. With a body length of about 18–30 inches from head to rump and a tail 15–34 inches long, the hind limbs are only moderately lengthened in comparison with the fore limbs. On the other hand the claws on the toes are curved and sharp, the hind toes (very large in ordinary kangaroos) are rather short; the hind foot is broad and provided with a rough, cushion-like gripping sole. The tail acts as a balancing organ. When moving fast on the ground a tree kangaroo holds its tail up in the air, unlike the terrestrial species which use the tail as a lever to assist the start of their jumps.

The fur which is very thick, of medium length and sometimes rather tufted in appearance, gives good protection against the heavy rainfall of the tropical forests. In its most characteristic pose, the head and neck are held lower than the shoulders and the middle of the back. In the region of the nape one lot of fur lies backwards and the other forwards, so that the rain water runs off freely. The species are dark brownish-black to pale golden red. One of the best known species, the black tree kangaroo, *Dendrolagus ursinus*, has a black or dark brown back with white or greyish-white underparts.

Tree kangaroos move briskly about the branches of trees where they feed on leaves, buds and fruits. They not only jump with yard-long leaps from branch to branch and from one tree-top to the next, but also climb up thick branches and trunks by gripping and embracing them with the arms, while supporting themselves with the hind-legs. The tail is also used for support and balance, but cannot be used for holding on as in the South American monkeys. Tree kangaroos can safely jump down to the ground from heights of 30 to 40 feet when they want to feed on grass and herbs. In general they live socially in groups. There is usually only one male to several females, for the males are very quarrelsome. They climb into a forked branch or squat on a broad branch when they go to rest.

The gestation period is about a month and the young, which is tiny at birth, remains in the pouch for months, until its fur is fully grown, its eyes open and its limbs are sufficiently well developed to make its first attempts at climbing.

At the present time there is no danger that the vast rain-forest areas of Queensland and New Guinea will be seriously reduced. The tree kangaroos have practically no enemies, apart from the natives who kill them for food, and so they should be able to continue their peaceful existence in the rain-forests for a long time yet.

Trumpeter Swan

Cygnus buccinator p. 95

The fate of the north American trumpeter swan is tragically involved with the settlement and development of an almost untouched continent.

When the white settlers began to explore the new land and reached the Mississippi, they saw huge flocks of aquatic birds in the autumn. Today such a wealth of birds would be regarded as well-nigh unbelievable. Among them were flocks of strikingly handsome swans which flew in from the north and dropped down on to the lakes. A few chroniclers, impressed by this, recorded something of their experiences and from their reports ornithologists of a later date have been able to extract some information. The swan was soon named trumpeter after its loud, melodious, horn-like call, to distinguish it from the similar but somewhat smaller whistling swan, which has a higher note.

At that time the trumpeter swan was a widely distributed and common species on the north American continent. Its nesting places lay in Canada and extended southwards into the United States. In the winter the migratory flocks shunned the cold and flew on a broad front to the Gulf coast but avoided the sea and remained faithful to fresh waters.

The trumpeter swan is thought to be analogous to the Eurasian whooper swan, to which it is closely related. In appearance it differs from the whooper in the absence of yellow on the bill; the bill of the trumpeter is entirely black. During the breeding season each pair requires an extensive territory which is defended strenuously against any member of their own species and also against geese and other large waterfowl. They pay no attention to the smaller species.

Towards the end of the 18th century the powerful Hudson Bay Company began to gain control over all trade, and swan skins soon came to be regarded as valuable articles of trade. It appears that at this time people in Europe preferred to use powder puffs made out of swan's down. The Indians quickly learned what the traders wanted. They were not paid much for a single skin so naturally they brought in a number. Transactions were carried on in a business-like manner and everything was recorded in detail in the company's books: at first there were records of thousands of swan skins per year, these dwindled to hundreds and then continued to decrease steadily. Except for the dry figures in the books of this famous trading company, only a few details are known of the history of the decimation of this marvellous bird. One traveller describes how he once saw Indians killing 50 swans but, in general, the process was hidden under the cloak of business secrecy.

By the beginning of the present century the trumpeter swan had already withdrawn from the major part of its original breeding range. It came to the brink of extinction. Part of the nesting area was taken over for agriculture and there was no control of shooting for sport. The relatively dense settlement of the area by man threatened the few birds that remained.

However, the same nation whose citizens in the pioneering days paid little heed to the result of their depredations now instituted an extensive programme for conserving what was left. Enormous reserves were established by an effective programme of legislation. The practical minded Americans did not set much store by legislation on paper; they prepared important schemes and found men to run them who worked out plans and experimented, learning from experience and finally succeeding.

The rescue operation was started just in time. It seemed

likely that the last areas in which trumpeter swans would ever breed would be in the states of Montana, Wyoming and Idaho, particularly around the Red Rock Lakes and in the Yellowstone National Park. As a result of strict protection and scientific control, the shrunken remnants of the population have been brought up to a level when numbers can be regarded as maximal in relation to the available breeding area. A constant rate of increase was observed until the population reached saturation in about 1954. After this the birds began to spread out beyond the reserves to the surrounding areas. There are now about 2000 trumpeter swans living in the whole of the north American continent of which at least 600 are in the United States. This species can now be regarded as no longer in danger.

Tuatara

Sphenodon punctatus p. 154

The tuatara is probably the most ancient living reptile in the world. Fossil remains show that a group of animals, which included the tuatara, lived on all continents about 170 million years ago. This group was represented by many different forms, of which the tuatara of New Zealand is the sole survivor today. In external form the tuatara closely resembles an ordinary lizard. However it differs so radically from the true lizards that it is classified not only in its own family but in its own order: the Rhynchocephalia, meaning 'snout-heads', a reference to the peculiar structure of the jaws.

This group is characterised by having a second bony bridge (the inferior temporal arch) in its skull. This character is also found in the crocodilians but has been lost in the lizards and snakes. A number of other characters also supports the separation of the tuatara from the other reptiles: for example, the immovable fixing of the quadrate bone to the skull and the absence of a pairing organ. The crest running along the nape and back, which is formed by elongated flat spines, is reminiscent of representatives of some families of lizards.

In contrast to the majority of lizards the scales in the tuatara are fixed to the skin without the posterior ends being free like the tiles on a roof. In the adults each of the scales, which are usually olive-brown, has a small yellow spot.

The habits of the tuatara are just as remarkable as its structure. It lives below ground in holes which it shares with various species of petrel. These holes, which are used as nesting-holes by the birds, are mostly under the canopy of a low tree of the genus *Coprosoma*, beneath which a deep layer of humus forms. The petrels and the tuataras make their homes together in burrows and the earth is often riddled by subterranean tunnels. Here and there the tuataras leave the burrows during the day to lie out in the sun. Generally speaking however this is a nocturnal reptile. It feeds chiefly on insects but also takes worms and snails. The eggs are laid in the spring in a shallow depression in the ground which is usually at some distance from the burrow in which it normally lives. The young do not usually hatch out until the following spring.

Originally the tuataras lived on the two main islands of New Zealand, but they were driven away by rats, mice, weasels, feral pigs and goats brought by the British colonists, which multiplied enormously. They only survived on a few offshore islands where they are now strictly protected.

By the subsequent removal of any introduced goats, it has been possible to maintain the correct habitat on some islands; bushy vegetation is essential together with the special soil conditions which are necessary for the construction of the subterranean burrows. In this way the necessary conditions for the future survival of this living fossil, the tuatara, have been guaranteed.

TURTLE see Leathery Turtle

Victoria Crowned Pigeon

Goura victoria p. 156

The fan of spatulate, lacy feathers which adorns the head of crowned pigeons gives these animals a strangely old-fashioned appearance. Although this pigeon looks larger than a domestic fowl, its weight is much the same.

The function of the crested crown is not yet fully understood because insufficient behaviour studies have been made to provide the necessary data. Is it a signal that serves only for species recognition? Or, is it a signal which is part of behaviour connected, for instance, with courtship display, or some other aspect of behaviour? Generally speaking little is known about the life history and habits of the crowned pigeons. People who have seen them in the wild have usually been intent on killing them, not on making scientific observations, and so our knowledge of these species is extremely sparse.

In recent times the American ornithologist Thomas Gilliard repeatedly saw crowned pigeons during his travels in New Guinea. He noticed that when disturbed, single individuals remained perching on the lower branches of the forest trees where they could easily be shot. They have now become rare, or have even disappeared completely in large areas.

There are three species of crowned pigeon which occur only in New Guinea and some neighbouring islands. They are closely related and all are birds of the forest. Like domestic fowls they spend a lot of time moving about on the ground where they pick up fruits in the clearings in the rain-forest. They are gregarious and keep together in small parties. They roost and nest in trees and evidently lay only a single egg in a typical pigeon nest, that is, in a thin flat structure built of twigs.

Crowned pigeons are seen quite frequently in zoos. Individual pairs breed in captivity or at least attempt to do so. In 1959 a young bird was even reared successfully in the Berlin Zoo. Centuries ago crowned pigeons were kept with poultry in the palaces of Indian maharajas.

In those parts of New Guinea where Europeans have settled, protective measures are taken. Unfortunately Gilliard's observations lend weight to the fears that the crowned pigeon can scarcely be expected to hold its own for much longer. It is all too easy to shoot and is valued as a hunting trophy.

VICUNA see South American camels

WALDRAPP see Bald Ibis

Walrus

Odobaenus rosmarus pp. 80, 81

The small roundish head with the big bristly moustache and the large barrel-shaped body give to the walrus the appearance of a jovial old beer-drinker. This makes it popular with visitors to zoos. It seems to cultivate public relations by looking at people with a friendly expression, apparently begging them to play with it and indulging in practical jokes such as spraying the public with water.

The walruses form their own family within the seal group. There is one genus containing a single species with two subspecies: one Atlantic and one Pacific. Its distribution is or was circumpolar. It lives on the islands in the Arctic Ocean and along the north coasts of Asia and America, into the Bering Sea, Davis Strait, Hudson Strait and Hudson Bay where its southern limit is at about latitude 60°N. It has unfortunately been exterminated by man in many areas. Its former range included Iceland and north Norway on the one hand and the Gulf of St. Lawrence on the other.

It was bludgeoned to death or shot by man in large numbers for commercial purposes. Under its wrinkled skin, which is 1½ inches thick, it has a substantial layer of fat from which a first quality oil could be extracted. An adult bull grows to a length of 10–11 feet, excluding the hindlimbs, and a weight of 3000 lb.; the females are about a third smaller. There is therefore plenty of fat to be obtained from every carcass. Both sexes have tusks which may grow to a length of 2 feet. They are of very hard ivory and are much prized.

Walruses live in places where the sea is not too deep; they dive down to the bottom where they use their tusks to loosen molluscs and other animals from the sea floor. Bottom-living fish, snails and crustaceans are thus disturbed and eaten. In areas where food is scarce on the bottom, the walrus will hunt seals, particularly the small ringed seal; it rips them open with the tusks and eats the entrails, muscles and blubber. The walrus also needs hauling out places on the shore, on rocks or on the ice; after feeding it rests there, apparently content to do nothing but laze. As its vision is poor and its hearing and sense of smell are not particularly well developed, it is not very difficult for man to approach them as they rest, to within shooting range.

Sealers have persistently adopted this technique and whole herds have been exterminated in just one expedition. Due to this the walruses have long since ceased to use suitable beaches for hauling out in their thousands. It is only in secluded places that one still finds herds with a few dozen or at the most hundreds. In addition the rate of reproduction is slow: the cows produce only a single pup after a gestation period of 10–11 months, and it is suckled for about 1½ years, so as a rule they only produce one pup every second year.

Some hundreds of years ago approximately half a million walruses lived along the coasts of the Arctic, today there are perhaps a tenth of that number. Since hunting is still permitted in certain areas, particularly by the Eskimos and other native peoples who are largely dependent on hunting seals for food, the total number shot exceeds the annual increment by about 10 per cent. The shooting must therefore be drastically reduced if the walrus is not to be exterminated shortly.

Weddell Seal

Leptonychotes weddelli pp. 114, 115

There are 30 species of seal living today and they are classified into three families: the eared seals, the walruses and the true seals. The latter contains 18 species. Of these only the monk seals are adapted to live in the warmer waters of the tropics and subtropics, the remainder being divided into a northern and a southern group. The southern group contains only a few species which live mainly in antarctic waters: southern elephant seal, crab-eating seal, Ross seal, leopard seal and Weddell seal.

The Weddell seal is named after the enormous bay discovered in 1823 by James Weddell, which pentrates deep into the antarctic continent. This seal occurs right round Antarctica and also extends to the southern island groups between latitude 30° and 60°S, to New Zealand, southern Australia and Tierra del Fuego. For preference it keeps close to land or the ice edge, and does not go far on the pack-ice or out to the open sea where there are icebergs and ice-floes; it likes to rest on the shore or at the edge of the ice. It does not undertake large-scale migrations.

It is a handsome, long-bodied animal with a small head, which is dark iron-grey on the upperparts and somewhat paler below.

It is about 9 feet in length and weighs 700–900 lb. The underparts are more strongly marked, with irregular yellowish-white flecks, than the upperparts. The young are much paler at first, almost whitish-grey.

Weddell seals hunt small fish and squid, which they can swallow easily. They keep their blow-holes free by constantly breaking the new ice as it forms. For most of the year they live in small groups or even singly; however, about a week before pupping, the females collect together on the edge of the ice in loose groups, of up to several dozen. The pups are born in September and October, after a gestation period of 310 days; at birth they are about half the length of the adult females and weigh about 70 lb. The mother's milk is extremely rich in fat and very nutritious. The young grow fast and by the time weaning takes place, when they are 2 months old, they have already quadrupled their weight. The mother does not leave her resting place from one week before to one week after the birth of the pup and by the end of the suckling period she will have lost 2½ cwt.; after this period, however, she soon puts on weight again. Two weeks after the birth of the young, the mother entices it into shallow pools, first of all, to accustom it to water; she then takes it into deeper water gradually, until it can swim and dive properly.

The population of Weddell seals in the Antarctic numbers several hundreds of thousands and at the moment this species is not threatened. It is not often hunted by man. Leopard seals prey upon the young Weddell seals and killer whales on the adults, but these losses are of no real significance.

White or Square-lipped Rhinoceros
Ceratotherium simum

and

Black or Narrow-lipped Rhinoceros
Diceros bicornis pp. 228, 229

Nowadays rhinoceroses are only to be found in south Asia and Africa, although earlier in the world's history they also occurred in Europe and North America. Of the five species still living, three are Asiatic: Sumatran, Javan and great Indian rhinoceroses. The black and the white rhinoceroses, on the other hand, are African. Like the Sumatran rhino they carry two horns on the front of the head.

The horns have no bony skeleton but are purely dermal structures formed by the fusion of horny filaments which are long, narrow and parallel to each other; the filaments are anchored in the skin itself. The horns are used as weapons and for digging out favourite roots, etc., rubbing against trees, termites' nests and so on. The horns become very sharp in the process and can be dangerous. On the average the white rhino has a longer anterior horn than the black rhino, but in the latter the posterior horn is longer than the front one. The longest front horn so far recorded in the black rhinoceros is 53 inches long, and of the white rhinoceros 62 inches, the posterior horns being 32 and 29 inches respectively.

Of the two African species the black rhino is the smaller and lighter. It attains a shoulder height of about 62 inches, a total length of approximately 155 inches and a weight of about 2 tons. The white rhinoceros, on the other hand, stands about 78 inches tall at the shoulders, is about 190 inches long and reaches a weight of about 2½ tons. Thus, after the elephant, the white rhinoceros is the largest living land mammal in the world. These figures suggest that the rhino is a heavy and cumbersome animal but in fact it is astonishingly active and can move fast. In a gallop, which admittedly cannot be kept up for long, they reach a speed of 30 miles per hour. It is not surprising that these colossi have no natural enemies in their home in Africa. Only a young calf unprotected by its mother might perhaps be taken by a lion or by a pack of hunting dogs. All quadrupeds move about with care in the vicinity of adult rhinos. Rhinos, particularly the black species, may become aggressive quite suddenly; they have poor sight and when they are suspicious and upset, they charge blindly at anything in front of them.

The black rhino is also known as the narrow-lipped from the elongated, pointed and finger-like upper lip which it uses in a prehensile manner when browsing on twigs and leaves. The white or square-lipped rhino, on the other hand, has a broad upper lip with which it grazes on grass and herbs. Since the latter holds its head lowered when grazing it needs a particularly powerful neck musculature to support the heavy head which is over 28 inches long. This musculature makes it look somewhat humped at the nape.

Both species live in grassy and bushy plains of the savannahs, singly or in pairs, sometimes a few join together in loosely-knit groups. They feed in the morning and evening, and in the heat of midday they rest in the shade. They like to wallow in mud. Their hide is undoubtedly thick but it is not insensitive and wallowing appears to be beneficial; it helps to keep down the ticks. These pests are also eaten by oxpeckers, small birds which look somewhat like starlings; they land on the rhinos' backs, perch and run about on them, pecking and nibbling at the ticks, searching in all the folds and cracks of the hide. They also do good service as sentinels. They give warning of anything suspicious by flying off and calling.

Young rhino calves can be seen at all times of the year. The gestation period of the white rhinoceros is 510–540 days, and 530–550 days in the black rhino. Only one calf is born which is suckled and tended for over two years. Therefore the cows only produce offspring every three to four years; they are sexually mature at three years at the earliest. Rhinos can live to be 35 years old.

The black rhino has already disappeared from several areas where it was once distributed, owing to the human settlement of many habitats and to poaching for its horn. The total population is still about 12,000 animals. This is alarmingly small for a huge continent such as Africa. Fortunately it does well in captivity and also breeds there. At the moment there are about 120 animals in the zoos of the world and so far over a dozen calves have been born in captivity.

The white rhinoceros, which occurs as a northern and a southern subspecies, is still rarer. At one time the southern subspecies survived only in the Umfolozi and Hluhluwe Game Reserves. In recent years, however, 150 of them have been transferred to other reserves in South Africa and Rhodesia. All in all there are not more than 3000 to 4000 white rhinos. They were first kept in zoos in about 1946 and there are now about 30 in captivity.

Whooping Crane

Grus americana p. 103

In 1834 the ornithologist Thomas Nuttall wrote the following eye-witness account of whooping cranes:

'In the month of December, 1811, while leisurely descending on the bosom of the Mississippi, in one of the trading boats of that period, I had an opportunity of witnessing one of these vast migrations of the Whooping Cranes, assembled by many thousands from all the marshes and impassable swamps of the north and west. The whole continent seemed as if giving up its quota of the species to swell the mighty host. . . . The clangor of these numerous legions, passing along, high in the air, seemed almost deafening.'

In 1952 R. P. Allen published a book giving the results of his investigations on this species of crane: he estimated that during the middle of the 19th century the total population for the whole of the North American continent was only 1300–1400 individuals. The decline in numbers took place of its own accord and the population continued to decrease steadily. In the spring of 1922 the last nest to be found for decades was located in a swamp in Saskatchewan. The population in the steadily shrinking winter quarters on the Gulf Coast were counted year by year and soon reached a 'low' of 21 specimens. The end appeared to be inevitable. Since then, however, the tiny remnant of the huge flocks which were once seen on migration has remained at approximately the same size. The population has even shown a slight increase in recent years. In 1963 thirty-three birds, of which six were immature, were counted in the winter quarters. Six specimens were living in captivity, to which they had mostly been taken owing to some accident.

The success of the protective measures for the sadly reduced relict of this outstanding bird species of the North American continent has been somewhat surprising. Over 2000 miles separate the last known breeding ground, right on the northern edge of the former range on Great Slave Lake in Canada, from the regular winter quarters in the Aransas National Wildlife Refuge on the coast of Texas. This unbelievably conspicuous snow-white giant bird undertakes a flight of 2000 miles twice a year, through areas full of hunters who would be only too glad to turn their guns on them if they could. Naturally there are individuals among them whose conscience would not be unduly troubled by shooting a whooping crane.

An annual publicity campaign is mounted in the press and on the radio. People in all areas which might be touched by the migrating cranes are told that this rare bird, the last of its race, must be protected. When the birds are sighted anywhere, there is usually at least one person who has heard of the importance of the cranes and can spread the news around. Naturally, however, it sometimes happens that a crane is shot or meets with an accident. If it is not fatally injured it usually ends up in a zoo where it is looked after. Even the remains of a dead specimen are of value and these are made available for scientific investigation. All this is the result of a tireless campaign to keep the public informed.

Naturally the cranes are also carefully guarded every year in their known winter quarters where they are easiest to control. If only it were possible, the birds would also be guarded everywhere they went but their present breeding grounds are only partly known. These lie in lonely areas, difficult of access, which still occur in the 'wide open spaces of Canada'.

How long will it be possible to preserve a population of 20–30 birds under these conditions? The rate of reproduction is low, the clutch normally consists of two eggs, of which usually only one is reared and it takes several years to reach sexual maturity. What are the chances of building up a large population from such a low level, even assuming that losses from human intervention can be avoided?

One characteristic of the whooping crane which works to its advantage is its exceptional shyness and secretiveness. Many of the older reports mention this characteristic. At a time when the whooping cranes were already rare and the finding of a nest created something of a sensation, many reports ended with an uninhibited account of an attempt at stealing the eggs, the collector expressing pride at his success or regret at his failure.

WILD CATTLE see Banteng; Bison; Cape Buffalo; Wisent

WILD HORSE see Tarpan

Wild Sheep

Ovis canadensis, O. dalli etc. pp. 75, 85, 87

There is scarcely any animal which would be more difficult to hunt than a wild sheep. It has extremely acute senses: it not only takes scent and hears excellently, but it also possesses remarkably keen sight over long distances.

The present-day sheep and goats are still remarkably similar in the skeleton—except for the skull—to those which from the evolutionary viewpoint first appeared about the beginning of the Ice Age. The goats became mountain-dwellers, browsing on leaves and shoots, and they developed into the most skilled climbers among the ungulates with paired hooves. The sheep became adapted as grazers, particularly of barren hill country and upland plateau. Sheep are also capable of climbing steep rocky cliffs and negotiating narrow ledges in mountainous country, and will seek refuge in this manner from man and to escape from the wolf.

With their preferred habitat the wild sheep have a very wide distribution. They extend from Corsica, Sardinia and Cyprus through the Near and Middle East to eastern Asia, and in north America from Alaska to north Mexico and Lower California. In these extensive areas wild sheep live in small flocks and have evolved into a range of several different forms or subspecies. They extend from the smallest, the mouflon of Corsica and Sardinia, which is only about 25 inches high at the withers up to the argali of eastern Asia which is about twice as tall and weighs up to 400 lb.

They vary in size and weight, and also in the colour of the coat and the shape of the horns. The colours range from pale grey, through reddish-brown, to black. The mouflon of Europe is reddish-brown with a whitish saddle. The Cyprian or red sheep of western Asia is also reddish-brown. The bighorn or Rocky Mountain sheep of North America is buff, greyish-brown or black, except for the muzzle, rump and the inner sides of the legs which are white. Stone's mountain sheep, a subspecies of the bighorn, which lives in Alaska, is white. The urial of the Caspian area is reddish. The argali of central Asia is greyish-brown.

In the rams the horns increase in size and in the number of spirals from east to west. The most powerful horns, up to about 72 inches long, are those of Marco Polo's argali in the Pamirs, eastwards from this area the horns are shorter but thicker. The females carry only short sabre-like horns.

In Europe after the Ice Age wild sheep only survived in Corsica, Sardinia and Cyprus as inhabitants of wooded mountains. In the last hundred years, however, they have been introduced into many places on the mainland of Europe as contented but timid animals. From the Near East to eastern Asia they inhabit the steppes, semi-deserts, deserts and the upland pastures of the hills and mountains. In north America before the colonisation by white men, they lived on the hilly grasslands of the Middle West as well as in the mountains; today they are almost entirely restricted to the big western mountain range of the continent. Even in this area there are large gaps in their distribution between Alaska and Lower California owing to human persecution.

In summer the females move about in flocks, each ewe with its one or two lambs; the rams remain apart from the females, living in small parties. In the autumn (September–October) the rams then join the females and fight for their favours. They rush at each other from a distance, crashing frontally with the horns, so that the sound of butting can be heard from afar. The butting continues until the weaker ram accepts defeat and retires. The sexes usually remain together during the winter.

Apart from man the main enemy of wild sheep is the wolf; in Asia they also fall prey to wild dogs, leopards and snow leopards; in north America they are killed by pumas. The lambs may be taken by eagles and other large birds of prey.

Nowadays the hunting of wild sheep is controlled in the United States, Canada and the USSR and there is no immediate danger of extermination. In the Near East too they are officially protected, but regulations are mostly not enforced and the sheep have to rely on the acuity of their senses and the lack of cover, which makes approach difficult for their enemies. In Cyprus, Corsica and Sardinia they are considerably threatened. Small remnant populations manage to survive owing to their shyness and alertness. The inhabitants of these islands take pride in carrying weapons and shoot regardless of the law.

Wisent

Bison bonasus pp. 44, 45

The wisent or European bison is a species of wild cattle which adapted itself to a woodland habitat in the post-glacial period when Europe was covered with forest. It has developed a marked preference for feeding on leaves and shoots. In this it differs from the auroch, the ancestor of our domestic cattle which became extinct in 1627, which fed on grass and herbaceous plants on virgin land.

The habitat of the wisent consists of open to dense forests of deciduous, coniferous and mixed species, up to altitudes of about 9000 feet in the mountains. These animals like to come out of the forest into meadows to sun themselves and dust-bathe in sandy clearings. They feed mainly on buds, leaves, shoots and bark of trees and bushes, but also eat fungi and lichens, grasses and herbaceous plants. The wisent normally rests in the middle of the day and is active chiefly in the morning and from afternoon to evening. Usually a powerful bull is seen in the company of several cows and their calves. Old bulls tend to go their separate ways and become solitary in their habits.

The cows come on heat in August–September. Young bulls which feel strong enough then challenge the old bulls and there are often vigorous fights. The gestation period is about 9 months; a single calf is usually born, occasionally two, which is then suckled for a year. A wisent becomes sexually mature at 3 years, more rarely when 2 years old; the bulls are not fully grown, however, until they are 7–9 years old. They live for about 20–25 years, rarely longer.

Like the alpine ibex the wisent was saved from extermination at the eleventh hour. In early times it was distributed from France in the west to the area of the River Lena in the east; in the second half of the 18th century it still occurred along the upper reaches of the rivers Irtysh and Ob and in the Altai region. In the Caucasus where a subspecies evolved, it hung on in the wild until the beginning of the 'twenties of this century. The Caucasus wisent was less heavy in form and was exterminated during the Russian revolution after the First World War. In other areas only a few wisent survived the First World War and the subsequent confusion.

In 1923 Dr Kurt Priemel, at that time Director of the Frankfurt Zoo, established in Berlin an International Association for the Preservation of the Wisent. A planned breeding programme was started with the 56 survivors of the wisent population. This programme was so successful that even the Second World War and its aftermath did not seriously endanger the wisent population. At the beginning of 1949 the number had risen again to 119 animals. These have bred so well that at the present time there are over 800. Some of these are distributed in over 30 zoos throughout the world and at least another 100 animals have already been released into the wild, primarily in the Bialowieza National Park.

A start has also been made in reconstituting the Caucasus wisent. A steer of this subspecies actually reached a zoo before the First World War and left behind descendants of mixed blood. It is now hoped to re-create the Caucasus wisent by careful selective breeding from these animals. The selected wisent have been taken to suitable mountain parks. Even if the hereditary material of a species once extinct does not allow the animal to be created again in its erstwhile character, in favourable circumstances, one can gradually breed back to a form which is very similar to the original. (See wild horse.)

The wisent has a good rate of reproduction and with the world-wide distribution of the populations, the future of this species should indeed be ensured. At the moment the problem is to find sufficiently large areas that are suitable for releasing further herds into the wild where they can be left completely free. (See also American bison.)

Wolverine or Glutton

Gulo gulo p. 77

The wolverine had already evolved to its present form and way of life long before the Ice Age. Its ancestor became adapted to moorland and swampy forest in the Miocene, diverging from the ancestors of the present-day species of marten and sable which are its nearest relatives. The interglacial periods, with their extensive formation of moorland, were its heyday and it was able to colonise a vast area which extends nowadays as a conifer forest belt through the whole of the boreal zone in the northern hemisphere. This has scarcely altered in historical times. Although the wolverine has lost ground in the Baltic and in eastern America north and south of the River St. Lawrence, due to hunting by man, it has made up by advancing into the northern tundras, some even reaching Greenland.

In spite of the enormous extent of its range, the wolverine is nowhere common and no subspecies have evolved. It is only by pure chance that one gets a glimpse of a wolverine in the wild. Each male has a very large territory of the order of a hundred square miles and, as it is extremely wary of man, it is easy for it to disappear completely. It has a reputation for being very aggressive and man is equally wary of meeting a wolverine face to face.

The wolverine is a large heavy animal weighing up to about 40 lb.; it has a body length of about 4 feet including the tail which is about 8 inches long; it stands 14 inches high at the shoulders. It eats almost any kind of food which in general is found on the moors, marshy ground and forests of the north. It is a solitary species and each animal needs a large area to satisfy its food requirements. The females occupy smaller territories than the males, namely between 20–30 square miles. The male mates with more than one female and a sexually mature male regards the territories of two or three females as belonging to him, hence the large size of the male's territory.

In its search for food a wolverine normally moves across country in a clumsy gallop, following a circular course for preference which may encompass several miles; it is therefore a difficult animal to track down. The land is free of snow for about a third of the year and after the thaw the wolverine goes in search of ground-nesting species, eating their eggs and young, together with any fresh green shoots that it finds. Later on it goes for the subterranean nests of wasps and devours the fat grubs and pupae. It also eats large quantities of all kinds of berries which are abundant in summer. In years when lemmings are numerous these constitute a welcome addition to its diet. It is also a carrion-eater and every carcass is investigated, carrion being a regular part of its diet. Tender flesh is relished and it springs on to young elk and caribou calves, killing them with lightning speed.

It is not able to overpower large healthy game in the snow-free period as it is unable to stalk its prey noiselessly but once the snow is on the ground the wolverine comes into its own. Its broad paws enable it to travel easily over snow and its incredible powers of endurance, enabling it to keep going for dozens of miles, undoubtedly give it superiority under these conditions. It does not hesitate to attack adult elk and caribou: it springs on to their backs, sometimes riding on the animal for several hundred yards, and brings it down by biting the neck vertebrae. It has exceptionally powerful jaws. On snow it will even attack a lynx and shows no sign of fear. Wolves and bears will make a detour rather than risk an encounter with a wolverine, in view of the latter's aggressiveness and its physical strength.

The wolverine does not become sexually mature until the third year. The male mates with several females, seeking out one after the other, from the end of April to the beginning of July. Two to three young are born in February or March in a den under fallen trees or in rock crevices. The young only weigh about 4 oz. at birth; they have fine yellow fur and are blind, the eyes opening after one month. They are suckled for 2½ months, get their milk dentition in the fourth month, and by the fifth month they are almost as large as the mother. They are not able to kill large prey by themselves until their second year. The females therefore only have a litter every second year.

Wood Ibis

Mycteria americana p. 102

Bird names like other names, serve primarily as a means of identification. For a variety of reasons, however, many names of birds convey an erroneous impression in that they are not strictly correct if their true meaning is applied. This is troublesome but once a name has been accepted in practice it only adds to the confusion if it is changed later.

The wood ibis is a case in point. With its naked head and neck, together with the slightly downward curve of the bill, the bird certainly looks like an ibis. In fact, however, it is not an ibis but a true stork. The error is, however, not very serious, because the ibises are classified in the same family as the spoonbill which is closely related to the true stork family.

The wood ibis is the only true stork in North America. It is, however, only distributed in the warm parts of the continent from South Carolina into the Gulf States, Mexico and some parts of South America down to Argentina. The wood ibis, unlike the European white stork, has never accustomed itself to living in the immediate vicinity of man. It prefers the secluded habitats of large swamps, in particular the Everglades in Florida, where spoonbills and numerous egrets also occur. The huge area of the Everglades, which consists of forest, swamp and water, still retains much of its original vegetation and is of unique importance in that it supports a rich aquatic bird fauna.

Here the wood ibises breed almost exclusively in large colonies, the largest containing several thousand birds. Giant cypresses are often densely crowded with their nests; some large trees have up to 50 nests. These storks also search for food gregariously. In this they hunt in small flocks over the numerous swamps and areas of shallow water; sometimes they also visit the seashore. Like some other aquatic birds, particularly cormorants and pelicans, wood ibises have developed a co-operative technique for exploiting their fishing grounds. A flock walks together through the swamp, and each bird stirs up the water in front of it with its bill. By this means the fish, frogs and other animals which are lurking in the water are forced to move fast to evade capture and are thus easier to spot. The bird nearest seizes the struggling prey and makes off with it, either eating it at a safe distance from the others or flying back with it to feed the young in the nest.

Zebras

Equus grevyi, E. burchelli, E. zebra pp. 232, 236, 237

Zebras carry a striking pattern of vertical dark stripes on the body. These stripes undoubtedly form a pattern on a pale background colour and not the reverse, that is to say the stripes do not constitute the ground colour. All the zebras have this feature in common but there are many differences in the detailed marking of the stripes. Africa is the only part of the world where zebras live. At the present time there are three species which differ from each other about as much as the pine marten, beech marten and sable.

The most northerly species, which is about 58 inches high at the withers is also the largest: Grévy's zebra. It occurs from central Ethiopia to Somaliland and north Kenya, and is geographically the closest to the other African group of the horse family, the wild asses which are restricted to the north of the continent. The second species is the common zebra which occurs from Kenya in the north to Cape Province in the south, and from Mozambique in the east to Angola in the west. With a height at the withers of about 48 inches, it is noticeably smaller than Grévy's zebra. The third species, the mountain zebra (*Equus zebra*) also occurs in the south. The type form *Equus zebra zebra* is slightly smaller than the common zebra. The other subspecies *E. zebra hartmannae* is a little larger, with a height at the withers of about 49 inches. Mountain zebras live in Cape Province and in south-west Africa northwards to central Angola.

The zebra which was described by Linnæus in 1758 was the mountain zebra from Cape Province. The most southerly representative of the common zebra was the quagga (now extinct), which also lived near the Cape. It was first made known to science in 1788 by Gmelin. Grévy's zebra, on the other hand, was not described until 1882; the French zoologist Oustalet named it after the then ruling President of the French Republic.

All three species of zebra differ not only in build and coloration but also in habits. The noticeably large-headed and big-eared Grévy's zebra has the narrowest and most densely arranged pattern of stripes; it also has a distinctive patterning on the rump, the stripes becoming even finer and closer on this part of the body. The mountain zebra also has narrow stripes but on the rump they are fewer, the individual stripes being broader. This species is also characterised by a small but distinct dewlap and steeply angled hard hooves. In the broad-striped common zebra the vividness of the pattern decreases from north to south, so that in the most southerly subspecies—the quagga—the back and the rump showed an overall shade of brown with no stripes visible in this area of the body.

Within its restricted range, Grévy's zebra has not developed any subspecies. The mountain zebras of western south Africa however have a somewhat narrower striping than the Cape mountain zebra and are known as Hartmann's zebra. In its enormous range the common zebra forms several subspecies, which from north to south bear the names Grant's or Boehm's, Burchell's and quagga, with Damaraland or Chapman's zebra in the west. Grant, Boehm and Burchell were explorers in the areas concerned; quagga is the hottentot word *kwucha*, bowdlerised by the Boers, from the neighing of this animal.

Grévy's zebra lives in small herds in semi-open country with scattered trees and bushes. The mountain zebra also lives in small herds; the terrain is rough in the mountainous and rocky country where it lives and is not suitable for large herds. The common zebra on the other hand lives in large to enormous herds, which are either widely scattered over the plains or densely congregated. They often move in long columns from one grazing ground to the next. When alarmed, the plains resound with the thudding of hooves as they gallop off.

So far Grévy's zebra has scarcely lost any of its population. Hartmann's zebra is still present in considerable numbers in south-west Africa and Angola, although it has had to vacate some areas owing to the pressure of human settlement. On the other hand, the Cape mountain zebra was never very numerous and has almost been exterminated: after the British took over Cape Colony in 1806, there was a relaxation of the hunting laws and this zebra was ruthlessly persecuted. Thanks to the foresight of some landowners it enjoyed protection on their large farms but in spite of full government protection, its population sank to 47 animals between 1910 and 1937. Today there are about 100 specimens but they breed slowly as the gestation period is one year and the mares only produce one foal every second year. At present they are distributed partly in the Mountain Zebra National Park at Cradock, partly on private farms in the vicinity of the Park, and also at Oudtshoorn, Jansenville and George.

Of the common zebras the two most southerly subspecies, the quagga and Burchell's zebra, were ruthlessly hunted and are now extinct. The quagga used to be present all over the plains of Cape Province up to the Orange River in hundreds of thousands, while Burchell's zebra occupied the Orange Free State and southern Bechuanaland. The last quagga died in 1875 in Berlin Zoo, the last Burchell's in 1910 in London Zoo. At the present time the other subspecies of common zebra are not threatened, even though they have had to vacate many areas on account of human settlement. It is only in the Serengeti that one can now see the larger herds which were such a common sight in former times.

The contributions on birds are by Dr G. Dieselhorst, on mammals by Dr T. Haltenorth, on reptiles and amphibians by Professor W. Hellmich. The articles on giant tortoises and marine iguana are by Dr I. Eibl-Eibesfeldt.

SOURCE OF PHOTOGRAPHS

All the photographs in this book were taken by Eugen Schuhmacher and Helmut Barth with the exception of the following:

page 41, Service de Photographie du Muséum National d'Histoire Naturelle, Paris;
page 55, Sven Gillsäter, Stockholm;
pages 75, 76, 230, Freimut Kalden, Geretsried, Obb., Germany;
page 103, Fred K. Truslow, Summit, N.J., U.S.A.;
pages 108, 110, Erwin von Dessauer, Rio de Janeiro;
page 142, Gary Lewis, Croydon, Vic., Australia;
pages 147, 152, Allen Gill, Gloucester, England;
page 239, Wolfgang Bell, Nairobi

Mt. McKinley
Banff, Yoho, Jasper, Kootenay
Montana National Bison Range
Yellowstone Nat. P.
NORTH AMERICA
Grand Canyon
Aransas Reserve
Everglades
Galapagos Is.
SOUTH AMERICA
Highlands of Peru
Highlands of Bolivia
Nahuel Huapí
Valdez Peninsula
Bass Roc
Farne Is.
Woburn
Texel
E U
Pontresin
Gran Paradisc
Coto Doñana
Gibraltar
A F R